DANDELIC ___ ...
OF
GREAT BRITAIN
AND IRELAND

B.S.B.I. HANDBOOK No. 9

A. A. DUDMAN and A. J. RICHARDS

WITH ILLUSTRATIONS BY
OLGA STEWART

EDITED BY P. H. OSWALD

BOTANICAL SOCIETY OF THE BRITISH ISLES
London
1997

Reprinted with minor alterations 2000

ISBN 0-901158-25-9

Dedicated to the memory of CHRIS HAWORTH,
who would, but for his untimely death,
have been one of the authors of this book,
and without whose pioneering work
its treatment would have been much less complete.

Published by the Botanical Society of the British Isles
c/o Natural History Museum
Cromwell Road, London SW7 5BD
Typeset by the Botanical Information Company Ltd
Printed and bound by CPI Group (UK) Ltd, Croydon, CR0 4YY

CONTENTS

ACKNOWLEDGEMENTS

British taraxacology in general and we ourselves in particular owe Chris Haworth a massive debt, as we have explained in the dedication of this book.

However, we are also indebted to many other sources. First, we should mention the small army of helpers, perhaps 80 in total, who have assiduously collected tens of thousands of specimens in Britain and Ireland over the last 25 years. Only through this help have we been able to cover our islands so thoroughly. A number of excellent and comprehensive local *Taraxacum* herbaria have thus been built up. Some still reside in private hands and some are in the public domain and can be found in local museums such as those at Maidstone, Colchester, Norwich and Lancaster as well as at the Natural History Museum in London, the National Museum of Wales, the Ulster Museum in Belfast and the National Botanic Gardens, Glasnevin, Dublin.

A number of these collectors have become expert taraxacologists and have guided us in our work. Of these, Richard Pankhurst, formerly of the Natural History Museum, London, and now at the Royal Botanic Garden, Edinburgh, deserves a special mention. Not only has he collected much excellent material, but he has also devised the computer programs which have made our work easier and more accurate. (He has also helped taraxacologists in other countries in the same way.) These computer programs were a database of species and records, which was used to sort the records for the dot maps, and a DELTA data file for the species descriptions. It is planned to make a dandelion identification program available through the B.S.B.I.

The most influential modern taraxacologist is without doubt the Dane Hans Øllgaard. For more than 15 years he has guided the study of dandelions in the British Isles, as elsewhere, with a benign but firm hand. For his interest, formidably high standards, intellectual rigour and great knowledge we offer our thanks. Several other taraxacologists have also contributed significantly in recent years, especially Piet Oosterveld, from the Netherlands, and two Czechs, Jan Kirschner and Jan Štěpánek.

Foremost amongst the workers in the British Isles has been Tom Edmondson, who, despite recent ill-health, has collaborated with Øllgaard to make an important and original contribution to the study of the dandelions of north-west England. Other significant contributors have included Merle Marsden, Michael Porter, Len Livermore and Len Margetts; but there are many others, too numerous to list here, to all of whom we extend our thanks.

Olga Stewart is a multi-talented botanist who has been interested in dandelions for many years. She has graced the present volume with her delightful and accurate drawings of involucres and other text figures and we thank her for the dedication and hard work that these have entailed. We also thank Mrs J. Gaunt for scanning these into the computer so that they could be sent to the printer on disk, Dr Chris Preston for his help in arranging this, and Clive Jermy for designing the cover.

The distribution maps in this publication were produced by using the computer program DMAP written by Dr Alan Morton of Imperial College, Silwood Park, Ascot, Berkshire SL5 7PY, whose help we gratefully acknowledge.

We are grateful to Professor Clive Stace for his permission to include a slightly modified version of the key to the sections of *Taraxacum* from his *New Flora of the British Isles* (1991). Thanks are also due to him, Douglas Kent and Peter Sell for nomenclatural and bibliographical assistance to the Editor and to Dr Max Walters for his help with material written in Scandinavian languages.

We are particularly grateful to Philip Oswald for his meticulous and scholarly editing.

Finally, we should like to thank the B. S. B. I. for publishing this book and also for granting both Chris Haworth and Andrew Dudman funds for the purchase of computer hardware and software.

A. A. D. & A. J. R.

I should like to add that, having been responsible for most of the management, processing and presentation of the material of this Handbook, I am likely to be the source of most of the inevitable mistakes; however it should be made clear that the source of virtually all the taraxacology in the book is A.J.R., to whom I, like most British taraxacologists, owe almost all of my knowledge of dandelions.

A. A. D.

AN INTRODUCTION TO BRITISH AND IRISH DANDELIONS

Historical

Until the start of the present century, only a very few dandelion species (*"T. palustre"*, *"T. laevigatum"* etc.) were recognised from western Europe, and they were of wide scope. Modern *Taraxacum* taxonomy starts with the Scandinavians Dahlstedt, Raunkiaer and, shortly afterwards, H. Lindberg, Palmgren, Marklund and others. These workers delimited many taxa of a much narrower scope, the so-called 'microspecies'. In his later years, Dahlstedt collaborated with G.C. Druce in describing and listing many such microspecies from Britain and Ireland. Much of this early work is unfortunately of poor quality, but it has been revised, rationalised, and 'tidied up' by Haworth & Richards (1990).

From 1930 to 1964 the dandelions of Britain and Ireland received little attention. Then the late D. H. Valentine suggested to one of us that a study of British *Taraxaca* would form a fit subject for a postgraduate thesis. Out of this youthful study developed Richards's publication of 1972. In this, the first attempt to catalogue systematically the dandelions of the British Isles, 132 species were listed. Of these, 98 have survived to appear in the present account of 235 species.

In his early years, Richards was helped by the veteran Johannes van Soest and by Carl-Frederik Lundevall. However, he worked largely alone. Further major advances in the study of British and Irish dandelions awaited the stimulus provided by the late Chris Haworth, to whose memory this book is dedicated, and by the collaboration of Richards and Haworth with Hans Øllgaard from about 1979. As a result of this collaboration, the 1980s were a fruitful decade for British taraxacology. Haworth took over and developed the extensive herbarium which had been originated by Richards and which is now in effect a *Taraxacum* Herbarium for the British Isles. By close examination of this herbarium, experimental cultivation and much fieldwork, and by his encouragement of a team of enthusiastic collectors throughout the country, Haworth laid the groundwork for the present account, which, but for his untimely death in 1990, he himself was hoping to write.

After Haworth's death, Dudman took over the mantle of his friend and the care of the herbarium. He also acquired not only Haworth's and Richards's records, but also all those which had been accumulated and collated by Richards and his students from various herbaria and which had been edited and validated by Richards and Haworth. These, with the annual records from the currently active British taraxacologists whom Haworth had welded into a team of enthusiasts over his last ten years or so, now constitute a database of some 30,000 records. With financial assistance from the B.S.B.I.'s Welch Fund, for a computer and software, and with invaluable help with programming from Richard Pankhurst, Dudman compiled the computer database which has made possible the distribution maps and the material for the multi-access keys. It will be clear that Haworth's work and this account would have been much less thorough without the contribution of collectors from many parts of the British Isles, whose invaluable help we gratefully acknowledge.

The nature of dandelion species

We have said that, until the present century, the only dandelion species that were recognised were those, like *"T. palustre"* and *"T. laevigatum"*, that were of a wide scope. However, the 'macrospecies' used in the 19th century and as recently as the second edition of Clapham, Tutin & Warburg (1962) are poorly defined and are often untypified. If they have been typified, as with *T. palustre* (Lyons) Symons, they are now used in a narrow sense. Thus we recommend that the sections of the genus (as described here) are used instead for wide-scope taxa. It is in the narrower sense that we describe the species of British and Irish dandelions in this Handbook.

Everyone knows what a dandelion looks like ..., but how do you tell them apart? Most botanists know that a select, or perhaps, rather, a self-selected, coterie recognises hundreds of 'microspecies' of *Taraxacum*. We suspect that most other botanists think they are mad. There is a method in their madness, however. In this Handbook we hope to expose the complexities of dandelion identification to a wider audience.

Apomixis

Dandelions are not like most other plants. Within the British Isles, virtually all dandelions reproduce apomictically, that is they produce seed asexually, each seedling usually being an exact copy of its mother. Sexual reproduction in dandelions, if it occurs at all, is very rare in our islands.

The consequences of this apomixis are of profound importance to the taxonomist. In most sexual groups of plants one can distinguish relatively few distinct species, each of which interbreeds and is to a greater or lesser extent

8

variable. However, dandelion populations consist of a number of genetically invariable mother–daughter lines, which can be thought of as 'seed-clones'. Each of these lines, at least in theory, can be recognised as a species.

Apomixis in dandelions is genetically dominant over sexuality. It seems likely that early pollen-bearing apomicts hybridised with sexual plants, instantaneously 'fixing' hybrid swarms as a large number of asexual lines (Richards 1973). Thus it might be thought that there should be an infinite number of such lines which could be described as microspecies. In practice, this seems not to be the case, and the number of native *Taraxacum* species known from Britain and Ireland probably does not exceed 150. Because of the ease of spread of wind-blown seeds, the proximity of continental Europe and the readiness of dandelions to prosper in man-made environments, there is a steady import of continental species, mostly in Section *Ruderalia*, and this accounts for the larger number of some 235 species recorded from the British Isles.

Evolution

Natural selection works on asexual lines as efficiently as it does on sexual phenotypes, so many of the less 'fit' lines will not have survived to the present day. Also, asexual lines fall prey to the mutants which accumulate within them. They cannot shed these mutants by the sexual processes of recombination and segregation (Richards 1986).

This is best illustrated by pollenless mutants. Approximately 16% of the British dandelion species lack pollen. (Informally we often call them 'females', although all asexual dandelions are effectively only female, even if they do produce pollen.) As they are asexual, lines which are spared the burden of producing pollen are presumably at an advantage compared to lines which produce pollen.

So why have not all dandelions become pollenless? The answer is that a line can only become pollenless if the correct mutation arises within that line. There is no way in which an asexual line can acquire beneficial mutants from other lines. Each line is 'stuck' with the mutants, successful or unsuccessful, that arise within it by chance. The relatively few lines which survive today have been able to do so as a result of the randomly arising mutational events, some beneficial, most harmful, which have occurred within each since those lines were first formed thousands of years ago.

Logically, one might expect that all lines would eventually acquire 'bad' mutations – that all asexual dandelions are therefore 'doomed to extinction'. In the distant future this may indeed prove to be true, but many dandelions still seem to be very successful today! Most seem to have been formed from hybridisation between genetically distant parents, so that they are fixed heterozygotes for many genes which may convey a 'hybrid vigour' (Hughes & Richards 1988).

Recent evidence suggests that dandelion lines may not be as invariable as was once thought. They do of course accumulate mutants, which provide some variability. This process has now been detected in dandelions at the molecular level (King & Schaal 1990). Also, although their genes are not usually recombined at meiosis, asexual dandelions have unusually high levels of chromosome breakage and refusion in dividing cells, probably due to 'transposons' (Richards 1989). This phenonemon may enable apomictic dandelions to 'shuffle off' potentially disadvantageous mutants into a position in the DNA where they are 'silenced' and can do no harm.

Plasticity

However, although it is necessary to note that dandelion lines can generate a small amount of variability, for all practical purposes the lines are genetically invariable. Take seeds from a plant, line the seedlings out in the experimental garden, and they develop as like as peas in a pod, like so many identical twins! In fact this type of comparative cultivation is an invaluable tool in dandelion taxonomy. If one is unsure whether two plants are different, a study of their progeny grown in standard conditions can be invaluable. The Czech workers Jan Kirschner and Jan Štěpánek have found that such investigations are best carried out in tomato boxes. The root restriction seems to produce phenotypes more 'characteristic' of the species.

This leads naturally to the subject which chiefly bedevils the successful identification of dandelions. If the species are genetically invariable lines, they might not differ by very much, but they should differ consistently. Sadly, this is far from the case. Dandelions are amongst the most plastic of all plants, the same clone being able to produce amazingly different phenotypes at different ages and times of year, in different soils and under different amounts of moisture stress, shade, grazing, etc.

As a result, it is usually only possible to identify material accurately for a short part of the year (in late bud and early flower) and when well grown (but not too well, as in the dreaded 'cowpat-forms'). Plants collected out of season or from grazed, mown, trodden, shaded or manured sites can rarely be identified successfully. With experience, one learns what to collect and, more importantly, what *not* to collect.

To illustrate the phenotypical plasticity of *Taraxacum*, we provide (opposite) silhouettes of two specimens of **89** *T. ekmanii*. Compare both of these with that on page 231.

In this book we illustrate nearly every species with one silhouette. Ideally it would be desirable to illustrate most species with several different specimens, thus illustrating a range of phenotypes. This is obviously impracticable, but it is important *not* to assume that any one specimen silhouette can be safely used to confirm or deny a determination. There is no simple alternative to having access to or assembling a collection of specimens to illustrate the range of possible forms.

Taraxacum plasticity is too complex to describe fully here, but there are some 'golden rules' which are worth listing.

1. Juvenile and shaded leaves are less complex in shape, often being essentially undivided.

2. Trodden, drought-stressed or insolated leaves are more complex in shape.

3. During the season, successive leaves develop increasing complexity in shape. If outer, early-season leaves are examined, these often reveal the 'basic phenotype' of the species.

4. In some 'heterophyllous' species, later inner leaves develop a large terminal leaf-lobe quite different from the small end-lobe of outer leaves.

5. Many species have leaf-shape characteristics, for instance rounded lobe or lobule ends or teeth on the proximal margins, which are diagnostic but occur only occasionally. Thus it is often worth examining several leaves on a specimen in the search for a distinctive character.

T. ekmanii *Dahlst.* from damp meadows in Bohemia

T. ekmanii *Dahlst.* from a roadside verge, Hexham, Northumberland

6. The shape, size, colour and posture of the exterior bracts is best judged in late bud, just before the capitulum opens. These bud characters are illustrated in this book.

7. In general, the colour, marking and texture of a leaf are a more reliable guide to identification than is its shape. However, reddish or blackish (anthocyanin) pigments develop more strongly in good light and on early (outer) leaves than on shaded or later leaves. Also, such pigments may fade with age, notoriously so for the leaf-spots of *T. pseudolarssonii*, which appear to be water-soluble.

8. Petiole colour, judged on the outside of the leaf in a fresh condition, may be modified by the habitat (see Glossary).

9. Hairiness characteristics are best judged on young organs, leaves, scapes, etc. Most species, even the hairiest, tend to be glabrescent with age.

10. The most reliable capitulum characters are also for colour, of the ligule stripes, ligule teeth, stigma, etc. However, these often change in dried material.

11. In some species considered to lack pollen, a small amount of pollen is sometimes produced in the outer florets. Note also that some pollen can be brought onto stigmas from other species by pollinators.

12. Differences in achene size tend to be consistent between species, but achenes vary considerably with respect to position on the head: inner achenes tend to be smaller and to have shorter cones.

13. Achene colours change considerably with maturity and insolation, and they fade easily.

Cytology

All diploid *Taraxaca* (2n = 16) are sexual, and almost all polyploids are apomictic. Most polyploids are triploids (2n = 24) including nearly all asexual members of Section *Ruderalia*. Other ploidy levels are more often found in other sections, as follows:

Erythrosperma	3×, 4×	*Naevosa*	3×, 4×
Obliqua	3×	*Celtica*	3×, 4×, 5×, 6×
Palustria	3×, 4×, 5×	*Hamata*	3×*
Spectabilia	5×	*Ruderalia*	3×
Taraxacum	4×, 5×		

*All *Hamata* are triploids, but with only two satellited (NOR) chromosomes (Mogie & Richards 1983), suggesting that they have a single asexual origin.

As all these polyploid *Taraxaca* are asexual, chromosome losses and gains are accumulated. These seem to be more often tolerated in the higher polyploids, so that triploids usually have 24 chromosomes (although 25, 26 and occasionally 23 are also found, some of the last being occasionally partially sexual). However, every number between 2n = 32 and 2n = 39 has been recorded for *T. ceratolobum* (Richards 1973).

The ecology, distribution and status of British and Irish dandelions

Dandelions are usually considered to be 'weedy', and indeed most are very well adapted to take advantage of human effects on the countryside. Being asexual, they set vast amounts of identical seed which is efficiently dispersed by wind (or vehicles). Being fixed hybrids, they seem to have a great deal of vigour, while their tap-rooted habit enables them to survive many types of disaster by propagation from buried root-cuttings.

However, dandelions seem to have one 'Achilles heel' in that, perhaps as a consequence of their hybrid origin, they seem to be poor competitors. Dandelions are best adapted to colonise open ground rapidly. Even species with specialised habitat requirements are often associated with some disturbance to the ground. Only in naturally open habitats such as sand-dunes and chalk downland (Section *Erythrosperma*), in fens and flushes (Sections *Palustria* and *Spectabilia*) and on mountain cliffs (Section *Taraxacum*) is one at all likely to see native dandelions growing in unmodified circumstances. (However, the familiar *T. hamatum* is sometimes found growing in what approximates to 'wildwood'.)

Nevertheless, *Taraxacum* species do have habitat preferences, and some dandelions can indeed be found in most British habitats. They are scarcest on mountain-top tundra, where our islands have no specialist species, in ancient woodland, and on wet acidic peat, where only *T. faeroense* is at all likely to be found. Elsewhere, most of the British native dandelion rarities are to be found in 'classy' seminatural habitats in the company of other rare species. Most famous British localities also have rare dandelions – *T. cymbifolium* on Ben Lawers (and *T. pycnostictum* on nearby Tarmachan); *T. scanicum* in the Breckland; *T. cornubiense* on the Lizard; *T. palustre* and *T. anglicum* at Wicken Fen; and *T. pseudonordstedtii* in Upper Teesdale, for instance.

However, to see dandelions *en masse*, with 30 or more species coexisting, an unmodified pasture or its modern equivalent, the road-verge, is the place to visit. Road-verges and urban wastelands usually provide the richest assemblages, most of the species occurring there being classified in Section *Ruderalia*.

In such habitats it can be very difficult to suggest which species are 'native'. Dandelions, especially those in Section *Ruderalia*, are amongst the most mobile of plants, the seed being readily imported in grass seed, in animal feed, on vehicles or on clothing. On recently sown motorway verges, many of the dandelions may prove to be rare species which have probably been imported from Scandinavia or the Netherlands, and some of these may not persist very long. On the urban motorway in Newcastle upon Tyne, which was finished in 1978, three species were recorded new to the British Isles in 1980, but none persisted more than a few years. After the Second World War, Arturi Railonsala described dozens of new species from northern Finland. Few of these persisted, and decades later it become evident that these species were in fact natives of Germany, then little studied. These had been imported with feed for horses engaged in the 'winter war'.

In this Handbook we have made suggestions as to the status of British and Irish dandelion species. In many cases this was not a difficult task. Endemic species or those with a mostly British and Irish distribution, such as *T. unguilobum*, are clearly native. Those species chiefly found in seminatural habitats which demonstrate coherent distributions, such as many *Celtica* species, are also considered to be native. Equally, where species have only been found a few times in the British Isles, are restricted to ruderal habitats and often do not persist, we have little hesitation in suggesting that they are adventive.

Between these two extremes there lie many difficult examples where the status of the species in the British Isles is far from clear. *T. polyodon* is a good example. It is a common and widespread species through much of western and central Europe, including most of the British Isles, but it only inhabitats highly disturbed, ruderal habitats. It is not at all clear where it is native anywhere in its range. Another type of status is exemplified by *T. edmondsonianum*. In Britain this is a localised species of ruderal habitats, but it has a coherent distribution in north-west England. Elsewhere, it is fairly widespread in Jutland, Denmark, with a single record from Germany. Is it native to both of its main, disjunct, areas or is it native to only one of them, and, if so, to which? The ruderal habit is in itself of little help. *T. stenacrum* is among the most ruderal of species, but it is known only from England and Wales, where it is presumably native.

In other examples, it seems likely that a species is native only in part of its British and Irish range. In southern England *T. subundulatum* usually forms a major component of the *Taraxacum* flora of species-rich seasonally flooded meadows, known as 'meads' in the Thames Valley, and it appears to be native in this habitat. Elsewhere it is found as an uncommon and inconstant ruderal, and here we judge that it is adventive.

Unlike adventive species, native dandelions have coherent distributions which are illustrative of most of the main phytogeographic elements in the

British and Irish flora. A few examples of these are listed below:

Lusitanian	*T. nietoi*
Continental	*T. parnassicum*
Boreal	*T. naevosum*
Arctic	*T. cymbifolium*
Northern Atlantic	*T. faeroense*
Western Atlantic	*T. unguilobum*
Southern Atlantic	*T. drucei*
Channel	*T. hygrophilum*
Broad endemic	*T. stenacrum*
Narrow endemic	*T. pseudonordstedtii*

There are no examples in our flora of dandelion species with Alpine, Arctic-alpine or Amphiatlantic distributions.

If one is most interested in the 'native' species, the most rewarding habitat type is often found to be an old sunken lane. Particularly in the west, the verges and lane banks often support a wide range of species in Sections *Naevosa*, *Celtica*, *Hamata* and *Erythrosperma*. Few 'adventive' *Ruderalia* intrude. Such sites can be taraxacological paradises!

The collection of dandelions

Dandelion identification is best carried out by comparing specimens with a reference herbarium. Serious students will need to accumulate as complete a collection of authentic material as possible. When picked, dandelions will regenerate from the root, so collection rarely presents a conservation threat. However, rarities, for instance native species which are known only from a few sites, should not normally be collected. This certainly includes all species in Sections *Taraxacum* and *Palustria*.

Material should be collected early in the season, preferably just as it is coming into flower. Well-grown, typical material should be selected, and diseased, grazed, mown, shaded, gross, stressed or juvenile material ignored.

One needs to excise the specimen at ground level, beneath the base of the rosette, using a knife or trowel. Large specimens should be subdivided, so that about ten leaves are pressed, not overlapping. Do not separate the leaves from the base. Material is best pressed immediately it is collected, in the field, and carefully arranged in the press. Overlapping or folded-back segments of leaves can be rearranged later. With most dandelions it is necessary to dry the specimen as quickly as possible if the colour is to be retained. Drying material should be changed at least daily, better twice daily. If a drying box or artificial heat from a radiator or boiler is used, better results will be achieved. Ideally, the specimen should be dried within two days.

As well as site details, it is helpful to make a few notes from fresh material, as some features tend to be lost in the herbarium:

> colour of petiole (outside) of inner and outer leaves
> leaf spots and/or interlobe blotches present
> posture of exterior bract
> dimensions of exterior bract
> diameter of capitulum when fully open (only in bright weather)
> colour of ligule stripe
> colour of stigma

It is sometimes helpful to have ripe achene material as well, and this is vital for material in Section *Erythrosperma* and to a lesser extent in Sections *Palustria* and *Taraxacum*. Material in fruit is usually too advanced to be usefully collected, but immature fruiting heads will often mature in the press. However, flowering heads can be kept in water in a vase until the fruits mature.

Do not stick the specimen down. It is often useful to examine it under a low-powered microscope or to turn it over, so keep it loose in folded paper. Never place material from two different individuals together, and, if two specimens originate from a single individual, indicate this by numbering. Give each specimen a unique reference number.

The identification of dandelions

The identification of dandelions in the field uses a different suite of characteristics, and even of skills, from their identification in the herbarium.

In the field, leaves are frequently arranged densely and three-dimensionally in a vertical posture, so that it is not possible to recognise the subtleties of leaf-shape. However, the involucre also carries a range of varied and subtle characteristics which are mostly lost in the herbarium. *T. aequilobum* can be readily identified in the field by its spreading, irregularly arranged, twisted bracts, but this plastic species can be much more difficult to recognise in the herbarium. Characters of leaf colour and texture are also much more evident in the field. The fleshy dark leaves of *T. ancistrolobum* or the pale green 'lettucy' leaves of *T. ekmanii* can often be identified in the field, but they are less easily recognised in the herbarium.

Once familiar with the local dandelions, one can usually recognise most specimens by their *Gestalt*. A 'stranger' is soon detected by its unfamiliar general appearance. If the specimen is large, it is better subdivided and dead leaves etc. removed. Only then can key characteristics such as the colour of the outside of the petiole and the leaf-shape be accurately examined. At this stage the identity of the specimen may become apparent, or the specimen can be put into the press.

However well preserved herbarium specimens may be, characters of colour, texture, posture and shape of the involucre inevitably become more difficult to discern, and one's attention is drawn more towards the subtleties of leaf-shape. As these can be greatly modified by plasticity, it can be difficult to identify material correctly by leaf-shape alone. It is important that attention is paid to other characteristics of colour, size and posture, which is why accompanying notes are often helpful. In the herbarium, rather cryptic characters such as style colour, the presence or absence of pollen, ligule stripe colour, exterior bract size, achene size, etc. should be examined closely with a lens. Generally speaking, for the experienced taraxacologist, it is easier to identify material in the field.

Constructing a key for the identification of dandelions presents considerable difficulties. A conventional key usually considers one character at a time and asks the inquirer to make a choice. However, because dandelions are so plastic, identification nearly always depends on the consideration of several characters of any one specimen at the same time. This has traditionally led many, perhaps most, taraxacologists to consider conventional keys to be impracticable; it certainly makes a perfect key impossible, and even a useful one very difficult to construct. Nevertheless, on balance, we have decided that (as well as providing a multi-access key – see below) we should provide a rudimentary conventional key as a possible aid to narrow the daunting field. The key does not always atttempt to distinguish individual species but only to reduce the choice to some suggestions, at which point the inquirer is left to consult the full accounts in order to take into consideration the combination of all characters.

In addition, we have provided a simple multi-access key, with two sets of character states, one based on more commonly occurring characteristics, the other on rarer ones. A high proportion of species possess one or more of these, giving each a distinctive 'character state profile'. These profiles are not always unique, but they do allow a relatively few species to be checked in the systematic account to see if features of leaf shape, involucre and general description match the specimen in question.

However, the reader is warned that neither key unlocks all doors – and there will still lie confusion and frustration ahead: dandelions are difficult!

KEY TO THE SECTIONS OF BRITISH AND IRISH DANDELIONS

(after Stace 1991)

1. Plants delicate, usually with strongly dissected (often nearly pinnate) leaves; outer row of exterior bracts rarely > 7 mm; capitula rarely > 3 cm across   2

1. Plants usually medium to robust, rarely with nearly pinnate leaves; outer row of exterior bracts usually > 7 mm; capitula usually > 3 cm across   3

2. Achenes grey-brown, with pyramidal cone ≤ 0.5 mm long; leaves often with 6 or more pairs of lateral lobes   **Section *Obliqua***

    Section Obliqua *Small plants with many leaves which are many-lobed and bright green. Achenes short-coned and brown. Bracts small and appressed. Confined to coastal habitats, especially dunes. Two species.*

2. Achenes usually violet-purple or reddish, to yellowish-brown, with cylindrical cone *c.* 1 mm long; leaves rarely with > 6 pairs of lateral lobes
                                                             Section *Erythrosperma*

    Section Erythrosperma *Usually small plants. Leaves dissected. Bracts small (3–9 mm). Achenes often reddish. Achene narrow, with fine spines and a cylindrical, narrow cone which can be up to 1.3 mm long. In dry, well-insolated habitats. 30 species. (For key, see page 20.)*

3. Outer row of exterior bracts appressed, ovate with broad scarious border; leaves very narrow, usually scarcely lobed   **Section *Palustria***

    Section Palustria *Very narrow-leaved plants with broadly scarious appressed bracts which are ovate. Fen plants. Four species.*

3. Outer row of exterior bracts appressed to recurved, linear to narrowly ovate, with narrow to very narrow scarious border or unbordered; leaves broader, usually distinctly lobed   4

4. Leaves simple, bright green, with green petioles; rare plants of a few mountain cliffs in Scotland **Section _Taraxacum_**

> **Section _Taraxacum_** _Medium-sized plants with orange-yellow heads and simple, smooth, bright green leaves, spotted in some species. Confined to high mountains in Scotland. Six species._

4. Lowland plants or, if on mountain cliffs, with leaves usually dark or blotched or spotted with purple and petiole usually purple 5

5. Achene (including cone but excluding beak) > 4.5 mm, nearly cylindrical; outer row of exterior bracts erect to appressed; ligules usually with red stripes on lower side; pollen usually 0 **Section _Spectabilia_**

> **Section _Spectabilia_** _Small to medium-sized plants with rather olive- to grey-green spathulate leaves which are entire or simply lobed. Bracts appressed to erect. Achenes broadly plump and long (4–5 mm). Leaves can be spotted. Plants of damp places, usually acid and mostly montane or submontane. Three species._

5. Achene body < 4 mm, narrowly top-shaped; outer row of exterior bracts rarely appressed; ligule stripes rarely red; pollen present or 0 6

6. Leaves with large dark spots covering > 10% of surface **Section _Naevosa_**

> **Section _Naevosa_** _Small to robust plants. Leaves typically rough, coarsely lobed and with spots. Pollen often absent. Bract orientation variable but mainly erect or spreading. Generally of a northern to western distribution. 12 species. (For key, see page 22.)_

6. Leaves unspotted or with spots covering < 10% of surface (but beware of damaged leaves) 7

7. Upper sides of petiole and midrib green or solid red or purple; outer row of exterior bracts usually > 10 mm, often recurved, not very dark on lower side; leaves often complexly lobed and folded in three dimensions **Section _Ruderalia_**

> **Section _Ruderalia_** _Typically robust. Leaves generally fairly complicated and multilobate. Bracts rarely erect and most often recurved to reflexed. Achenes short and stubby, to 3.5 mm, and with short, broad-based cones. Anthocyanin development various, but many species are totally 'green'._

Apart from a few select native and endemic species, they have a great tendency to weedy behaviour. By far the largest section, with many introduced species. 120+ species. (For key, see page 26.)

7. Upper sides of petiole and midrib usually minutely striped red or purple (use lens); outer row of exterior bracts rarely > 10 mm, usually patent to erect and dark on lower side; leaves ± flat, relatively simply lobed   8

8. Lateral leaf-lobes broad-based, with convex front and concave rear edge, commonly in four pairs; outer row of exterior bracts usually arched to various degrees, often subobtuse, pruinose above, dark olive-green below
Section *Hamata*

> **Section *Hamata*** *Medium-sized or robust plants. Leaves dark olive green with simple lobation of hamate lobes and with a most characteristic midrib of 'interwoven' purple and green strands (use lens). Bracts regular, spreading and arcuate. Related to at least some of the Celtica but, like those of the last section, their ecology is predominantly 'weedy'. 18 species. (For key, see page 25.)*

8. Lateral leaf-lobes rarely as above, often 5–6 pairs; outer row of exterior bracts erect to recurved all ± to same degree, often acute   **Section *Celtica***

> **Section *Celtica*** *Medium-sized plants. Leaves generally smooth with a mid- or bluish-green colour. Petioles and midribs often bright purple or red. Leaves not usually spotted. Bracts spreading to erect. As the name suggests, with a generally western distribution. They are plants of 'good' habitats, occurring in old hedges, at woodland edges and on riversides, on generally damp soils. 30+ species. (For key, see page 23.)*

Key to Section *Erythrosperma*

1	Petioles narrow, deep purple	2
1	Petioles not as above	4
2	Scapes completely glabrous	**5 T. rubicundum**
2	Scapes pubescent, at least at top at first	3

3	Achenes pale brown; open capitulum diameter < 25 mm	**14 T. tortilobum**
3	Achenes dark violet when mature	**6 T. dunense**
3	Achene colour otherwise; open capitulum diameter > 25 mm	**1 T. lacistophyllum, 4a T. commixtum, 9 T. oxoniense**

| 4 | Exterior bracts strongly recurved | 5 |
| 4 | Exterior bracts spreading to erect | 7 |

5	Achenes chestnut; styles blackish	**8c T. disseminatum**
5	Achenes dark brown or puce; styles discoloured	**8 T. proximum**
5	Achenes pale; styles yellow or discoloured	6

| 6 | Pollen absent; styles yellow | **12 T. glauciniforme** |
| 6 | Pollen present; styles discoloured | **11c T. retzii, 12a T. wallonicum** |

| 7 | Pollen absent | 8 |
| 7 | Pollen present | 14 |

| 8 | Achenes chestnut to dark red | 9 |
| 8 | Achenes brown or puce | 11 |

| 9 | Leaves spotted | **1a T. inopinatum** |
| 9 | Leaves unspotted | 10 |

| 10 | Ligules inrolled, striped reddish-orange | **3 T. argutum** |
| 10 | Ligules flat, striped otherwise | **4 T. arenastrum, 5a T. parnassicum** |

| 11 | Achenes cinnamon or pale brown | 12 |
| 11 | Achenes dark brown or puce | **8 T. proximum** |

| 12 | Styles yellow | **8a T. proximiforme, 11 T. fulvum, 13c T. tanylepis** |
| 12 | Styles discoloured | 13 |

| 13 | Ligule teeth yellow; exterior bracts conspicuously bordered | **13 T. degelii** |
| 13 | Ligule teeth dark; exterior bracts not or slightly bordered | **8a T. proximiforme, 10 T. fulviforme, 11 T. fulvum** |

| 14 | Achenes chestnut to red | 15 |
| 14 | Achenes brown or dark purple | 17 |

15	Styles yellow; ligule teeth dark	**7a T. gotlandicum**
15	Styles usually discoloured; ligule teeth yellow	16

16	Ligule stripe purple-violet	**2 T. brachyglossum, 4 T. arenastrum**
16	Ligule stripe grey-purple	**1 T. lacistophyllum, 2a T. scanicum**

17	Achenes dark violet; styles yellow	**7 T. haworthianum**
17	Achenes pale; styles usually discoloured	18

18	Ligule teeth yellow, stripe grey-violet	**11b T. falcatum**
18	Ligule teeth dark	19

19	Ligule stripe grey-violet	**8a T. proximiforme, 11a T. scoticum**
19	Ligule stripe dark violet	**13a T. acutum**
19	Ligule stripe silver-grey	**13b T. placidum**

Key to Section *Naevosa*

1	Pollen absent or confined to marginal florets and very sparse	2
1	Pollen present in all florets	4

2	Leaves with scattered small spots	3
2	Leaves with many, larger, often confluent spots	
		24 T. euryphyllum, 25 T. maculosum

3	Exterior bracts recurved	**27 T. subnaevosum**
3	Exterior bracts suberect to spreading	**29a T. richardsianum**

4	Leaves with scattered spots or none; western and/or northern spp.	
	24a T. hirsutissimum, 27a T. cornubiense, 28 T. drucei,	
		29 T. stictophyllum
4	Leaves with many, larger, often confluent spots	5

5	Open capitulum diameter > 50 mm	**23 T. naevosum, 23b T. rubellum**
5	Open capitulum diameter < 50 mm	6

6	Spots fading; leaves ± glabrous; exterior bracts spreading, curved	
		26 T. pseudolarssonii
6	Spots permanent; leaves hairy; exterior bracts spreading to suberect	
		23a T. naevosiforme

Key to Section *Celtica*

1	Pollen absent	2
1	Pollen present	10
2	Styles yellow	3
2	Styles discoloured or dark	4

3 Exterior bracts spreading to erect, pruinose, with a clear white border
46 T. unguilobum
3 Exterior bracts spreading to recurved, pruinose or not, ± unbordered
43 T. ostenfeldii, 43a T. breconense

4	Exterior bracts spreading to recurved	5
4	Exterior bracts spreading to erect or appressed	6
5	Terminal leaf-lobe ± obtuse	**38 T. inane**
5	Terminal leaf-lobe trilobate	**35 T. celticum**

6 Lateral leaf-lobes coarsely dentate; exterior bracts pruinose throughout;
achenes cinnamon (oxidising to brown)   **45 T. fulvicarpum**
6 Not as above   7

7	Exterior bracts clearly bordered	8
7	Exterior bracts not or scarcely bordered	9

8 Exterior bracts dark green, glaucous; ligules short, striped grey
42e T. lancastriense
8 Exterior bracts green, pruinose or not; ligules striped purple
42c T. olgae, 42f T. palustrisquameum

9 Exterior bracts pruinose; ligules rather short, striped puce
42 T. nordstedtii, 42b T. berthae, 44 T. caledonicum
9 Exterior bracts not pruinose; ligules striped purple   **41 T. landmarkii**

10	Ligules lacking a stripe	**46a T. luteum**
10	Ligules striped	11

11 Proximal lateral leaf-lobes filiform or acuminate   **33a T. oellgaardii,
34 T. duplidentifrons, 34a T. porteri, 40 T. haematicum**
11 Proximal lateral leaf-lobes acute to obtuse   12

12 Leaves heavily and distinctly dark-blotched on lower surface of
interlobes   13
12 Leaves unblotched or indistinctly blotched   14

13 Terminal leaf-lobe obtuse to rounded
37 T. excellens, 39 T. fulgidum, 39a T. tamesense
13 Terminal leaf-lobe acute to trilobate
**33 T. subbracteatum, 35 T. celticum, 36 T. hesperium,
36a T. 'cestrense', 40 T. haematicum**

14 Midrib bright purple almost to apex   15
14 Midrib not bright purple or, if so, not distally   18

15 Lateral leaf-lobes 2–3(–4) on each side; rare spp.   **31a T. orcadense,
31b T. nietoi, 39b T. texelense**
15 Lateral leaf-lobes (3–)4 or more on each side   16

16 Ligules short, striped puce, brown or purple
42 T. nordstedtii, 42a T. pseudonordstedtii
16 Ligules longer, stiped grey to purple   17

17 Exterior bracts blackish on lower surface; styles blackish
32 T. britannicum
17 Exterior bracts dark green on lower surface; styles not blackish
31 T. bracteatum, 33 T. subbracteatum, 42d T. cambricum

18 Lateral leaf-lobes 2–3 on each side; rare spp.
39c T. hygrophilum, 40a T. akteum, 40b T. beeftinkii
18 Lateral leaf-lobes (3–)4 or more on each side   19

19 Exterior bracts pruinose   **32 T. britannicum, 34 T. duplidentifrons,
35 T. celticum, 42 T. nordstedtii**
19 Exterior bracts green
30 T. gelertii, 33a T. oellgaardii, 34 T. duplidentifrons

Key to Section *Hamata*

1   Exterior bracts with a narrow but ± clearly demarcated border   2
1   Exterior bracts unbordered, or border indistinct   3

2   Exterior bracts with a white border   **47a T. hamatulum,**
52b T. pruinatum, 55 T. lamprophyllum
2   Exterior bracts with a border, but not white
49a T. quadrans, 50 T. pseudohamatum, 50b T. prionum

3   Buds very dark, pruinose, inky-black at apex; involucre of exterior bracts
stellate   **47 T. hamatum**
3   Not as above   4

4   Terminal leaf-lobe ± obtuse   5
4   Terminal leaf-lobe subacute, acute or acuminate   6

5   Terminal leaf-lobe typically with one or more teeth
52 T. atactum, 52a T. sahlinianum
5   Terminal leaf-lobe entire   **51 T. boekmanii**

6   Terminal leaf-lobe toothed   7
6   Terminal leaf-lobe ± entire   8

7   Terminal leaf-lobe not larger than pairs of lateral lobes, with elongated
apex   **48a T. marklundii, 54 T. kernianum,**
55 T. lamprophyllum
7   Terminal leaf-lobe obtuse or subacute, without elongated apex
50a T. fusciflorum

8   Terminal leaf-lobe with elongated apex   9
8   Terminal leaf-lobe without elongated apex   10

9   Midrib green or weakly coloured   11
9   Midrib strongly coloured purple   12

10   Midrib bright purple to apex, usually with red side-veining
51 T. boekmanii
10   Not as above   13

11 Lateral leaf-lobes recurved, with distal margin strongly dentate
throughout; exterior bracts suffused purple   **48a T. marklundii**
11 Lateral leaf-lobes with distal margin slightly dentate proximally; exterior
bracts pruinose, pale green on upper surface   **48 T. subhamatum**

12 Interlobes heavily blotched; maximum width of exterior bracts > 3.5 mm
50b T. prionum, 55 T. lamprophyllum
12 Interlobes blotched or unblotched; maximum width of exterior bracts
< 3.5 mm   **50b T. prionum, 53 T. hamatiforme,
53a T. spiculatum, 53b T. lancidens**

13 Ligule stripe brown, without yellow border at apex; uncommon sp.
50a T. fusciflorum
13 Ligule stripe bordered yellow at apex   14

14 Inner involucral bracts not equally broad, usually irregularly connate
49 T. hamiferum
14 Inner involucral bracts ± equally broad   15

15 Maximum width of exterior bracts > 3.5 mm   **50 T. pseudohamatum**
15 Maximum width of exterior bracts < 3.5 mm
49a T. quadrans, 53 T. hamatiforme

Key to Section *Ruderalia*

1   Pollen absent; bracts ± erect   **81b T. exsertiforme**
1   Pollen absent; bracts recurved   **63b T. subhuelphersianum,
67a T. cherwellense, 69b T. speciosum**
1   Pollen present   2

2   Underside of petioles green to white with little or no trace of red
Key A (page 27)
2   Underside of petioles of outer leaves green to white, but of inner leaves
pink   **Key B** (page 29)
2   Underside of petioles of all leaves uniformly pink, red or purple
Key C (page 30)

(N.B. Lead 2 is best assessed on fresh material in the open and with the base
of the plant exposed.)

Key A: Underside of petioles green to white with little or no trace of red

1	Styles yellow or yellowish	**67b T. porrigens, 69 T. undulatiflorum, 69a T. chloroticum, 76 T. aequisectum**
1	Styles discoloured	2

2	Upper surface of midrib darker than petiole, usually coloured	3
2	Upper surface of midrib not darker than petiole	6

3	Leaves flat; terminal lobe large, subacute to obtuse; lateral lobes 2–3(–4) on each side	**73 T. ancistrolobum**
3	Not as above	4

4	Some exterior bracts > 5 mm in maximum width; midrib discoloured, often bordered by black lines	**74 T. sellandii**
4	Exterior bracts < 5 mm wide	5

5	Bracts violet on upper surface	**70a T. cyanolepis, 70b T. curtifrons, 70c T. acutifrons**
5	Bracts leaden-violet on upper surface	**70 T. piceatum**
5	Bracts pale green on upper surface	**70d T. chrysophaenum, 102d T. sublongisquameum**

6	Plant small, with fleshy, grey-green leaves; petiole and midrib chalk-white	**68a T. obtusilobum**
6	Not as above	7

7	Petioles unwinged in basal half	8
7	Petioles winged basally, sometimes narrowly so	10

8	Exterior bracts erect to appressed or erect to spreading	**57 T. pannucium, 57a T. subexpallidum, 59a T. tenebricans**
8	Exterior bracts spreading to recurved	9
8	Exterior bracts recurved	**67 T. stenacrum, 69 T. undulatiflorum**

9	Exterior bracts spreading, bordered, 4–5 mm wide	**63d T. margettsii, 75 T. altissimum**
9	Exterior bracts often recurved, unbordered, usually < 4 mm wide	**57a T. subexpallidum, 64a T. lepidum, 67 T. stenacrum, 72 T. intumescens, 72a T. angulare**

10 Petiole wings parallel, narrow; exterior bracts recurved or reflexed but
   spreading at apex   **60 T. alatum, 60b T. densilobum**
10 Petiole wings not usually parallel; exterior bracts not as above   11

11 Exterior bracts usually < 3 mm in maximum width   12
11 Exterior bracts usually > 3 mm in maximum width   15

12 Exterior bracts suffused purple, narrow, spoke-like   **61 T. insigne**
12 Not as above   13

13 Lateral leaf-lobes with patent, often double, linear processes
                                                         67 T. stenacrum
13 Not as above   14

14 Ligule tips dark   **62a T. nigridentatum**
14 Ligule tips orange-red   **66 T. croceiflorum**
14 Ligule tips yellow   **63a T. pallescens, 64a T. lepidum,**
                            65 T. expallidiforme, 65a T. subcyanolepis

15 Upper surface of exterior bracts whitish   16
15 Upper surface of exterior bracts pale green or darker   18

16 Terminal leaf-lobe abruptly acuminate   **68 T. leucopodum**
16 Not as above   17

17 Leaves greyish green, usually hairy or at least matt   **60a T. horridifrons**
17 Leaves rather pale green, sometimes hairy
                            63c T. necessarium, 65b T. pallidipes

18 Leaves ± strongly crisped   **56a T. macrolobum, 58 T. corynodes,**
                    59 T. undulatum, 59b T. dilaceratum, 89c T. lunare
18 Leaves not strongly crisped   19

19 Terminal leaf-lobes of outer leaves narrowly protracted
             56a T. macrolobum, 57 T. pannucium, 57a T. subexpallidum,
                        61a T. laciniosum, 85a T. procerisquameum
19 Terminal leaf-lobes sometimes acute but not protracted   20

20 Leaf-lobes crowded, ± overlapping
                    63 T. laticordatum, 63c T. necessarium
20 Leaf-lobes not crowded   21

21 Plant very large with rather regular lateral leaf-lobes with large teeth; rare sp.   **67c T. 'broddesonii'**
21 Not as above **56 T. laeticolor, 59b T. dilaceratum, 61b T. atonolobum, 62 T. pannulatiforme, 64 T. sublaeticolor, 89c T. lunare**

Key B: Underside of petioles of outer leaves green to white, but of inner leaves pink

1 Styles yellow   **67b T. porrigens, 80c T. edmondsonianum**
1 Styles discoloured   2

2 Exterior bracts reflexed or recurved   3
2 Exterior bracts recurved, spreading or erect   5

3 Scapes heavily arachnoid-hairy throughout when young **78b T. stereodes**
3 Scapes ± glabrous   4

4 Petioles coloured, clearly demarcated from the parallel-sided green wings
                                   79 T. adiantifrons, 80c T. edmondsonianum
4 Petioles unwinged or, if winged, with petiole colour not clearly demarcated   **84 T. lingulatum**

5 Pink petioles clearly demarcated from the parallel-sided green wings
               79b T. semiglobosum, 80b T. latens, 86a T. remanentilobum, 93a T. diastematicum, 93b T. tanyphyllum, 99a T. planum
5 Pink petioles unwinged or with midrib indistinct   6

6 Some leaves at least with terminal lobe larger than pair of lateral lobes below it   **63a T. pallescens, 70 T. piceatum, 84a T. macranthoides, 88 T. sagittipotens, 89 T. ekmanii, 96a T. fagerstroemii**
6 Terminal lobe not larger than pair of lateral lobes below it, except sometimes on inner leaves   7

7 Interlobes blotched dark below   **62 T. pannulatiforme, 96 T. huelphersianum, 102c T. maculatum**
7 Interlobes not usually blotched dark   8

8 Some lateral leaf-lobes with long linear processes; open capitulum exceeding 50 mm in diameter   **89b T. aurosulum**
8 Not as above   9

9	Exterior bracts somewhat twisted	**99a T. planum**
9	Exterior bracts not twisted	10

10	Lateral leaf-lobes sometimes divided	**66a T. lacerifolium,**
		78b T. stereodes, 96a T. fagerstroemii
10	Lateral leaf-lobes never divided	**87 T. cordatum**

Key C: Underside of petioles of all leaves uniformly pink, red or purple

1	Exterior bracts claw-shaped, coloured; interlobes blotched dark on young leaves	**100 T. polyodon, 103b T. acutifidum**
1	Not as above	2

2	Terminal lobe large and rounded or helmet-shaped on all or most leaves	
		88a T. hexhamense, 90 T. aberrans,
		90a T. 'non-severum', 91a T. cophocentrum
2	Terminal lobe large and rounded only on inner leaves or not at all	3

3	Styles yellow or yellowish	4
3	Styles discoloured	7

4	Interlobes strongly blotched dark below	5
4	Interlobes unblotched or scarcely so	6

5	Lateral leaf-lobes 5 or more on each side	
		76 T. aequisectum, 80c T. edmondsonianum,
		100a T. multicolorans, 100b T. nitidum
5	Lateral leaf-lobes 2–5 on each side	
		80c T. edmondsonianum, 102 T. xanthostigma,
		102a T. longisquameum, 102b T. scotiniforme

6	Most terminal leaf-lobes with a protracted apex	
		79a T. retroflexum, 81a T. exsertum, 82c T. leptodon
6	Terminal leaf-lobes lacking an obviously protracted apex	
		80c T. edmondsonianum, 88b T. amplum,
		89d T. coartatum, 96b T. hepaticum

7	Some exterior bracts not exceeding 3 mm in maximum width	8
7	Exterior bracts exceeding 3 mm in maximum width	11

8   Exterior bracts recurved or hanging vertically; petiole usually vivid
    purple   **95 T. dahlstedtii, 95b T. pachylobum,**
                                  98 T. pectinatiforme, 98a T. caloschistum
8   Exterior bracts erect to recurved; petiole not vivid purple   9

9   Petiole very broadly winged, short; terminal leaf-lobe tripartite
                                                   99 T. trilobatum
9   Not as above   10

10 Exterior bracts twisted   **80 T. aequilobum, 80a T. latissimum**
10 Exterior bracts not twisted
                        62a T. nigridentatum, 78 T. angustisquameum,
             91 T. oblongatum, 100 T. polyodon, 103b T. acutifidum

11 Petiole shining purple; exterior bracts broad and spreading
          82b T. obtusifrons, 97 T. subundulatum, 97a T. pulchrifolium
11 Petiole rarely shining purple but, if so, then exterior bracts not broad   12

12 Terminal leaf-lobe very acute or acuminate or at least protracted   13
12 Terminal leaf-lobe obtuse to acute, but not ending in a fine point   14

13 Leaves flat, hairy, at least when young; scapes arachnoid-hairy, at least
    when young   **81 T. acroglossum, 82 T. exacutum**
13 Leaves often ± crisped; leaves and scapes ± glabrous
                    77 T. interveniens, 78a T. mimulum, 80b T. latens,
                        90b T. pseudoretroflexum, 99a T. planum

14 Lateral leaf-lobes 2–3 on each side
                        82a T. valens, 105 T. lucidum, 105a T. sundbergii
14 Lateral leaf-lobes usually 4 or more on each side   15

15 Exterior bracts twisted
            80 T. aequilobum, 80a T. latissimum, 99a T. planum
15 Exterior bracts not twisted   16

16 Petiole narrowly parallel-winged with a clearly demarcated red midrib
        80c T. edmondsonianum, 93 T. dilatatum, 103a T. subxanthostigma
16 Not as above   17

17 Interlobes strongly blotched dark below   18
17 Interlobes unblotched or weakly coloured   22

18 Leaf-lobes strongly dentate, cut almost to midrib   **101 T. incisum**
18 Leaf-lobes sometimes strongly dentate, but not cut as far as midrib   19

19 Leaves grey-green with scattered punctate spots   **104 T. melanthoides**
19 Not as above   20

20 Leaves smudged blackish on upper surface; leaf-lobes more or less over-
     lapping   **92 T. pachymerum**
20 Distal margins of lateral leaf-lobes with many dark teeth
     62a T. nigridentatum
20 Not as above   21

21 Midribs pink to purple   **100b T. nitidum, 103a T. subxanthostigma**
21 Midribs green to slightly coloured   **71 T. tumentilobum,**
     80c T. edmondsonianum, 100 T. polyodon, 103 T. fasciatum

22 Midribs golden-brown on upper surface, especially in centre of leaf
     (in fresh specimen)   **83 T. pannulatum, 89a T. ochrochlorum**
22 Midribs not golden-brown on upper surface   23

23 Petioles very short, more or less obsolete, broadly winged
     83 T. pannulatum, 94a T. laciniosifrons
23 Petioles not very short or, if short, then not broadly winged   24

24 Leaves bright green, shiny, crisped, with omnidirectional lobes
     94 T. sinuatum
24 Leaves with lateral lobes somewhat divided
     78b T. stereodes, 96a T. fagerstroemii
24 Not as above   25

25 Apex of inner ligules blackish   **95c T. latisectum**
25 Apex of inner ligules reddish   **95a T. obliquilobum**
25 Apex of inner ligules yellow   26

26 Scapes arachnoid-hairy, at least when young
     78b T. stereodes, 82a T. valens, 86a T. remanentilobum
26 Scapes ± glabrous   27

27 Exterior bracts < 14 mm long   **80b T. latens, 85 T. rhamphodes,**
     86 T. vastisectum, 90b T. pseudoretroflexum, 96a T. fagerstroemii
27 Exterior bracts > 14 mm long   **80b T. latens,**
     80c T. edmondsonianum, 83 T. pannulatum, 96a T. fagerstroemii

MULTI-ACCESS KEY

Introduction

This key is designed for use with living material in good condition. Examine the specimen to see whether any of the character states are present. From this examination, construct an alphabetical list based on the character states that seem to be present in your specimen. If the character is not very clear or is variable, the letter may be placed in brackets.

Compare the resultant list with the alphabetical list of profiles; this should enable you to narrow the choice to a few species. The silhouettes, involucre pictures, descriptions and distributions of these species should then be consulted to make a final choice.

Common character states

A   Upper surface of leaf-blade with large irregularly-shaped black spots > 1 mm in diameter
B   Upper surface of leaf-blade with small punctate spots < 1 mm in diameter
C   Midrib coloured red or purple to extreme apex
D   Petiole white but midrib becoming increasingly dark towards leaf apex
E   Petiole (underside) and midrib white to green throughout
F   Petiole brilliantly coloured purple or violet
G   Interlobes blotched blackish on underside of leaf
H   Interlobes clearly plicate
I   Petiole unwinged, at least for basal third
J   Proximal margin of lateral leaf-lobes often with at least one marked tooth
K   Proximal margin of lateral leaf-lobes uniformly convex
L   Apex of terminal leaf-lobe with a well-differentiated tip
M   Most or all lateral leaf-lobes strongly subdivided so as to appear 'double'
N   Interior bracts noticeably corniculate at apex
O   Bud involucre strongly pruinose
P   Exterior bracts closely appressed to the involucre in bud and early flower
Q   Exterior bracts strongly reflexed into a vertical position in late bud and early flower

R   Exterior bracts irregularly arranged in late bud and early flower, often twisted

S   Upper surface of exterior bracts strongly coloured red, purple or blue in late bud and early flower

T   Exterior bracts all < 6 mm in length

U   Exterior bracts all > 15 mm in length

V   Apical teeth of inner florets dark (red, grey or black)

W   Stigmas yellow or yellowish in fresh and dried states

X   Stigmas blackish in fresh and dried states

Y   Pollen absent or rudimentary (remaining in anther tubes)

Z   Achenes reddish or red-brown

Rarer character states

a   Spots fading

b   No ligule stripes

c   Ligule stripes incomplete, crimson

d   Ligules inrolled

e   Scapes completely glabrous, even just below capitulum (Use lens.)

f   Scapes thickly arachnoid-hairy

g   Leaves very narrow, lacking clear leaf-lobes

h   Achenes blackish-purple

j   Capitulum orange

k   Upper surface of leaf thickly scabrid with short stiff hairs

l   Involucre black or blackish

m   Exterior bracts with white or scarious border > 0.5 mm

n   Inner bracts of markedly different widths

o   Achene body almost smooth throughout

p   Achene cone > 1.1 mm long

q   Achene body excluding cone > 4.0 mm long

r   Occasional lateral lobes of leaves strongly rounded (the remainder acute)

s   Ligule apex completely brown beneath

Taraxacum key profiles

(Brackets denote character states which commonly vary for the species or which are not clear cut.)

A(B)(C)(D)F(G)O(S)VY	
	24 euryphyllum
A(B)(C)(F)(G)OY	25 maculosum
A(B)(C)Hk	23 naevosum
A(B)(C)HZ(k)	23b rubellum
(A)B(C)(J)(P)k	29 stictophyllum
(A)BDWY(k)	27 subnaevosum
A(B)(H)(k)	23a naevosiforme
A(C)(G)a	26 pseudolarssonii
(B)CFG(K)(S)V(X)	39 fulgidum
BC(F)(G)(P)VY	29a richardsianum
BCF(H)IPVYc(g)oq	18 faeroense
BCFIPVYcq	18b serpenticola
BDILPVXY	42c olgae
(B)(E)H(I)OP(V)(Y)	42 nordstedtii
(B)EIPY(g)	42f palustrisquameum
BEO(j)	22 pycnostictum
(B)FIPe	17 anglicum
(B)(F)I(P)Y	42e lancastriense
B(G)(H)Q	104 melanthoides
(B)I(G)(J)(K)O(S)VYZ	
	45 fulvicarpum
BIKOP(l)o	28 drucei
BILNOYZ	1a inopinatum
B(I)(L)(W)	27a cornubiense
Bk	24a hirsutissimum
BOP(V)Y	42b berthae
C(D)GH(M)(P)	33 subbracteatum
CFGI(M)O(S)V	36 hesperium
(C)FGIS	39a tamesense
CFGJKMO(S)	37 excellens
(C)(F)GJK(S)	100b nitidum
C(F)GJMO(S)V	36a 'cestrense'
(C)(F)G(M)(O)W	100a multicolorans
CF(I)LOPlo	32 britannicum
(C)FIO(P)b(k)	46a luteum
CF(I)OV	51 boekmanii
CFIP	31 bracteatum
CF(I)PVoq	18a geirhildae
C(F)(L)(M)Q	98 pectinatiforme
C(F)(L)O	53a spiculatum
CFNW	13b placidum
(C)GHJMf	94a laciniosifrons

(C)(K)Oo	42d cambricum
DGH(I)LV	75 altissimum
DGH(J)(M)(R)(V)	62a nigridentatum
D(G)H(J)O(S)(U)(V)	74 sellandii
D(G)(H)KS(V)	70b curtifrons
DGH(L)S	70 piceatum
DG(M)V	102c maculatum
DG(U)	102d sublongisquameum
D(G)(V)	73 ancistrolobum
D(H)	103b acutifidum
DH(Q)U(k)	85a procerisquameum
DIWYd	43a breconense
E	12a wallonicum
Eejoq	19a clovense
E(G)(H)(I)(L)(M)	57 pannucium
E(G)HILWYZdjs	3 argutum
(E)GH(J)KV	72 intumescens
(E)GH(J)M	62 pannulatiforme
E(G)(H)(J)(S)r	65a subcyanolepis
E(G)(H)(J)(U)	65b pallidipes
E(G)H(L)M	59b dilaceratum
EG(H)(M)(R)	61a laciniosum
EGHQV	84a macranthoides
(E)(G)(J)	64 sublacticolor
E(G)(J)(K)(P)(S)	56 laeticolor
E(G)(K)(Q)(V)(W)	63c necessarium
EG(L)	69 undulatiflorum
EGMU	67c 'broddesonii'
EH(I)(L)NPTV(W)cde(j)	
	15 obliquum
EH(J)(K)f	59 undulatum
(E)H(J)(K)(U)V	105a sundbergii
EH(J)(L)P	59a tenebricans
EH(J)(M)	58 corynodes
EH(J)(M)OQk	60b densilobum
EH(J)(M)V(j)	66 croceiflorum
EHJ(R)(U)(W)f	89d coartatum
EHJ(U)f	89c lunare
EH(K)V	70d chrysophaenum
E(H)(L)	65 expallidiforme
E(H)L(M)OQ(V)k	60a horridifrons
E(H)M	66a lacerifolium
EHMNVWYZ	12 glauciniforme

E(H)(Q)V	61b atonolobum	FIL(M)OV(s)	53b lancidens
EHW(Y)ej(q)	19 ceratolobum	FILNOPTV(Y)eh	5 rubicundum
E(I)	63d margettsii	FILN(T)YZ	5a parnassicum
E(I)(J)Or	64a lepidum	FILNVh(p)	6 dunense
E(I)(K)LS(r)	70c acutifrons	FI(L)VY	41 landmarkii
EI(L)	69a chloroticum	(F)I(P)	31a orcadense
E(I)LM	56a macrolobum	FIPgm	16b sarniense
E(I)LM	67 stenacrum	FIPYgm	16a webbii
E(I)LM(W)	67b porrigens	(F)IPYgm(o)	16 palustre
E(I)(L)NPTVW	15a platyglossum	F(I)Q	98a caloschistum
EILNVYZe	5b cenabense	FIVXZ	8c disseminatum
EIMY	67a cherwellense	FIWm	31b nietoi
(E)(I)(O)	87 cordatum	FIZ	9 oxoniense
E(I)WY	13c tanylepis	F(K)	33a oellgaardii
E(J)(K)	63 laticordatum	FK(O)(S)(W)(Z)	88a hexhamense
E(J)(K)RSV	61 insigne	F(K)P	30 gelertii
EJLO(R)U	68 leucopodum	(F)(L)Y	81b exsertiforme
EKSV	70a cyanolepis	GH	90 'non-severum'
EL	39c hygrophilum	GHf	96 huelphersianum
ELNSVWZ	7a gotlandicum	GHI(J)(K)(L)R	80a latissimum
ELS	68a obtusilobum	(G)H(I)(J)(L)	78 angustisquameum
E(L)(U)V	72a angulare	GH(I)(J)V	101 incisum
E(M)	57a subexpallidum	(G)(H)ILr	77 interveniens
(E)(O)(Q)	88 sagittipotens	(G)(H)(I)L(V)f	82 exacutum
EO(Q)(V)	60 alatum	GHILYZ	11b falcatum
E(P)W	40b beeftinkii	(G)(H)I(M)Qf	78b stereodes
EQ(Y)	63b subhuelphersianum	GHI(M)V	71 tumentilobum
(E)r	63a pallescens	GHIV(W)	102a longisquameum
EV(e)jq	19b xiphoideum	(G)HJKQ	92 pachymerum
EWY(j)	20 craspedotum	GHJ(K)QW	80c edmondsonianum
EWZj	21 cymbifolium	(G)(H)(J)(O)qs	50a fusciflorum
(F)GHILMO	54 kernianum	GHJVW	102 xanthostigma
FGHIL(M)(S)V	40 haematicum	(G)H(L)R	80 aequilobum
FGH(I)LOSV(s)	55 lamprophyllum	(G)(H)LV	89b aurosulum
F(G)HJ	97 subundulatum	GHLVWZ	11a scoticum
(F)(G)HO(R)	93 dilatatum	(G)H(M)U	83 pannulatum
FGHVY	38 inane	(G)HQVW	76 aequisectum
(F)(G)IO	53 hamatiforme	G(H)V	103 fasciatum
F(G)LOV(X)Y	35 celticum	GHV	80b latens
FHI(J)LNOPTX	14 tortilobum	GHV	103a subxanthostigma
FH(I)J(O)(V)	94 sinuatum	G(H)VWf	102b scotiniforme
FHIKV	105 lucidum	GILOVYZ	10 fulviforme
(F)HI(L)OPSVY(d)	44 caledonicum	(G)I(L)O(W)m	47a hamatulum
F(H)IQ	95 dahlstedtii	(G)ILWf(k)	82c leptodon
FHJLM(Q)VX	99 trilobatum	(G)(I)O	82b obtusifrons
F(H)r	95b pachylobum	(G)IOl	47 hamatum
(F)(H)U	93b tanyphyllum	(G)IOn	49 hamiferum
FIJM	97a pulchrifolium	G(J)LVWYj	69b speciosum
(F)I(K)WY	43 ostenfeldii	(G)L	34a porteri

G(L)(f)(k)	81 acroglossum	(I)(K)(L)Q	79 adiantifrons
(G)LO(S)	48a marklundii	IKNOWY(h)	8 proximum
(G)LO(S)	48 subhamatum	IL	13a acutum
(G)LQr	84 lingulatum	ILNOSVZ	2 brachyglossum
GLSV	100 polyodon	ILNOVW	8a proximiforme
G(M)	93a diastematicum	ILNOZ	1 lacistophyllum
(G)O(V)	50 pseudohamatum	I(L)OV	52b pruinatum
(G)W	96b hepaticum	(I)L(Y)p	13 degelii
H	89 ekmanii	IMNVZ	2a scanicum
(H)(I)JLO	90 aberrans	(I)M(Q)(S)	96a fagerstroemii
(H)(I)(K)O	49a quadrans	INO	8b pseudoproximum
(H)I(K)Q	78a mimulum	IOP(S)V	42a pseudonordstedtii
HILNPVWh	7 haworthianum	I(O)V	52 atactum
HILWZ(f)	4 arenastrum	(I)(S)V	95c latisectum
(H)(I)Q(W)	79a retroflexum	(I)VWYZ	11 fulvum
(H)J	86 vastisectum	JVZ	11c retzii
HJf	89a ochrochlorum	KL(O)(V)f(k)	50b prionum
H(K)Or	85 rhamphodes	(L)(N)(W)	81a exsertum
HL(R)	99a planum	LQ	90b pseudoretroflexum
(H)Of	86a remanentilobum	MV(X)(k)	34 duplidentifrons
(H)Q	79b semiglobosum	OPWYZ	46 unguilobum
(H)Qf	82a valens	(O)(S)(V)	52a sahlinianum
(H)(R)UV	95a obliquilobum	(S)	91 oblongatum
H(S)Wf	88b amplum		91a cophocentrum
I	40a akteum		39b texelense
IJNWYZ	4a commixtum		

Profiles of species in alphabetical order

aberrans	(H)(I)JLO	atonolobum	E(H)(Q)V
acroglossum	G(L)(f)(k)	aurosulum	(G)(H)LV
acutifidum	D(H)	beeftinkii	E(P)W
acutifrons	E(I)(K)LS(r)	berthae	BOP(V)Y
acutum	IL	boekmanii	CF(I)OV
adiantifrons	(I)(K)(L)Q	brachyglossum	ILNOSVZ
aequilobum	(G)H(L)R	bracteatum	CFIP
aequisectum	(G)HQVW	breconense	DIWYd
akteum	I	britannicum	CF(I)LOPlo
alatum	EO(Q)(V)	'broddesonii'	EGMU
altissimum	DGH(I)LV	caledonicum	(F)HI(L)OPSVY(d)
amplum	H(S)Wf	caloschistum	F(I)Q
ancistrolobum	D(G)(V)	cambricum	(C)(K)Oo
anglicum	(B)FIPe	celticum	F(G)LOV(X)Y
angulare	E(L)(U)V	cenabense	EILNVYZe
angustisquameum	(G)H(I)(J)(L)	ceratolobum	EHW(Y)ej(q)
arenastrum	HILWZ(f)	'cestrense'	C(F)GJMO(S)V
argutum	E(G)HILWYZdjs	cherwellense	EIMY
atactum	I(O)V	chloroticum	EI(L)

chrysophaenum	EH(K)V	haworthianum	HILNPVWh
clovense	Eejoq	hepaticum	(G)W
coartatum	EHJ(R)(U)(W)f	hesperium	CFGI(M)O(S)V
commixtum	IJNWYZ	hexhamense	FK(O)(S)(W)(Z)
cophocentrum		hirsutissimum	Bk
cordatum	(E)(I)(O)	horridifrons	E(H)L(M)OQ(V)k
cornubiense	B(I)(L)(W)	huelphersianum	GHf
corynodes	EH(J)(M)	hygrophilum	EL
craspedotum	EWY(j)	inane	FGHVY
croceiflorum	EH(J)(M)V(j)	incisum	GH(I)(J)V
curtifrons	D(G)(H)KS(V)	inopinatum	BILNOYZ
cyanolepis	EKSV	insigne	E(J)(K)RSV
cymbifolium	EWZj	interveniens	(G)(H)ILr
dahlstedtii	F(H)IQ	intumescens	(E)GH(J)KV
degelii	(I)L(Y)p	kernianum	(F)GHILMO
densilobum	EH(J)(M)OQk	lacerifolium	E(H)M
diastematicum	G(M)	laciniosifrons	(C)GHJMf
dilaceratum	E(G)H(L)M	laciniosum	EG(H)(M)(R)
dilatatum	(F)(G)HO(R)	lacistophyllum	ILNOZ
disseminatum	FIVXZ	laeticolor	E(G)(J)(K)(P)(S)
drucei	BIKOP(l)o	lamprophyllum	FGH(I)LOSV(s)
dunense	FILNVh(p)	lancastriense	(B)(F)I(P)Y
duplidentifrons	MV(X)(k)	lancidens	FIL(M)OV(s)
edmondsonianum	GHJ(K)QW	landmarkii	FI(L)VY
ekmanii	H	latens	GHV
euryphyllum	A(B)(C)(D)F(G)O(S)VY	laticordatum	E(J)(K)
exacutum	(G)(H)(I)L(V)f	latisectum	(I)(S)V
excellens	CFGJKMO(S)	latissimum	GHI(J)(K)(L)R
expallidiforme	E(H)(L)	lepidum	E(I)(J)Or
exsertiforme	(F)(L)Y	leptodon	(G)ILWf(k)
exsertum	(L)(N)(W)	leucopodum	EJLO(R)U
faeroense	BCF(H)IPVYc(g)oq	lingulatum	(G)LQr
fagerstroemii	(I)M(Q)(S)	longisquameum	GHIV(W)
falcatum	GHILYZ	lucidum	FHIKV
fasciatum	G(H)V	lunare	EHJ(U)f
fulgidum	(B)CFG(K)(S)V(X)	luteum	(C)FIO(P)b(k)
fulvicarpum	(B)I(G)(J)(K)O(S)VYZ	macranthoides	EGHQV
fulviforme	GILOVYZ	macrolobum	E(I)LM
fulvum	(I)VWYZ	maculatum	DG(M)V
fusciflorum	(G)(H)(J)(O)qs	maculosum	A(B)(C)(F)(G)OY
geirhildae	CF(I)PVoq	margettsii	E(I)
gelertii	F(K)P	marklundii	(G)LO(S)
glauciniforme	EHMNVWYZ	melanthoides	B(G)(H)Q
gotlandicum	ELNSVWZ	mimulum	(H)I(K)Q
haematicum	FGHIL(M)(S)V	multicolorans	(C)(F)G(M)(O)W
hamatiforme	(F)(G)IO	naevosiforme	A(B)(H)(k)
hamatulum	(G)I(L)O(W)m	naevosum	A(B)(C)Hk
hamatum	(G)IOl	necessarium	E(G)(K)(Q)(V)(W)
hamiferum	(G)IOn	nietoi	FIWm

nigridentatum	DGH(J)(M)(R)(V)	retzii	JVZ
nitidum	(C)(F)GJK(S)	rhamphodes	H(K)Or
'non-severum'	GH	richardsianum	BC(F)(G)(P)VY
nordstedtii	(B)(E)H(I)OP(V)(Y)	rubellum	A(B)(C)HZ(k)
obliquilobum	(H)(R)UV	rubicundum	FILNOPTV(Y)eh
obliquum	EH(I)(L)NPTV(W)cde(j)	sagittipotens	(E)(O)(Q)
oblongatum	(S)	sahlinianum	(O)(S)(V)
obtusifrons	(G)(I)O	sarniense	FIPgm
obtusilobum	ELS	scanicum	IMNVZ
ochrochlorum	HJf	scoticum	GHLVWZ
oellgaardii	F(K)	scotiniforme	G(H)VWf
olgae	BDILPVXY	sellandii	D(G)H(J)O(S)(U)(V)
orcadense	(F)I(P)	semiglobosum	(H)Q
ostenfeldii	(F)I(K)WY	serpenticola	BCFIPVYcq
oxoniense	FIZ	sinuatum	FH(I)J(O)(V)
pachylobum	F(H)r	speciosum	G(J)LVWYj
pachymerum	(G)HJKQ	spiculatum	C(F)(L)O
pallescens	(E)r	stenacrum	E(I)LM
pallidipes	E(G)(H)(J)(U)	stereodes	(G)(H)I(M)Qf
palustre	(F)IPYgm(o)	stictophyllum	(A)B(C)(J)(P)k
palustrisquameum	(B)EIPY(g)	subbracteatum	C(D)GH(M)(P)
pannucium	E(G)(H)(I)(L)(M)	subcyanolepis	E(G)(H)(J)(S)r
pannulatiforme	(E)GH(J)M	subexpallidum	E(M)
pannulatum	(G)H(M)U(r)	subhamatum	(G)LO(S)
parnassicum	FILN(T)YZ	subhuelphersianum	EQY
pectinatiforme	C(F)(L)(M)Q	sublaeticolor	(E)(G)(J)
piceatum	DGH(L)S	sublongisquameum	DG(U)
placidum	CFNW	subnaevosum	(A)BDWY(k)
planum	HL(R)	subundulatum	F(G)HJ
platyglossum	E(I)(L)NPTVW	subxanthostigma	GHV
polyodon	GLSV	sundbergii	(E)H(J)(K)(U)V
porrigens	E(I)LM(W)	tamesense	(C)FGIS
porteri	(G)L	tanylepis	E(I)WY
prionum	KL(O)(V)f(k)	tanyphyllum	(F)(H)U
procerisquameum	DH(Q)U(k)	tenebricans	EH(J)(L)P
proximiforme	ILNOVW	texelense	
proximum	IKNOWY(h)	tortilobum	FHI(J)LNOPTX
pruinatum	I(L)OV	trilobatum	FHJLM(Q)VX
pseudohamatum	(G)O(V)	tumentilobum	GHI(M)V
pseudolarssonii	A(C)(G)a	undulatiflorum	EG(L)
pseudonordstedtii	IOP(S)V	undulatum	EH(J)(K)f
pseudoproximum	INO	unguilobum	OPWYZ
pseudoretroflexum	LQ	valens	(H)Qf
pulchrifolium	FIJM	vastisectum	(H)J
pycnostictum	BEO(j)	wallonicum	E
quadrans	(H)(I)(K)O	webbii	FIPYgm
remanentilobum	(H)Of	xanthostigma	GHJVW
retroflexum	(H)(I)Q(W)	xiphoideum	EV(e)jq

SYSTEMATIC ACCOUNT

Introduction

Although 235 species are described in this account, many are casual adventives and others localised and rare natives. In most parts of Britain and Ireland one is likely to encounter no more than about 100 species, perhaps less. So we have selected 105 numbered 'lead' species; 'subsidiary' species have a letter after the number of the relevant lead species.

We give full descriptions of most species, in which all relevant character states are listed in a standard order. The account of each lead species ends with some key character states; for subsidiary species the principal differences from the lead species are noted. Details of the status, habitat and range of each species are also given, and there are also distribution maps for 178 species, including records to the end of 1996. Silhouettes of herbarium specimens are provided for all except a few rare casuals. We are fortunate to be able to provide drawings of bud involucres for the majority of species. The choice of these has been dictated by our ability to provide fresh material to Olga Stewart, who painstakingly drew them for us.

In the systematic account we provide the current binomial for each of the species, with the author and date, but no synonymy. Accounts containing much of the synonymy of the British and Irish species can be found in Richards (1972) and in Haworth & Richards (1990). The nomenclature and synonymy of the sections is discussed in Richards (1985) and in Kirschner & Štěpánek (1987). We provide a list of some of the more frequently occurring alternative names. References to the works in which the British and Irish species were named and described are listed at the end of this book.

In the distributional accounts of each species, we list, by giving vice-county numbers, the British and Irish Watsonian vice-counties for which we hold records. These vice-counties and their numbers are listed below. Their limits bear scant resemblance to modern political boundaries but are accurately detailed by Dandy (1969).) The distribution maps at the end of the systematic account use the 10-km squares of the British and Irish National Grids and are based only on our own database. In this account we have rarely attempted to detail distributions outside the British Isles, but we have stated when the species is endemic.

On the whole, the coverage of Britain has become reasonably even. Such bias as exists tends to result from localised pockets of very intensive activity by expert recorders, for instance Tom Edmondson in Cheshire, Merle Marsden in Gloucestershire, Michael Porter in Breconshire, Len Livermore in Lancashire, Tom Margetts in Devon and Cornwall, or ourselves and Chris Haworth in Cumberland and Northumberland. This bias is mostly shown by the unevenly recorded distribution of casual adventives. However, some British vice-counties have received a much less adequate cover than most. These are: 5, 6, 7, 8, 9, 10, 13, 14, 25, 26, 32, 38, 47, 52, 53, 54, 63, 64, 78, 79, 86, 87. The coverage of Ireland is still far from adequate, and for some vice-counties few if any records exist. However there is quite good cover for: H9, H12, H13, H15, H16, H17, H20, H21, H22, H23, H26, H27, H37, H38, H39, H40.

Vice-county list

1	West Cornwall	39	Staffordshire
2	East Cornwall	40	Shropshire
3	South Devon	41	Glamorgan
4	North Devon	42	Breconshire
5	South Somerset	43	Radnorshire
6	North Somerset	44	Carmarthenshire
7	North Wiltshire	45	Pembrokeshire
8	South Wiltshire	46	Cardiganshire
9	Dorset	47	Montgomeryshire
10	Isle of Wight	48	Merionethshire
11	South Hampshire	49	Caernarvonshire
12	North Hampshire	50	Denbighshire
13	West Sussex	51	Flintshire
14	East Sussex	52	Anglesey
15	East Kent	53	South Lincolnshire
16	West Kent	54	North Lincolnshire
17	Surrey	55	Leicestershire
18	South Essex	56	Nottinghamshire
19	North Essex	57	Derbyshire
20	Hertfordshire	58	Cheshire
21	Middlesex	59	South Lancashire
22	Berkshire	60	West Lancashire
23	Oxfordshire	61	South-east Yorkshire
24	Buckinghamshire	62	North-east Yorkshire
25	East Suffolk	63	South-west Yorkshire
26	West Suffolk	64	Mid-west Yorkshire
27	East Norfolk	65	North-west Yorkshire
28	West Norfolk	66	Durham
29	Cambridgeshire	67	South Northumberland
30	Bedfordshire	68	North Northumberland
31	Huntingdonshire	69	Westmorland and Furness
32	Northamptonshire	70	Cumberland
33	East Gloucestershire	71	Man
34	West Gloucestershire	72	Dumfriesshire
35	Monmouthshire	73	Kirkcudbrightshire
36	Herefordshire	74	Wigtonshire
37	Worcestershire	75	Ayrshire
38	Warwickshire	76	Renfrewshire

77	Lanarkshire	96	East Invernessshire
78	Peeblesshire	97	West Invernessshire
79	Selkirkshire	98	Argyll Main
80	Roxburghshire	99	Dunbartonshire
81	Berwickshire	100	Clyde Islands
82	East Lothian	101	Kintyre
83	Midlothian	102	South Ebudes
84	West Lothian	103	Mid Ebudes
85	Fifeshire	104	North Ebudes
86	Stirlingshire	105	West Ross
87	West Perthshire	106	East Ross
88	Mid Perthshire	107	East Sutherland
89	East Perthshire	108	West Sutherland
90	Angus	109	Caithness
91	Kincardineshire	110	Outer Hebrides
92	South Aberdeenshire	111	Orkney
93	North Aberdeenshire	112	Shetland
94	Banffshire	S	Channel Islands
95	Moray		

H1	South Kerry	H21	Dublin
H2	North Kerry	H22	Meath
H3	West Cork	H23	West Meath
H4	Mid Cork	H24	Longford
H5	East Cork	H25	Roscommon
H6	Waterford	H26	East Mayo
H7	South Tipperary	H27	West Mayo
H8	Limerick	H28	Sligo
H9	Clare	H29	Leitrim
H10	North Tipperary	H30	Cavan
H11	Kilkenny	H31	Louth
H12	Wexford	H32	Monaghan
H13	Carlow	H33	Fermanagh
H14	Leix	H34	East Donegal
H15	South-east Galway	H35	West Donegal
H16	West Galway	H36	Tyrone
H17	North-east Galway	H37	Armagh
H18	Offaly	H38	Down
H19	Kildare	H39	Antrim
H20	Wicklow	H40	Londonderry

BRITISH AND IRISH *TARAXACUM* SPECIES LIST

Note: * denotes an illustration of the capitulum and † a distribution map.

Section **Erythrosperma** (H. Lindb.) Dahlst.

1 lacistophyllum*†
1a inopinatum*†
2 brachyglossum*†
2a scanicum†
3 argutum*†
4 arenastrum*†
4a commixtum†
5 rubicundum*†
5a parnassicum*†
5b cenabense†
6 dunense†
7 haworthianum*†
7a gotlandicum†
8 proximum†
8a proximiforme†

8b pseudoproximum
8c disseminatum†
9 oxoniense*†
10 fulviforme*†
11 fulvum*†
11a scoticum†
11b falcatum†
11c retzii†
12 glauciniforme*†
12a wallonicum†
13 degelii†
13a acutum†
13b placidum
13c tanylepis
14 tortilobum*†

Section **Obliqua** (Dahlst.) Dahlst.

15 obliquum*†
15a platyglossum*†

Section **Palustria** (H. Lindb.) Dahlst.

16 palustre*†
16a webbii†

16b sarniense†
17 anglicum*†

Section **Spectabilia** (Dahlst.) Dahlst.

18 faeroense*†
18a geirhildae*†

18b serpenticola*†

44

Section **Taraxacum**

19 ceratolobum*†
  19a clovense†
  19b xiphoideum†

20 craspedotum†
21 cymbifolium*†
22 pycnostictum†

Section **Naevosa** M.P. Christ.

23 naevosum*†
  23a naevosiforme*†
  23b rubellum*†
24 euryphyllum*†
  24a hirsutissimum*†
25 maculosum*†

26 pseudolarssonii*†
27 subnaevosum*†
  27a cornubiense†
28 drucei†
29 stictophyllum*†
  29a richardsianum*†

Section **Celtica** A.J. Richards

30 gelertii*†
31 bracteatum*†
  31a orcadense†
  31b nietoi†
32 britannicum*†
33 subbracteatum*†
  33a oellgaardii†
34 duplidentifrons*†
  34a porteri*†
35 celticum*†
36 hesperium*†
  36a 'cestrense'
37 excellens*†
38 inane*†
39 fulgidum†
  39a tamesense*†
  39b texelense†
  39c hygrophilum†

40 haematicum†
  40a akteum†
  40b beeftinkii†
41 landmarkii*†
42 nordstedtii*†
  42a pseudonordstedtii†
  42b berthae*†
  42c olgae*†
  42d cambricum*†
  42e lancastriense†
  42f palustrisquameum†
43 ostenfeldii*†
  43a breconense*†
44 caledonicum*†
45 fulvicarpum*†
46 unguilobum*†
  46a luteum†

Section **Hamata** H. Øllg.

47 hamatum*†
  47a hamatulum*†
48 subhamatum*†
  48a marklundii*†
49 hamiferum*†
  49a quadrans*†
50 pseudohamatum*†
  50a fusciflorum†
  50b prionum

51 boekmanii*†
52 atactum*†
  52a sahlinianum*†
  52b pruinatum
53 hamatiforme*†
  53a spiculatum
  53b lancidens
54 kernianum*†
55 lamprophyllum*†

Section **Ruderalia** Kirschner, H. Øllg. & Štěpánek

56 laeticolor*†
  56a macrolobum†
57 pannucium*†
  57a subexpallidum*†
58 corynodes*†
59 undulatum*†
  59a tenebricans†
  59b dilaceratum*†
60 alatum*†
  60a horridifrons*†
  60b densilobum*
61 insigne*†
  61a laciniosum
  61b atonolobum
62 pannulatiforme*†
  62a nigridentatum*†
63 laticordatum*†
  63a pallescens†
  63b subhuelphersianum
  63c necessarium*†
  63d margettsii†
64 sublaeticolor*†
  64a lepidum*†
65 expallidiforme*†
  65a subcyanolepis†
  65b pallidipes*†

66 croceiflorum*†
  66a lacerifolium†
67 stenacrum*†
  67a cherwellense†
  67b porrigens
  67c 'broddesonii'*
68 leucopodum
  68a obtusilobum
69 undulatiflorum*†
  69a chloroticum
  69b speciosum
70 piceatum*†
  70a cyanolepis*†
  70b curtifrons
  70c acutifrons
  70d chrysophaenum
71 tumentilobum*†
72 intumescens*
  72a angulare
73 ancistrolobum*†
74 sellandii*†
75 altissimum†
76 aequisectum*†
77 interveniens†
78 angustisquameum*†
  78a mimulum*

78b stereodes*
79 adiantifrons*†
79a retroflexum†
79b semiglobosum
80 aequilobum*†
80a latissimum*†
80b latens
80c edmondsonianum†
81 acroglossum*†
81a exsertum†
81b exsertiforme
82 exacutum*†
82a valens
82b obtusifrons*
82c leptodon
83 pannulatum*†
84 lingulatum*†
84a macranthoides
85 rhamphodes*†
85a procerisquameum†
86 vastisectum*†
86a remanentilobum*
87 cordatum*†
88 sagittipotens*†
88a hexhamense†
88b amplum*
89 ekmanii*†
89a ochrochlorum
89b aurosulum*†
89c lunare*
89d coartatum
90 aberrans
90a 'non-severum'
90b pseudoretroflexum
91 oblongatum*†

91a cophocentrum*†
92 pachymerum*†
93 dilatatum*†
93a diastematicum*
93b tanyphyllum
94 sinuatum*†
94a laciniosifrons*†
95 dahlstedtii*†
95a obliquilobum†
95b pachylobum
95c latisectum*†
96 huelphersianum*†
96a fagerstroemii*†
96b hepaticum
97 subundulatum*†
97a pulchrifolium*†
98 pectinatiforme*†
98a caloschistum
99 trilobatum*†
99a planum*
100 polyodon*†
100a multicolorans*†
100b nitidum
101 incisum*†
102 xanthostigma*†
102a longisquameum*†
102b scotiniforme*
102c maculatum
102d sublongisquameum
103 fasciatum*†
103a subxanthostigma
103b acutifidum
104 melanthoides*†
105 lucidum*
105a sundbergii

DESCRIPTIONS AND ILLUSTRATIONS

The illustrations of capitula accompanying the descriptions are drawn from living material and are all life-size. The plant silhouettes are of specimens in our own herbarium. They are not all to the same scale: note the individual 6-cm scale-bars. In many cases some of the leaves have been removed in the preparation of herbarium specimens.

Measurements and shapes of leaves relate to both the blade and the petiole, but leaf colours relate to the blade alone, the colour of the petiole being given separately. The numbers of lateral lobes refer to those on *one* side of the leaf. See the glossary (pages 325–327) for notes on petiole colour, petiole wings, exterior bracts, ligule stripes and teeth, style colour, presence of pollen, and achene colour.

Authors of names of species are given in the forms recommended by Brummitt & Powell (1992). Authors for *Taraxacum* sections are as given by Kirschner & Štěpánek (1977).

Section ERYTHROSPERMA (H. Lindb.) Dahlst. (1921)

1 T. lacistophyllum (Dahlst.) Raunk. (1906)

Map 1

A small to medium-sized plant, with deeply dissected leaves 30–200 mm.

Leaves mid-green, without spots, almost glabrous, interlobes without blotches, midrib green to faintly coloured; lateral lobes 3–5, patent to somewhat recurved, broader proximally but with apex linear and acute, forming a *sigmoid distal margin when well developed, only proximal lobes dentate*; terminal lobe subsagittate with an acute, somewhat elongated apex; petiole unwinged proximally, narrow, purple. Scapes often purplish, somewhat arachnoid-hairy below capitulum. Involucre usually *pruinose*; exterior bracts usually spreading, sometimes arcuate or erect, about 7 × 2 mm, *bordered, pruinose*, grey-green often lightly suffused with purple on upper surface, blue-green on lower surface, somewhat corniculate. Capitulum rather pale yellow, to 30 mm in diameter; outer ligules flat, *to 2× the involucre*, striped *grey-purple*, with *yellow* teeth; styles *discoloured*; pollen *present*. Achenes chestnut (to purple); body *3.0 mm*; cone 0.8–1.0 mm. 2n=24.

Native. Frequent on light, well-drained neutral to calcareous soils, often in species-rich grasslands but also on walls, cliffs etc., throughout the British Isles. V.cc. 1–26, 28–30, 32–53, 55, 57–62, 64–75, 78, 80–83, 85, 88, 89, 91, 94–99, 101, 106, 109, 110, S, H21, H26, H39.

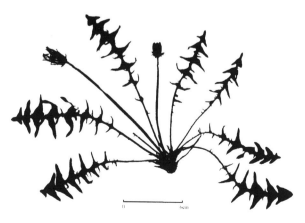

Diagnosed by the combination of reddish achenes, pollen-rich, discoloured styles, and usually spreading, bordered and pruinose exterior bracts. In well-developed specimens the leaf-shape is characteristic. **2** *T. brachyglossum* has short ligules which scarcely exceed the involucre. See also **4a** *T. commixtum* and **14** *T. tortilobum*.

1a T. inopinatum C.C. Haw. (1990)

Map 1a

A small to medium-sized plant, with oblanceolate leaves to 200 mm.

Leaves mid to dark olive-green, *usually with scattered faint purple spots*; lateral lobes 4–6, triangular or deltoid; interlobes rather narrow and *usually dentate* with narrow teeth of various lengths; terminal lobe medium-sized, ± acutely trilobate, with an elongated acute or subacute apex; petiole to one quarter length of leaf, unwinged, usually green but occasionally slightly dull purple. Exterior bracts erect or suberect, 7–8 × 2–3 mm, pale, glaucous and pruinose on upper surface, very dark glaucous and pruinose on lower surface, usually with a narrow white border, scarcely corniculate. Capitulum 25–35 mm; styles grey-yellow; pollen *absent or sometimes present in small quantity*. Achene dark orange-brown or red; body *3.2–3.4 mm*; cone 0.6–0.9 mm.

Native and endemic. More western than **1** and more typical of bare, rocky and sandy sites. V.cc. 1, 3, 25, 35, 40, 42, 44, 50, 51, 52, 58, 60, 65, 69, 70.

Differs from **1** in having leaves more often dentate throughout, which are usually marked with small purple spots; the achene is somewhat longer (3.2–3.4 mm), and pollen is absent or sparse. This is the only member of the British *Erythrosperma* to be characterised by leaf-spots.

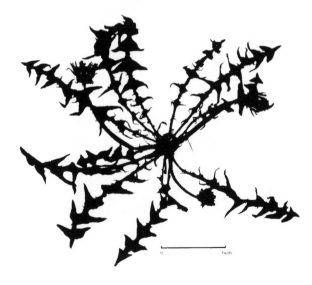

50

Section *Erythrosperma*

2 T. brachyglossum (Dahlst.) Raunk. (1906) **Map 2**

A small to medium-sized plant, with leaves 30–200 mm.

Leaves usually a rather dull green, without spots, interlobes without blotches, midrib green to faintly coloured; lateral lobes 4–6, patent or somewhat recurved, narrow, pointed, sometimes linear; terminal lobe with apex sometimes shortly lingulate; petiole dull purple, unwinged. Scapes 30–150 mm, usually suffused purple, arachnoid-hairy below the involucre. Involucre *very dark* and strongly pruinose in bud; exterior bracts 7 × 2 mm, spreading to erect, glaucous, usually suffused purple on upper surface, corniculate, ± *unbordered*. Capitulum 20–30 mm, yellow; ligules *very short, scarcely exceeding inner bracts,* striped *purple*; styles exserted, *discoloured*; pollen *present*. Achenes *chestnut red*; body 2.9–3.2 mm; cone 0.4–0.7 mm.

A widespread British and Irish species of dry sites, often growing with **1** *T. lacistophyllum* but sometimes in more acidic situations. V.cc. 1–7, 9, 11–17, 19–30, 32–52, 54–62, 64–76, 78–83, 85, 87–104, 106, 109, 110, 112, S, H9, H12, H15, H16, H20, H21, H27, H31, H38, H40.

It is readily distinguished from **1** *T. lacistophyllum* by its dark, unbordered, purplish exterior bracts and short ligules with purple stripes.

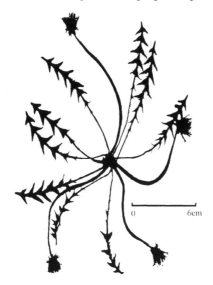

0   6cm

2a T. scanicum Dahlst. (1911b)   **Map 2a**

A small to medium-sized plant, with deeply dissected leaves 100–180 mm.

Leaves mid-green, without spots, almost glabrous, interlobes unblotched, midrib coloured; lateral lobes 4–6, long, often sublaciniate, patent or somewhat recurved, often *appearing double*, often narrowed in the waist, acute, usually dentate on distal margin, sometimes on both margins; terminal lobe often double, typically with a *somewhat elongated, lingulate apex*; petiole unwinged, purple. Scapes equal to or longer than leaves, often purplish, somewhat arachnoid-hairy below capitulum. Exterior bracts spreading, *about 8 × 2 mm,* bordered, not corniculate. Capitulum rather dark yellow, 35–40 mm in diameter; ligules striped *grey-purple*; styles exserted, discoloured; pollen present. Achenes chestnut to dark brick-red; body 3.0 mm; cone 1.0 mm.

Native in Breckland grasslands and in the Channel Islands; probably introduced in Shetland. V.cc. 26, 28, 112, S.

Related to both **1** and **2**, but lacking the short ligules and purple exterior bracts of **2** and distinguished from both by the distinctive leaf-shape in which the terminal leaf-lobe has a somewhat elongated, lingulate apex and the lateral lobes typically bear a large lobule, thus appearing double.

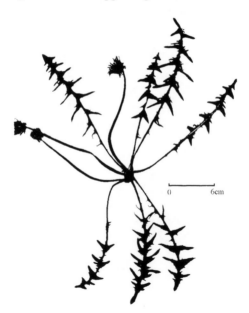

0   6cm

A small to medium-sized plant, with erect leaves 50–100 mm.

Leaves dark green, usually without spots, interlobes sometimes blotched, midrib green to faintly coloured; lateral lobes 4–5, *regular, deltoid*, scarcely dentate; terminal lobe *triangular*, sometimes with a somewhat lingulate apex; petiole *white to green* or dull purple, scarcely winged. Scapes 100–150 mm, arachnoid-hairy below capitulum. Exterior bracts 6 × 2 mm, spreading, dark green, scarcely corniculate, *unbordered*. Capitulum deep yellow-orange, *closed*; ligules *involute*, with reddish-orange backs; styles inserted, *yellow*; pollen *absent or infrequent*. Achenes deep red; body 3.0 mm; cone 0.8 mm. 2n=24.

Native. More frequent in western Britain; found especially in limestone areas. Considered endemic until recently recorded in central Bohemia. V.cc. 3, 4, 11, 13, 16, 17, 19–22, 24–26, 30, 34, 35, 37, 39, 42–44, 50, 51, 55, 57, 58, 60–62, 64, 67–70, 72, 73, 75, 80–83, 88, 89, 94, 95, 98, 99, 101, H39.

This is the only member of the British *Erythrosperma* with habitually closed capitula and involute ligules. This condition is occasionally found in other species, from which it can satisfactorily be distinguished by its dark green, regularly deltoid-lobed leaves. Seed production is rather poor, and it may be that this species has evolved from triploid facultatively agamospermous forms of **2** *T. brachyglossum*, achieving obligate agamospermy through structural isolation (the closed ligules and capitulum) rather than meiotically (Richards 1970).

4 **T. arenastrum** A.J. Richards (1981)

Map 4

A small delicate plant, thickened at the base with the remnants of dead leaf-bases, with ± prostrate leaves not exceeding 80 mm.

Leaves mid-green, without spots, ± glabrous, interlobes unblotched, midrib green to faintly coloured; lateral lobes 4–5, *strongly recurved*, acute, scarcely dentate, often contracted from a broad base to *a very narrow, falcate, downward-pointing tip*; terminal lobe with a narrow, attenuate apex or at least markedly mucronate; petiole short or up to one quarter length of leaf, unwinged, somewhat purple, or green. Scapes equalling leaves, arachnoid-hairy, dull green or coppery. Exterior bracts erect at base, spreading distally, *about 6–9 × 2–3 mm*, green, *with well-marked white margins*, scarcely corniculate. Capitulum pale yellow, to 25 mm in diameter; ligules striped *purple-violet*; styles exserted, *yellow* or somewhat discoloured; pollen *present or absent*. Achenes *chestnut or dark red*, shortly spinulose above but otherwise smooth, narrow; body 3.0 mm; cone abruptly demarcated, narrow, 0.7–0.8 mm; pappus white. 2n=24.

Native. Apparently local and rare. Sand-dunes and chalk and limestone grassland, usually near the sea. Great Britain, western Ireland, the Netherlands and probably northern France. V.cc. 1, 4, 6, 15, 28, 42, 50, 52, 58, 62, 66–68, 70, 74, 90, 101, 103, H9.

0   6cm

This characteristic little species is diagnosed by its deep reddish achenes, erect exterior bracts with a white margin, and yellowish styles. The leaf-shape combines the expanded lobe bases of **1** *T. lacistophyllum* with the recurved lobe apices of **7** *T. haworthianum.*

4a T. commixtum G.E. Haglund (1942)   Map 4a

A medium-sized plant, with erect leaves 70–200 mm.

Leaves dull green, without spots, interlobes unblotched, midrib green; lateral lobes 4–6, pointing forwards, patent or somewhat recurved, linear, often swollen at apex or bifurcate; interlobes with lobules and long teeth; terminal lobe tripartite with a linear, elongated apex; petiole unwinged, narrow, purple. Scapes 150–250 mm, often purplish, arachnoid-hairy, rather stout, ascending to erect. Exterior bracts usually erect, *about 8–10 × 5 mm, ± bordered*, dark green, sometimes corniculate. Capitulum deep yellow, to 40 mm in diameter; ligules striped *reddish-purple*; styles exserted, *yellow*; pollen present. Achenes *dark red*; body 3.5 mm; cone 1.0 mm.

Apparently native on sand-dunes and sandy heaths north to Flintshire and Northumberland. Local and rare. V.cc. 11, 15, 22, 25, 26, 28, 29, 51, 67, 68, S.

A distinctive plant, often more robust than its relatives, with very long linear processes to the lateral leaf-lobes, which are usually swollen or even divided at the apex. From extreme forms of **1** *T. lacistophyllum*, which can look similar, *T. commixtum* is readily distinguished by the large (8–10 mm), usually erect, dark exterior bracts, reddish-purple ligule stripes, yellow styles and large (3.5 mm) achene bodies. In recent years it has been suggested that western European material placed here differs from the Swedish type, and for Dutch material the workname *T. 'bifurcatum'* has been proposed by Hagendijk, Oosterveld and Zevenbergen. It seems likely that British material is closer to the Dutch taxon.

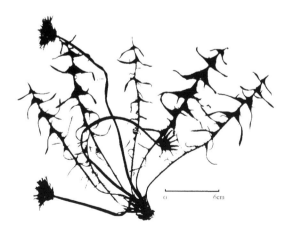

0 ———— 6cm

5 T. rubicundum (Dahlst.) Dahlst. (1906)

Map 5

A small and delicate plant, with deeply dissected leaves 20–70 mm.

Leaves dull green, without spots, almost glabrous, inter-lobes without blotches, midrib coloured; lateral lobes 4–7, patent or pointing forward, narrow to linear; interlobes narrow, straight, dentate; terminal lobe trilobate, linear; *petiole unwinged, narrow, dark violet-purple; persistent dark leaf-bases conspicuous.* Scapes many, 50–80 mm, thin, wiry, purplish, *glabrous.* Exterior bracts ± erect, *5 × 1.5 mm, ovate, dark glaucous green* often suffused with purple, ± bordered, conspicuously corniculate. Capitulum pale yellow, 15–20 mm in diameter; ligules short, striped dark violet; with *blackish* teeth; styles exserted, *discoloured*; pollen usually absent. Achenes *dark violet*; body 2.5 mm; cone 1.0 mm. 2n=24.

Native. Dry places; mostly restricted to calcareous downland, but locally on sandy heaths. Widespread and locally common in southern England, becoming rarer northwards; not recorded from Ireland. V.cc. 1–7, 9–12, 14–17, 20, 22–26, 28–30, 33, 34, 36, 37, 39, 41–43, 45, 47, 49–52, 55, 57, 59–62, 65, 67–71, 80–83, 95, 96, 101, 108, S.

Diagnosed by the glabrous scapes (even just below the involucre), the ± erect ovate exterior bracts and the dark violet achenes. However, the whole plant has a most distinctive appearance. It is a most attractive little species and one of the easiest to identify.

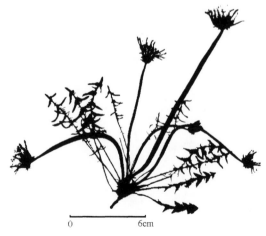

0   6cm

Section *Erythrosperma*

5a T. parnassicum Dahlst. (1929b)

Map 5a

A small plant, with very regularly lobed leaves 30–100 mm.

Leaves *pure green*, without spots, almost glabrous, interlobes unblotched, midrib green to faintly coloured; lateral lobes 4–5, crowded, slightly recurved, with distal margin convex, mostly entire but proximal lobes sometimes dentate on distal margin; interlobes frequently with a solitary tooth; terminal lobe triangular or shortly trilobate with a short, subacute tip; petiole winged, short, purple. Scapes 30–120 mm, often purplish, *arachnoid-hairy when young*. Exterior bracts erect to spreading, recurved at apex, *about 6 × 2 mm, scarcely bordered*, green, somewhat corniculate. Capitulum yellow, 20–30 mm in diameter; ligules striped purple, with *yellow* teeth; styles exserted, discoloured; pollen ± absent. Achenes *dark red*; body 3.2 mm; cone 1.0 mm. 2n=24.

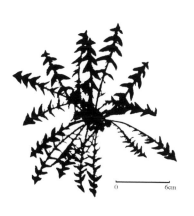

Native but local in dry calcareous grassland, especially in the west, northwards to south-west Northumberland; also in West Galway. A widespread species, extending to eastern Europe. V.cc. 1, 3, 14, 17, 22, 23, 28, 34, 36, 37, 39, 41, 42, 47, 49–51, 55, 57, 60, 67, H16.

Similar to **5**, but diagnosed by the scapes slightly arachnoid-hairy under the capitulum (use a lens) and the yellow ligule teeth. The exterior bracts are recurved at the apex and slightly longer (about 6 mm) and the mature achenes are a dark red. In well-developed specimens the leaf-shape differs.

5b T. cenabense Sahlin (1983)

Map 5b

Closely related to and intermediate between **5** and **5a**, differing from the former by its larger, reddish achenes, pale petioles and darker flower colour, and from the latter by the scapes glabrous at the apex, pale petioles and purple ligule teeth.

A rare native. Occurs in West Sussex and in northern France. V.c. 13 only.

6 **T. dunense** Soest (1956) **Map 6**

A small to medium-sized plant, with deeply dissected leaves 50–120 mm.

Leaves dark green, often purplish, without spots, almost glabrous, interlobes without blotches, midrib green to coloured; lateral lobes 5–10, patent, narrowly linear to the base and acute but with a narrowed middle; terminal lobe usually trilobate with a lingulate apex (but note that early leaves can be scarcely lobed or entire, and thus highly misleading); petiole unwinged, very narrow, dark violet-purple. Scapes 50–150 mm, often purplish, decumbent to erect, arachnoid-hairy. Exterior bracts spreading, 7 × 2 mm, scarcely bordered, green, corniculate. Capitulum deep yellow, 20–30 mm in diameter; ligules striped purple; styles exserted, *discoloured*; pollen present. Achenes dark violet to red; body 3.5 mm; cone *1.2 mm.* 2n=24.

Native. Sand-dunes, extending north to Cheshire in the west and Northumberland in the east. V.cc. 11, 13–16, 25, 28, 34, 41, 52, 58, 66, 67, S.

A most distinctive species, with very narrow leaf-lobes, narrow midribs and large violet (red when immature) achenes with long cones.

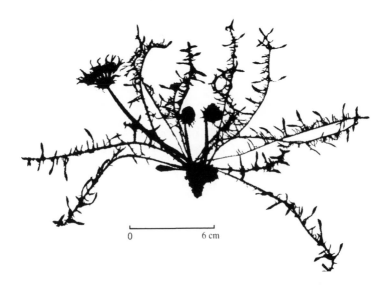

0   6 cm

Section *Erythrosperma*

7 **T. haworthianum** Dudman & A.J. Richards (1994)   **Map 7**

A small plant, with leaves 50–100 mm.

Leaves mid-green, without spots, almost glabrous, interlobes without blotches, midrib green to faintly coloured; lateral lobes *6–8*, somewhat recurved, regular and triangular or with sinuate distal margin, subacute to obtuse at apex, sometimes narrowing to an elongated apex; terminal lobe subsagittate with an acute, somewhat elongated apex; petiole unwinged, narrow, green or purple at base. Scapes often purplish, somewhat arachnoid-hairy below capitulum. Exterior bracts erect to appressed, ovate, *about 6 × 2 mm, bordered white or rose, somewhat scarious, markedly purple-corniculate.* Capitulum rather pale yellow, to 30 mm in diameter; ligules striped violet or grey, with purple teeth; styles yellow; pollen present. Achenes *dark violet-purple when mature*; body 3.0 mm; cone 0.8–1.0 mm. 2n=24.

Endemic. Sand-dune grassland. Commonest in the north and west. V.cc. 1–4, 6, 13, 15, 25, 27–29, 41, 42, 45, 46, 48, 49, 51, 52, 55, 57–60, 66–69, 73–75, 82, 85, 90, 93–95, 101–104, 106, 107, 109, 110, S, H9, H12, H21, H28, H39, H40.

Diagnosed by the combination of violet achenes, yellow styles and short, appressed, bordered exterior bracts, with purple cornicula. Difficult to separate from **15a** *T. platyglossum* without achenes.

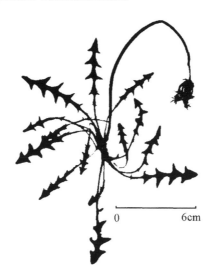

0   6cm

7a T. gotlandicum (Dahlst.) Dahlst. (1909)   Map 7a

A small to medium-sized plant, with leaves 50–100 mm.

Leaves mid-green, without spots, almost glabrous, interlobes unblotched, midrib green; lateral lobes 4–6, patent, short, often obtuse, usually entire, *with distal margin concave*; terminal lobe distinctly trilobate; petiole winged or unwinged, usually green. Scapes rather numerous, 80–150 mm, decumbent to erect, not coloured, arachnoid-hairy. Exterior bracts erect, about 7 × 2 mm, glaucous, suffused violet, bordered. Capitulum rather pale yellow, to 30 mm in diameter; ligules striped violet; styles exserted, *yellow*; pollen present. Achenes *brick-red*; body 3.0 mm; cone 0.8 mm. 2n=24.

Calcareous grassland in eastern Scotland and possibly in western Ireland. Apparently rare and has not been recorded in recent years. V.cc. 90, 94, 109, ?H9.

Resembles **7**, but usually has narrowly winged petioles which are green to the base. The lateral leaf-lobes are subobtuse with a concave notch on the distal margin, and the achenes are brick-red at maturity.

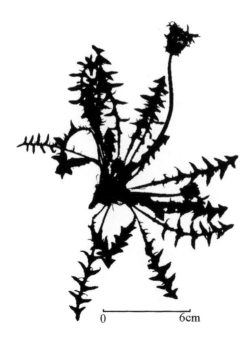

0 ——— 6cm

There is some doubt as to the correct identity of this distinctive little plant, and when new material can be critically compared with *T. gotlandicum* it may turn out to be a new species. However, *T. gotlandicum* does have a strange and apparently relict distribution (Gotland, Öland, adjacent areas of Sweden, the extreme west of Estonia, and the Oslofjord, Norway (Wendelbo 1959)).

8 T. proximum (Dahlst.) Raunk. (1906) Map 8

A small to medium-sized heterophyllous plant, with leaves 50–200 mm.

Leaves dull green, without spots, almost glabrous, interlobes without blotches, midrib green to faintly coloured; leaves regularly lobate, unlobed but dentate, or lobate only proximally and with a large dentate or sublobate terminal lobe; lateral lobes 5–8, triangular, acute, regularly dentate, with acute or subacute apex; terminal lobe subacute, acute or subsagittate with acute, somewhat elongated apex; petiole unwinged, dull purple. Scapes green, erect, arachnoid-hairy when young. Exterior bracts spreading to recurved, sometimes rather strongly so, *8 × 2 mm*, slightly bordered, purplish-green, *pruinose*, slightly corniculate. Capitulum deep yellow, 35 mm in diameter; ligules striped purple; styles exserted, *discoloured*; pollen *absent*. Achenes *dark brown to purple-brown (puce)*; body 2.8 mm; cone 0.8 mm. 2n=24.

Native. Dry grassland and meadows. Local throughout Great Britain. V.cc. 1, 3, 4, 6, 15, 17, 19, 20, 26, 28, 35, 42, 43, 47, 48, 50–52, 58, 61, 62, 64–70, 74, 75, 78, 95, 102, 103, 108, 110.

Diagnosed by the combination of the characteristic leaf-shape, the urn-shaped, pruinose involucre, and the achenes, whose colour is unique among British species.

0   6cm

Section *Erythrosperma* 61

8a T. proximiforme Soest in Lambinon & Soest (1962)   Map 8a

A small to medium-sized heterophyllous plant, with leaves 50–250 mm.

Leaves bright green, without spots, interlobes unblotched, midrib green to faint-ly coloured; leaves varying markedly, from entire, through dentate and partly lobed, to ± deeply dissected; lateral lobes, if present, 3–6, somewhat recurved to patent or even forward-pointing, dentate only on proximal interlobes, with apex sometimes linear and very acute, sometimes subacute or obtuse from a broad base; terminal lobe triangular, trilobate or subsagittate with an acute, somewhat elongated, apex; petiole winged, dull purple. Scapes 80–250 mm, erect, arachnoid-hairy. Exterior bracts spreading, *about 8 × 2 mm*, scarcely bordered or corniculate. Capitulum mid-yellow, 30 mm in diameter; ligules striped *grey-violet*, with *purple* teeth; styles exserted, *yellowish*; pollen present or absent. Achenes *straw-coloured*; body 3.0 mm; cone 0.8–1.0 mm. 2n=24 (counts made on British material).

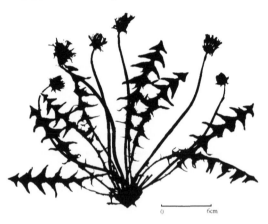

0 ──── 6cm

Native. Dry mesic grass-land. England, southern Scotland and the Channel coasts of France, Belgium and the Netherlands. V.cc. 15, 23, 28, 33, 42, 66–70, 79, 80, 82, 91, 94.

Very similar to **8**, differing chiefly by the straw-coloured achenes, yellowish styles which sometimes bear pollen, and purple ligule teeth.

8b T. pseudoproximum Soest (1961)

A close relative of **8** and **8a**, dubiously differing from **8a** in being non-hetero-phyllous (with leaves with 4–5 very regular triangular lateral lobes) and having unwinged petioles and discoloured styles invariably bearing pollen. The achenes are grey-brown.

A few records from the south of England; possibly introduced. V.c. 19 only.

Section *Erythrosperma*

8c T. disseminatum G.E. Haglund (1947)

A small to medium-sized plant, with leaves 50–150 mm.

Leaves pale green, almost glabrous, without spots, interlobes unblotched, midrib green to faintly coloured; lateral lobes 2–3, triangular, *with several and sometimes large teeth on the distal margin*, the distal lobes sometimes double; terminal lobe triangular, subacute, sometimes lingulate; petiole unwinged, narrow, violet. Scapes 100–200 mm, erect, rarely coloured, arachnoid-hairy below capitulum. Exterior bracts *recurved, about 6 × 2 mm*, bordered, somewhat corniculate. Capitulum rather pale yellow, to 30 mm in diameter; ligules striped *grey-violet*, styles exserted, *blackish*; pollen present. Achenes golden-brown, spinulose; body 3.0–3.2 mm; cone 0.8 mm. 2n=24.

Probably introduced. Short, dry grassland and lawns. From Scandinavia and England to central Europe. V.cc. 4, 5, 17, 28, 41, 50.

A close relative of **8**, **8a** and **8b**, differing chiefly by the shorter, recurved outer bracts, blackish styles, and golden-brown achenes with large, broad-based spines. The rather pale green leaves typically have few (2–3) dentate lateral lobes.

0 ⟶ 6cm

9 T. oxoniense Dahlst. (1923)

Map 9

A small to medium-sized plant, with leaves 30–250 mm.

Leaves, including the midrib, pure green, without spots, varying from entire, through entire but toothed and partly lobed, to deeply and narrowly lobed; lateral lobes, if present, 3–6, irregular, narrow, acute to obtuse, patent to somewhat recurved; interlobes with teeth and lobules; terminal lobe often long and divided; petiole *unwinged, narrow, bright purple.* Scapes 50–280 mm, decumbent to erect, purplish, slightly arachnoid-hairy under capitulum. Exterior bracts erect, the outer ovate, *about 7 × 2 to 9 × 4 mm, white-bordered, dark green,* scarcely corniculate. Capitulum mid-yellow, to 30 mm in diameter; ligules striped *grey-violet*, with yellow teeth; styles exserted, slightly discoloured; pollen present. Achenes *cinnamon*; body 3.0 mm; cone 1.0 mm. 2n=32.

Native. Dry neutral or calcareous ground, especially downland and sand-dunes. Widespread and locally common throughout the British Isles, though only more locally in Scotland. V.cc. 1–7, 9–20, 22–62, 64–71, 73, 75, 78, 80–83, 85, 93, 98, 101, 102, 107, 110, 112, S, H9, H12, H15, H16, H20, H21, H30, H33, H35, H38, H40.

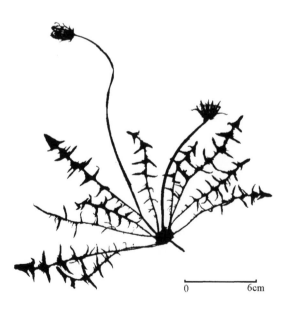

0   6cm

This is often the commonest member of Section *Erythrosperma* in England and Wales. The leaf morphology, although varying from highly dissected to almost entire, is nevertheless characteristic, especially in combination with the contrasting bright green leaves and purple petioles. The erect, dark green, white-bordered, ovate exterior bracts are also distinctive. This is also the only cinnamon-fruited species with erect ovate bracts and possessing pollen.

Section *Erythrosperma*

10 **T. fulviforme** Dahlst. (1923)

Map 10

A small to medium-sized plant, with leaves 40–100 mm.

Leaves dull-green, without spots, almost glabrous, interlobes often dark-blotched, midrib green to faintly coloured; lateral lobes 3–5, patent to somewhat recurved, dentate only on distal lobes; terminal lobe subsagittate with a mucronate apex and, in well-developed leaves, *larger than in most of this section*; petiole *unwinged or narrowly winged distally*, dull pink. Scapes 10–150 mm, not coloured, somewhat arachnoid-hairy below capitulum. Exterior bracts green, *erect (to spreading)*, acute, giving a star-shaped involucre, about 7 × 2–3 mm, scarcely corniculate, slightly bordered, scarcely pruinose. Ligules striped *grey-violet*, with teeth tipped *reddish*; styles *discoloured*; pollen *absent*. Achenes *cinnamon*; body 3.0 mm; cone 0.8 mm. 2n=32.

Native. Dry places, especially sand-dunes, cliff-tops and calcareous grassland. Locally frequent. Also in paths and lawns. V.cc. 1–4, 6, 7, 9–30, 33–43,45–62, 64, 66–70, 73–75, 80, 81, 85, 86, 88, 90, 91, 93, 98, 99, 101–103, 105, 108–110, S, H13, H16, H20, H21, H39, H40.

T. fulviforme is the only British cinnamon-fruited and pollenless species that has erect to spreading green exterior bracts.

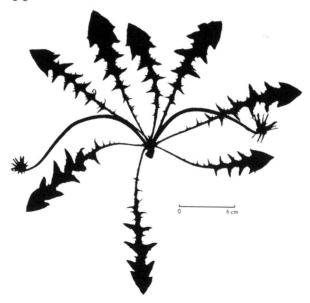

0   6 cm

11 T. fulvum Raunk. (1906)

Map 11

A small to medium-sized plant, with leaves 50–180 mm.

Leaves dull green, without spots, almost glabrous, inter-lobes without blotches, midrib green to faintly coloured; lateral lobes *4–5*, recurved, *dentate*; terminal lobe trilobate with an acute, elongated apex; petiole unwinged below, purple. Scapes 60–150 mm, arachnoid-hairy above. Exterior bracts *spreading to recurved, shortly lanceolate, about 7 × 2 mm, dark green, ± bordered.* Capitulum mid-yellow, 25 mm in diameter; ligules striped *grey-violet,* with teeth tipped *reddish*; styles exserted, yellowish; pollen *absent.* Achenes *cinnamon*; body *3.0 mm*; cone 0.7–1.0 mm. 2n=32.

Native. Locally scattered on light, well-drained neutral to calcareous soils, often in species-rich grasslands; also on walls, cliffs etc. Occurs throughout the British Isles. V.cc. 1, 2, 5–7, 9–11, 13, 15–24, 26, 27, 29, 31, 32, 34, 37, 41, 42, 49, 50, 53–57, 60, 62, 64, 67–70, 80, 88, 90, 91, 95, 96, 98, 101–104, 106, 109, 110, S, H9, H38, H39.

Related to the more common **10** *T. fulviforme*, but with narrower, more dentate leaf-lobes, an untidy leaf-shape and rather more recurved exterior bracts.

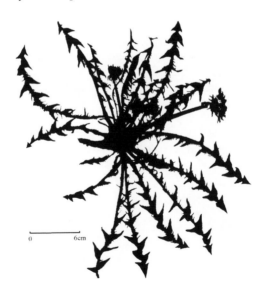

0 ——— 6cm

Section *Erythrosperma*

11a T. scoticum A.J. Richards (1981)

Differs from **11** by the exterior bracts, which are more ovate (5–6 × 2–3 mm), by the presence of pollen, and by the longer achenes (3.2–3.5 mm).

Native and endemic. Scattered in a number of sandy localities in England and Scotland.

V.cc. 6, 22, 39, 56, 67–69, 74, 83, 88, 94, 101, 106.

11b T. falcatum Brenner (1907)   Map 11b

A small to medium-sized plant, with deeply dissected to *laciniate* leaves 50–150 mm.

Leaves *grey-green*, without spots, interlobes unblotched, midrib green to faintly coloured; lateral lobes *5–8*, pointing forward, patent or somewhat recurved, with *the whole lobe linear*, acute; interlobes with lobules and teeth; terminal lobe *trilobate* with an acute, elongated apex; petiole unwinged, narrow, purple. Scapes 40–100 mm, green, ascending, arachnoid-hairy. Exterior bracts *spreading, about 7 × 2 mm, slightly bordered*, somewhat corniculate. Capitulum mid-yellow, to 30 mm in diameter; ligules striped grey-violet, with *yellow* teeth; styles discoloured to *yellowish*; pollen *present* but sometimes sparse. Achenes *warm straw-brown*; body *3.5 mm*; cone 1.0 mm. 2n=24.

Probably introduced. A few records from dry grassland, mostly in central and southern England. V.cc. 2–4, 21, 24, 28–30, 43, 50, 51, 55, 58, 70.

A close relative of **11** and **11a**, differing chiefly by the more numerous (5–8) and longer, linear lateral lobes which are variously directed. The achene body (3.5 mm) is longer and the ligule teeth are yellow. Pollen is present, even if sparse.

11c T. retzii Soest (1961)

A medium-sized plant, with leaves 80–180 mm.

Leaves dull green, without spots, almost glabrous, interlobes unblotched, midrib green to faintly coloured; lateral lobes 4–7, *slightly recurved, very long, dentate,* often on both margins; terminal lobe triangular and subacute or subsagittate with an acute, somewhat elongated, apex; petiole winged or unwinged, dull reddish. Scapes 100–300 mm, greenish, arachnoid-hairy above. Exterior bracts recurved, *8 × 2–4 mm*, green, bordered, not corniculate. Capitulum yellow, 35 mm in diameter; ligules striped *grey-violet*, with *pink* teeth; styles exserted, *discoloured*; pollen *present*. Achenes cinnamon; body *3.5 mm*; cone 1.2 mm.

Native. Acid sandy heaths in southern Britain, very local. V.cc. 10, 16, 20, 22, 27–29, 50, 51, S.

A relative of **11** and **11a**, but usually with broader (up to 4 mm) exterior bracts and pollen present. The cinnamon achenes have a long body (3.5 mm), as in **11b**.

0   6 cm

Section *Erythrosperma*

12 T. glauciniforme Dahlst. (1929)

Map 12

A small to medium-sized plant, with linear-oblong laciniate leaves of a characteristic shape, 40–200 mm.

Leaves greyish-green, without spots, almost glabrous, with complex dissection, interlobes without blotches, midrib *green* (to faintly coloured); lateral lobes 6–12, patent, narrow, linear; interlobes toothed; terminal lobe with an acute apex; petioles *winged*, narrow, usually *green*. Scapes green, somewhat arachnoid-hairy below capitulum. Involucre somewhat pruinose; exterior bracts spreading to recurved, about 6–6.5 × 2 mm, bordered, grey-green, sometimes suffused purple, somewhat corniculate. Capitulum pale yellow, 30 mm in diameter; ligules striped *pale grey*, with purple teeth; styles greenish to *yellow*; pollen *absent* or rare. Achenes *cinnamon* to chestnut-puce; body *2.5–2.8 mm*; cone 0.8–1.0 mm.

Native. Frequent on light, sandy, well-drained neutral to calcareous soils, often in garden lawns; also on walls, cliffs etc. Widespread and locally common in England and Wales, mainly in the south; also in the Channel Isles, the Isle of Man and Ayrshire. V.cc. 1, 6, 11, 12, 14–17, 19–26, 28–31, 33–35, 37–39, 41, 42, 46, 47, 50, 51, 55, 57–60, 66, 71, 75, S.

This most characterful little species is instantly recognised by its leaf-shape.

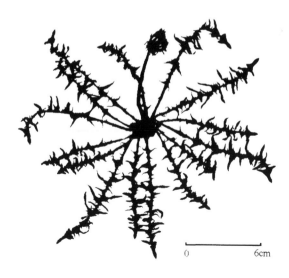

0   6cm

12a **T. wallonicum** Soest in Lambinon & Soest (1962) Map 12a

A small to medium-sized plant, with regularly lobed leaves 80–150 mm.

Leaves mid-green, without spots, almost glabrous, interlobes unblotched, midrib green; lateral lobes 4–8, patent to somewhat recurved, triangular with a broad base, dentate only on distal margin of proximal lobes; interlobes dentate on larger leaves; terminal lobe subsagittate with an acute, somewhat elongated apex; petiole unwinged proximally, narrow, green. Scapes equal to or over-topping leaves, somewhat arachnoid-hairy below capitulum. Exterior bracts spreading to recurved, *about 8 × 2 mm*. Capitulum rather pale yellow, to 30 mm in diameter; ligules striped *grey-purple*; styles exserted, *discoloured*; pollen *present*. Achenes *straw-coloured*; body *3.0 mm*; cone 0.8–1.0 mm.

A few sites in London, Essex and Kent, possibly introduced. V.cc. 16, 18, 19, 21.

It has a similar leaf-shape and colouring to **12**, but the discoloured styles bear pollen, and the longer achene (body 3.0 mm) is straw-coloured.

Section *Erythrosperma*

A small plant, with leaves 30–100 mm.

Leaves mid-green, without spots, interlobes without blotches, midrib green to faintly coloured; lateral lobes 5–8, *regular*, triangular-acute to ± linear, almost entire; terminal lobe acute to tripartite; petiole narrowly winged, rose-coloured. Scapes 50–150 mm, erect, green, arachnoid-hairy. Exterior bracts erect to spreading, *about 8–9 × 2 mm, pale green*, somewhat corniculate, *with a conspicuous white or rose-coloured border.* Capitulum rather pale yellow, to 30 mm in diameter; ligules striped *grey*; styles exserted, *discoloured*; pollen present or absent. Achenes grey-brown; body 3.0 mm; cone *1.3 mm*. 2n=24.

Endemic. Rocky places, usually near the sea, mainly in south-west England, Wales, south-west Scotland and western Ireland. V.cc. 2, 4, 36, 42, 43, 48–50, 75, 101–103, H9, H16, H21.

Amongst brown-fruited *Erythrosperma, T. degelii* is best identified by the wide white or rose borders of the pale green exterior bracts and by the regular lobation of the leaves.

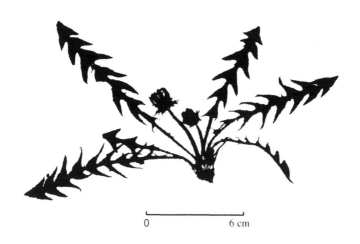

0   6 cm

13a T. acutum A.J. Richards (1972)   Map 13a

A small plant, with leaves 30–100 mm.

Leaves dark green, unspotted, almost glabrous, interlobes unblotched, midrib green to purple; lateral lobes 4–5, *regular*, recurved, acute, with 1 or several teeth, mainly on proximal lobes; terminal lobe *subsagittate, sometimes with a single tooth*; petiole unwinged, green or purple. Scapes 50–100 mm, narrow, green, arachnoid-hairy. Exterior bracts ascending to erect, *about 7 × 2 mm,* ± bordered, dark green, not corniculate. Capitulum deep yellow, to 30 mm in diameter; outer ligules flat, to 2× the involucre, striped *dark violet*; styles exserted, *discoloured*; pollen *present*. Achenes straw-coloured; body 3.0 mm; cone *0.7 mm*. 2n=24.

Endemic. A few locations, mainly in southern England, on species-rich chalk grassland. V.cc. 11, 19, 20, 22, 23, 26, 28, 30, 57.

A close relative of **13**, best distinguished by the ± bordered exterior bracts, the dark violet ligule stripes and the shorter (0.7 mm) cone to the achene. Pollen seems always to be present.

13b T. placidum A.J. Richards (1972)

A small to medium-sized plant, with leaves 60–200 mm.

Leaves pale green, narrow, unspotted, midrib coloured; lateral lobes 5–8, short, deltoid, entire or denticulate; terminal lobe small (larger in later leaves), entire, triangular; petiole long, narrrowly winged, *bright purple*. Scapes 100–300 mm, erect, purple, arachnoid-hairy above. Exterior bracts spreading, *7 × 3 mm, bordered*, corniculate. Involucre narrow. Capitulum mid-yellow, *40–45 mm in diameter*; ligules striped *silver-grey*; styles exserted, *yellow*; pollen *present*. Achenes grey-brown; body 3.0 mm; cone *0.8 mm*. 2n=24 (counts made on British material).

Native. Dry grassy paths in Alderney (Channel Islands), central France and northern Spain. V.c. S only.

Another close relative of **13** and **13a**, but with purple midribs and brilliant purple petioles, large capitula (to 45 mm in diameter) and yellow styles bearing pollen. The exterior bracts are bordered, but not so strongly as in **13**, and the ligule stripes are silver-grey; achene cone 0.8 mm.

Section *Erythrosperma*

13c   T. tanylepis Dahlst. (1923)

A medium-sized plant, with leaves 70–150 mm.

Leaves dull green, unspotted, interlobes unblotched, midrib green to somewhat coloured; lateral lobes 4–6, patent to somewhat recurved, entire or filiform-dentate; terminal lobe sometimes sagittate, with a subacute apex; petiole up to a quarter or half length of leaf, unwinged, narrow, green or somewhat coloured. Scapes 50–170 mm, ascending to erect. Exterior bracts erect to spreading, about 9 × 3 mm, bordered, dark green. Capitulum yellow, *40 mm in diameter*; ligules striped grey-purple; styles exserted, *yellow*; pollen *absent*. Achenes straw-coloured; body *3.5 mm*; cone *to 0.5 mm*.

Endemic. Wet marshy ground. Known only from Orkney, but could be elsewhere. V.c. 111.

Another relative of **13**, but closely resembling **13b** in the large capitulum and the yellow styles, which however lack pollen. Diagnostically in this group, the achene body is long (3.5 mm) and the cone short.

A single plant of a central European relative, *T. pseudolacistophyllum* Soest, was discovered, presumably adventive, in Surrey (v.c. 17) in 1995. This species has a leaf-shape somewhat resembling **1** *T. lacistophyllum*, but has pale brown achenes and spreading to recurved, conspicuously bordered exterior bracts.

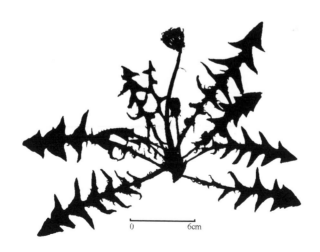

0   6cm

14 T. tortilobum Florstr. (1914)

Map 14

A small plant, with *highly contorted*, deeply dissected leaves 70–150 mm.

Leaves mid-green, without spots, almost glabrous, interlobes sometimes blotched, midrib green to faintly coloured; lateral lobes 3–5, patent to somewhat recurved, broader proximally but with apex linear and acute to form a *strongly sigmoid distal marginal hump*, dentate only on proximal lobes; interlobes frequently dentate; terminal lobe trilobate with an acute, somewhat elongated apex; petiole unwinged, narrow, purple. Scapes often purplish, ± glabrous. Exterior bracts erect, *5–6 × 2–2.5 mm, bordered, pruinose*, grey-green often suffused with purple on upper surface, strongly purple-corniculate. Capitulum pale yellow, to 25 mm in diameter; ligules striped *grey-purple*, with *yellow* teeth; styles *blackish*; pollen present. Achenes *pale to straw-coloured*; body 2.5–3.0 mm; cone 0.7–0.9 mm.

Native. Mainly in coastal grasslands in eastern England. V.cc. 14, 15, 17, 26, 66.

In many ways resembling a highly contorted **1** *T. lacistophyllum*, but with pale brown achenes.

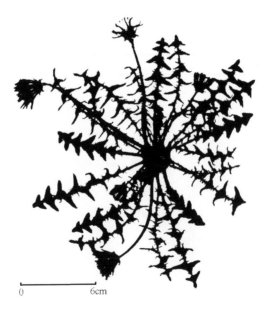

0   6cm

Section *Erythrosperma*

Section OBLIQUA (Dahlst.) Dahlst. (1921)

15 T. obliquum (Fr.) Dahlst. (1905)

A small plant, with highly dissected leaves 30–80 mm.

Leaves *pale green,* without spots, ± glabrous, interlobes without blotches, midrib green; lateral lobes 7–10, *patent,* short, *obtuse,* scarcely dentate; terminal lobe triangular or slightly trilobate; petiole green, narrow, sometimes slightly winged. Scapes many, 20–100 mm, slender, green, glabrous. Exterior bracts appressed, *about 6 × 2 mm,* with a purple corniculation and pale border. Capitulum *orange-yellow, 10–15 mm in diameter,* usually closed; ligules *involute or flat, striped red*; styles ± exserted, yellowish; pollen present. Achenes *grey-brown*; body 3.0 mm; cone 0.4 mm. 2n=24.

Native. Dune-slacks and grey-dunes. Coasts of Scotland, northern England and Ireland. V.cc. 58, 69, 82, 95, 101–103, 106–110, H21.

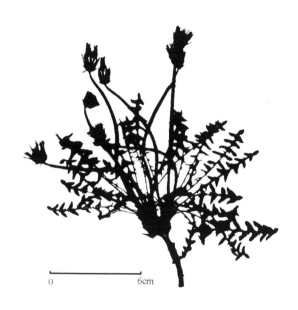

0   6cm

75

15a T. platyglossum Raunk. (1906)

A small to medium-sized plant, with leaves 30–120 mm.

Leaves *mid-green to dark green*, unspotted, almost glabrous, interlobes unblotched, midrib green to faintly coloured; lateral lobes 7–12, recurved, *acute, filiform-dentate* proximally; terminal lobe trilobate with a subacute, sometimes somewhat elongated apex; petiole ± winged proximally, narrow, green or ± coloured. Scapes many, 20–100 mm, slender, often coloured, glabrous. Exterior bracts erect to appressed, about 7 × 2 mm, green, with a purple or green corniculation and pale border. Capitulum *deep yellow, 25–30 mm in diameter*, usually flat, sometimes closed; ligules usually flat, sometimes involute, striped red; styles exserted, discoloured; pollen present or absent. Achenes *grey-brown*; body 3.0 mm; cone 0.4 mm.

Native. Sand-dunes. Scottish coasts and isolated localities in north-east England, the Isle of Man, Anglesey, Caerns, Somerset, Guernsey and Antrim. V.cc. 6, 49, 52, 66–68, 71, 74, 75, 82, 85, 90, 94–96, 101, 103, 105, 108–110, S, H39.

Very closely allied to **15** *T. obliquum*, into which, in some senses, it merges and of which it may possibly be best treated as a form. It is best distinguished by its darker leaves, more acute, dentate lateral lobes and a larger, usually flat, deep yellow capitulum. Very similar to **7** *T. haworthianum* except for the very different achenes.

It has been suggested (1995) that at least one new taxon in Section *Obliqua* occurs in the British Isles. As yet the situation is unclear, and for the present we are maintaining these two traditional taxa.

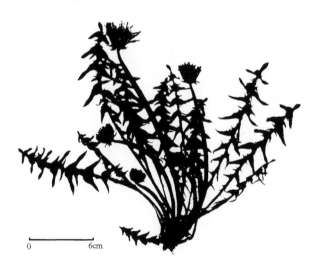

0 _____ 6cm

Section PALUSTRIA (H. Lindb.) Dahlst. (1921)

16 T. palustre (Lyons) Symons (1798)   Map 16

A small to medium-sized slender plant, with decumbent to erect leaves 20–150 mm.

Leaves dull green, without spots, glabrous, *linear or narrowly oblanceolate, entire to denticulate*; *leaf-lobes absent* or lateral lobes 2–3, distant, very short, triangular, entire; midrib green to faintly coloured; petiole unwinged or narrowly winged, purple. Scapes 40–200 mm, decumbent to erect, often purplish, arachnoid-hairy above. Exterior bracts *appressed*, 7 × 3 mm, green or suffused with purple, *with a broad, scarious border*. Capitulum flat, deep yellow, to 40 mm in diameter; ligules flat, striped purple; styles scarcely exserted, discoloured; pollen *absent*. Achenes straw-coloured, oblong, scarcely spinulose; body 4.0 mm; cone 0.5 mm. 2n=40.

Native. In hay-meadows liable to seasonal flooding; less often in calcareous flushes, sometimes near the sea. V.cc. 4, 11, 20, 22, 23, 27–30, 34, 37, 52, 61, 62, 64, 69, 73, 82, S, H8, H9, H15, H16, H19, H23–H27.

In 'The *Taraxacum* Flora' (1972) A.J. Richards wrote: "Rare, apparently only surviving in Norfolk, Cambridgeshire, Berkshire, Hampshire and Co. Clare. There are probably less than 500 plants left in the British Isles, and the world population may well number less than 1,000." It is a measure of the progress in taraxacology in Britain in the last twenty years that there are now records from 29 vice-counties, with records from 65 10-km squares, including at least one colony of some 500 plants in Kirkcudbrightshire.

0   6cm

T. palustre is readily distinguished as it is the only British or Irish species with such narrow leaves which lacks pollen.

16a T. webbii A.J. Richards (1981)

Map 16a

A medium-sized plant, with linear or narrowly spathulate leaves 50–120 mm.

Leaves pale green, without spots, almost glabrous, *lacking lobes*, entire or with short teeth arising from a slightly sinuate leaf-margin; apex entire, acute or sub-obtuse; midrib purplish to green; petiole unwinged proximally, narrow, purple, a third or half length of leaf. Scapes green, *glabrous*. Exterior bracts appressed, 6 × 4 mm, ovate or ovate-lanceolate, *strikingly bordered with a very distinct white border 1 mm wide*, mid-green often suffused with purple on upper surface, not corniculate. Capitulum *rather pale yellow*, flat, *to 30 mm* in diameter; ligules striped purple; styles exserted, discoloured; pollen *absent*. Achenes straw-coloured, shortly tuberculate distally, otherwise smooth; body 4.0–4.3 mm; cone 0.5 mm.

Apparently endemic. Rough grassland by turloughs subject to flooding. Known only from v.cc. H9, H18, H25, H26 and H28.

Distinguished from **16** *T. palustre*, to which it is closely related, by its often broader leaves, a smaller capitulum of a paler colour, and exterior bracts with a distinct white margin.

0   6cm

Section *Palustria*

16b T. sarniense A.J. Richards in A.J. Richards & C.C. Haw. (1984)

A medium-sized plant, with *erect, narrowly oblanceolate-spathulate* leaves 80–150 mm.

Leaves mid-green, without spots, glabrous, *not lobed*, entire or more usually with 3–5 distant, regularly spaced, triangular, short teeth proximally; apex acute; midrib green or purplish proximally; petiole half length of leaf, unwinged proximally, narrow, purple. Scapes usually suffused purple distally, arachnoid-hairy below capitulum at first, glabrescent. Exterior bracts appressed, 3–6 × 1.5–3.5 mm, ovate-acuminate with apex itself somewhat rounded, medium-green on lower surface with a darker vein and with a ± clearly demarcated white border about one quarter of the area of the bract, all sometimes suffused pinkish, especially in bud. Capitulum mid-yellow, 25–35 mm in diameter; ligules flat, striped grey-violet, with purple teeth; styles discoloured; pollen *present.* Achenes straw-coloured, shortly spinulose at apex, otherwise ± smooth; body 3.0 mm; cone cylindrical, *0.9 mm.* 2n=32.

Endemic. Known only from grassy fens in the Channel Islands. V.c. S.

Diagnosed by the characteristic erect, narrowly oblanceolate-spathulate leaves, usually with regularly spaced teeth proximally, the presence of pollen, discoloured styles, short, turbinate achenes with a long cylindrical cone, and scapes arachnoid-hairy when young. Possibly conspecific with the French species *T. ciliare* Soest.

17 T. anglicum Dahlst. (1920) Map 17

A small to medium-sized plant, with narrowly oblanceolate *lobate* leaves 60–200 mm (rarely 300 mm).

Leaves dull green, without spots or with scattered small punctate spots, glabrous, interlobes unblotched, midrib coloured or green; lateral lobes 2–3, short, *acute, often forming sagittate pairs, upper ones entire, lower ones filiform-dentate*; interlobes sometimes dentate; terminal lobe subsagittate, *long* to one quarter length of leaf, with an acute, somewhat elongated apex; petiole unwinged, *vivid purple*. Scapes 50–200 mm, erect, greenish, glabrous. Exterior bracts *appressed*, 7 × 3 mm, *ovate, dark green with a paler narrow border*. Capitulum deep yellow, to 40 mm in diameter, flat; ligules flat, striped leaden-grey (sometimes reddish-brown); styles exserted, discoloured; pollen *present*. Achenes straw-coloured; body 3.5 mm; cone 0.8–1.0 mm. 2n=24.

Native. Very locally frequent in hay-meadows liable to seasonal flooding. Southern England. V.cc. 12, 17, 22, 23, 29–31, 33, 34.

Diagnosed by its smooth, slender, shortly lobate leaves, by the ovate, tightly appressed exterior bracts, and by the presence of pollen. See also **42f** *T. palustrisquameum*.

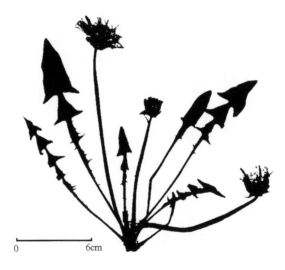

0   6cm

Section *Palustria*

Section SPECTABILIA (Dahlst.) Dahlst. (1921)

18 T. faeroense (Dahlst.) Dahlst. (1925a)

Map 18

A small to medium-sized plant, with oblanceolate-spathulate leaves 50–250 mm.

Leaves *dark green, often spotted*, rough, lobed or *unlobed*, midrib coloured; lateral lobes, if present, 2–4, patent to somewhat recurved, *broad*, acute; petiole unwinged proximally, *purple*. Scapes 20–200 mm, often purplish, ± glabrous. Exterior bracts erect, appressed, 8 × 3 mm, unbordered, dark green. Capitulum bright yellow, *to 40 mm in diameter*; ligules *striped carmine*; styles exserted or ± inserted, dirty yellow; pollen *absent*. Achenes straw-coloured, oblong, almost lacking spines; body 4.0 mm; cone 0.3 mm; rostrum *stout, 5–6 mm*. 2n=40.

Native. Our most widespread dandelion. Throughout the British Isles, particularly in the north and west; very scarce in fens in the south-east. Often very common and the only species in wet places in hilly districts; less frequently on lowland heaths and road-sides, where it is probably introduced. It ascends to 1,000 m (3,300 ft) in Scotland. V.cc. 1–6, 8, 9, 11–14, 17, 22–24, 27–29, 34, 35, 37–52, 55, 57–83, 85–112, S, H1, H2, H9, H11, H12, H16, H20, H21, H31, H38, H39.

The dark, often spotted, often unlobed leaves with coloured petioles, appressed exterior bracts, carmine-striped ligules and large pale achenes distinguish this from all other species.

0   6cm

18a T. geirhildae (Beeby) R. Palmer & Walter Scott (1995)   Map 18a

A medium-sized plant, with broadly obovate thick leaves (60–)90–100(–140) mm.

Leaves yellowish-green to dark apple-green, very sparingly and lightly spotted brownish-red, *rough on upper surface, with very short stout hairs, unlobed,* with up to 5 teeth or small denticulations on either side of the proximal margin; midrib conspicuously *dark brownish-red*; petiole short or absent. Scapes to 180 mm, dull brownish-red. Exterior bracts appressed, dark green, ovate-triangular, 7–8 × 3 mm, with narrow pale border. Capitulum deep yellow, *45–50 mm in diameter*; ligules *striped dark purplish-grey*; styles discoloured; pollen *present.* Achenes straw-coloured; body 4.3–4.6 mm; cone 0.3–0.4 mm.

Endemic. Known only from Lang Clodie Loch and towards the south end of Birka Water, North Roe, Shetland. V.c. 112.

Differs from **18** *T. faeroense* in the leaves being always undivided, broader (to 30 mm) and usually paler yellowish-green (thus contrasting strongly with the dark brownish-red midrib). The capitula are 45–50 mm in diameter, of a darker yellow, with dark purplish-grey ligule stripes, and pollen is present.

0   6cm

Section *Spectabilia*

18b T. serpenticola A.J. Richards in A.J. Richards & C.C. Haw. (1984)

Map 18b

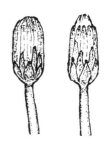

A small to medium-sized plant, with prostrate to ascending, oblanceolate- to obovate-spathulate, thick and leathery leaves to 110 mm.

Leaves *dark olive or brownish green*, with sparse irregular dark spots on upper surface, ± *unlobed*, obtuse with a short mucronate tip, with 1–3 large deltoid, obtuse teeth or very short lobes proximally and smaller irregular, acuminate teeth distally; midrib and petiole dark brown-purple, with some lateral veins also purple; petiole unwinged proximally. Scapes shorter than or equalling leaves at flowering, slightly arachnoid-hairy below capitulum, purplish. Exterior bracts appressed, 5–7 × 2–4 mm, scarcely bordered, olive green on lower surface, *suffused purple*, especially towards apex. Capitulum mid-yellow, *30–35 mm in diameter*; ligules flat, striped deep carmine, with purple teeth; styles ± included, discoloured; pollen *absent*. Achenes straw-coloured; body *4.8–5.0 mm*; cone 0.4 mm.

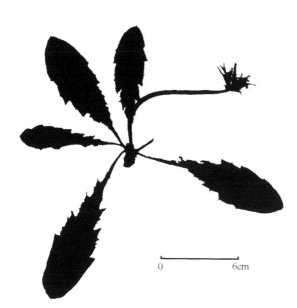

0   6cm

Endemic. Known only from serpentine rocks on Unst, Shetland. V.c. 112.

The leaves are nearly entire, even when well developed, and are dull brownish green, thick and leathery. The exterior bracts are suffused purple, especially towards the apex. Differs from **18** *T. faeroense* in its achenes, the bodies being longer (4.8–5 mm), with short spines on the apical quarter, otherwise faintly rugose.

Section TARAXACUM

19 T. ceratolobum Dahlst. (1912)

Map 19

A small to medium-sized plant, with narrow leaves 50–150 mm.

Leaves *pure green, without spots, glabrous*, midrib green; lateral lobes *5–8*, regular, patent, *short, narrow*, acute, entire; terminal lobe *narrow*, acute, entire; petiole narrowly winged, green. Scapes 80–200 mm, pale, glabrous. Exterior bracts spreading, *7 × 2 mm, bordered*, green. Capitulum very deep orange-yellow, to 40 mm in diameter; ligules striped violet; styles exserted, *yellow*; pollen *present* or absent. Achenes *light brown*; body 4.0 mm; cone 0.7 mm.

Native. Basic rock-ledges at 900–1,070 m (3,000–3,500 ft). V.cc. 88, 90, 92, 94, 96–98, 105.

This species is easily recognised by its bright green leaves with many regular narrow lobes and by its restricted habitat. The styles are yellow.

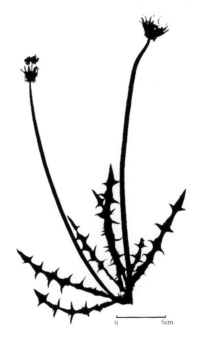

19a T. clovense A.J. Richards (1981)   Map 19a

A medium-sized plant, with erect oblanceolate leaves 100–280 mm.

Leaves green or pale green, unmarked, lobed in the mature condition; lateral lobes 2–3(–4), slightly recurved, short, acute, entire and straight-sided to somewhat concave on the distal margin; interlobes entire; petiole long, green, narrowly winged, ± entire, to half length of leaf. Scapes green, ± equalling leaves. Exterior bracts erecto-patent to suberect, 9–14 × 3–4 mm, green, pruinose on upper surface, with pale border. Capitulum about 40 mm in diameter, deep yellow; styles exserted, *discoloured*; pollen present. Achenes large, straw-coloured; body *4.8–5.3 mm, nearly smooth, almost imperceptibly narrowed into a very short cone.*

Native. Apparently endemic. Known only from Glen Doll, Angus. V.c. 90.

Distinguished from other members of this high-arctic section by its exserted, discoloured styles and its very large (body 4.8–5.3 mm), nearly smooth achenes, which almost lack a cone. It is generally more robust than **19**.

0   6cm

19b T. xiphoideum G.E. Haglund in G.E. Haglund C.G. Lill. (1941)

A small to medium-sized plant, with ± *parallel-sided, obtuse* leaves 50–200 mm.

Leaves mid-green, without spots, glabrous, *unlobed, regularly though sparsely deltoid-dentate*; petiole poorly differentiated, winged, green. Scapes sub-glabrous, erect, pale, copper-coloured. Exterior bracts spreading, 9 × 2 mm, bordered, green. Capitulum deep yellow, to 45 mm in diameter; ligules striped grey-violet; styles exserted, *discoloured*; pollen present. Achenes straw-coloured, spinulose above; body 3.8 mm; cone 1.0 mm. 2n=24.

Native. Moy Corrie, Loch Laggan, Inverness, and Loch Lyon, Argyll. Scotland, southern Iceland and south-west Norway. V.cc. 97, 98.

Distinguished from **19** by its ± parallel-sided, obtuse, unlobed leaves with short, regularly spaced, deltoid teeth. The exterior bracts are more spreading, the achene body rugose throughout, and the styles discoloured. However, juvenile forms of **19** can have a leaf-shape similar to *T. xiphoideum*.

0   6cm

A small to medium-sized plant, with leaves 40–100 mm.

Leaves *rather pale, slightly bluish-green, without spots, almost glabrous*; lateral lobes 3–4, patent, short, ± deltoid, entire, (or dentate proximally); terminal lobe short, *obtuse, often rounded*; petiole *short, green, winged*. Scapes 50–100 mm, erect, pale, glabrous even below capitulum. Exterior bracts spreading, *7 × 2 mm, conspicuously bordered*. Capitulum deep yellow, to 35 mm in diameter; ligules striped violet; styles exserted, *yellow*; pollen *absent*. Achenes *pale brown*; body *3.2 mm*; cone *0.3 mm*. 2n=32.

Native. Acid but mineral-rich rock-ledges at 900–1,200 m (3,000–4,000 ft) in Scotland. V.cc. 88, 89, 92, 94, 96–98, 105.

This rare and geographically disjunct species is best recognised by its pale green leaves and deep yellow flowers, with bordered exterior bracts, yellow styles and no pollen. The small, pale brown achenes with short cones are very characteristic.

21 T. cymbifolium H. Lindb. ex Dahlst. (1930b)   Map 21

A small to medium-sized plant, with leaves 50–150 mm.

Leaves *pure green*, without spots, glabrous; lateral lobes 3–4, patent, ± short, acute or obtuse, scarcely dentate; terminal lobe acute or subacute; petiole winged, green. Scapes 50–100 mm, ascending, pale, somewhat arachnoid-hairy below capitulum. Exterior bracts spreading to recurved, 7 × 2 mm, *unbordered*, green. Capitulum *deep yellow*, 40 mm in diameter; ligules striped violet; styles exserted, *discoloured*; pollen *present*. Achenes *rust-coloured*; body 3.5 mm; cone 0.8 mm. 2n=32.

Native. Rare, at 1,000 m (3,200 ft) in the south-west corrie of Ben Lawers, Perth, on calcareous schist. This species shows a most remarkable disjunct distribution in the arctic. The Ben Lawers station is 10° latitude south of any other in Europe, and this species is a notable addition to its famous relict flora. V.c. 88 only.

T. cymbifolium is the only reddish-fruited species with bright green leaves and orange-yellow heads in Britain. The spreading to recurved, unbordered exterior bracts are also distinctive.

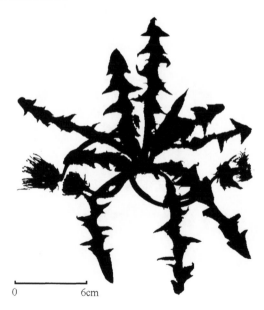

0   6cm

Section *Taraxacum*

22 T. pycnostictum M.P. Christ. (1942) Map 22

A small to medium-sized plant, with narrowly oblanceolate leaves 50–150 mm.

Leaves bluish, *punctate-spotted, rough*; lateral lobes 3–5, patent, short, entire, with distal margin usually concave; terminal lobe a quarter or a third length of leaf, subacute or mucronate, sometimes with a solitary tooth; petiole winged, green. Scapes 100–200 mm, erect, pale. Exterior bracts erect to spreading, imbricate, *9 × 2 mm, scarcely bordered, stiff and thistle-like, glaucous.* Capitulum deep yellow, 40 mm in diameter; ligules striped *grey-purple*; styles exserted, *discoloured*; pollen present. Achenes straw-coloured, spinulose; body 3.8 m; cone 0.7 mm. 2n=32.

Native. Very wet ledges on calcareous schist at 600–900 m (2,000–3,000 ft). Central Highlands, Iceland and Faeroe. V.cc. 88–90, 92, 98.

Although very plastic, this is a most characteristic species with a unique involucre. While it is aberrant in several respects (rough, spotted leaves; involucre), the colour of the leaves and flowers and the shape of the achenes suggest that this species belongs here in Section *Taraxacum* rather than in Section *Naevosa.*

Section *Taraxacum*

Section NAEVOSA M.P. Christ. (1942)

23 T. naevosum Dahlst. (1907)

Map 23

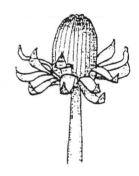

A squat, very robust, medium-sized plant, with leaves 80–250 mm.

Leaves *dark grey-green*, usually with irregular spots, *very rough, bristly*, midrib coloured, sometimes with coloured veins; lateral lobes 5–7, *rather crowded*, patent to somewhat recurved, short and broad, with acute apex, often with a concave-angled distal margin, dentate on distal margins; interlobes ± dentate; terminal lobe a ± equilateral triangle; petiole winged, dull purple. Scapes 50–180 mm, thick, pale. Exterior bracts erect to spreading, *10–12 × 3–5 mm,* scarcely bordered, green or with pink tips. Capitulum flat, mid-yellow, *50–60 mm in diameter*; ligules striped purple; styles exserted, *discoloured*; pollen present. Achenes straw-coloured, *with thick spinules above*; body 3.7–4.0 mm; cone 0.7–0.9 mm. 2n=32.

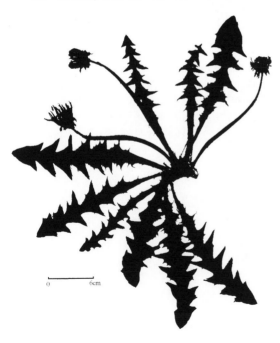

0   6cm

Native. Damp hay-meadows; locally common in the Scottish Highlands; less frequent south to northern England and North Wales. V.cc. 49, 57, 60, 62, 64, 65, 67–70, 85, 88, 89, 91, 93–96, 101, 104, 109–112.

This is a most characterful species with large rough leaves, broadly-winged petioles, and larger involucres and capitula than any other species in this section. Pollen is abundantly present.

Section *Naevosa*

23a T. naevosiforme Dahlst. (1912)

A robust medium-sized plant, with leaves 50–200 mm.

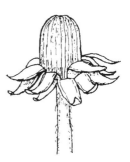

Leaves yellow-green or dark grey-green, spotted, rough, midrib coloured; lateral lobes 4–7, *recurved*, with acute apex, with distal margin convex, ± dentate; terminal lobe a ± equilateral triangle; petiole narrowly winged, purple. Scapes 60–200 mm, erect, often purplish, somewhat arachnoid-hairy below capitulum. Exterior bracts spreading, *10 × 2.5–4 mm*, scarcely bordered, dark green suffused with purple on upper surface, purple-tipped. Capitulum deep yellow, convex, *40 mm in diameter*; ligules striped *grey-purple*; styles exserted, *discoloured*; pollen present. Achenes straw-coloured, spinulose; body 3.5 mm; cone 0.6 mm. 2n=32.

Native. Wet grassland, cliffs etc. Commonest in northern Scotland, becoming progressively rarer southwards. Also in Ireland. V.cc. 41, 42, 48–51, 55, 57–60, 66–70, 72–74, 76, 80, 85, 88, 89, 91, 93, 94, 96–99, 101, 104, 105, 109, 111, 112, H6, H40.

Related to **23** but with smaller capitula (about 40 mm in diameter), longer, more recurved lateral leaf-lobes, and rather narrower exterior bracts. Pollen is abundant.

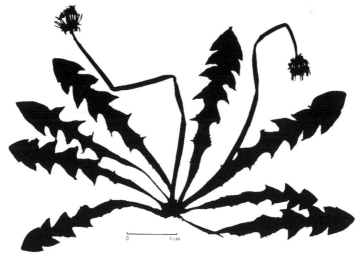

A medium-sized plant, with leaves 150–200 mm.

Leaves dark green, with many spots, almost glabrous, midrib coloured; lateral lobes 6–9, regular, patent, triangular-deltoid, with linear, acute apex, but broader proximally to form a *sigmoid distal margin when well developed*, dentate only on proximal lobes; terminal lobe triangular-hastate, with acute, somewhat elongated apex; petiole unwinged, narrow, purple. Scapes often purplish, somewhat arachnoid-hairy below capitulum. Exterior bracts loosely erect to spreading or recurved, *about 12 × 2–3.5 mm, bordered*, pruinose, pale green on upper surface, dark green on lower surface. Capitulum large, bright yellow, *to 60 mm in diameter*; ligules *striped grey-purple* or green; styles exserted, *discoloured*; pollen present. Achenes *brick-red*, narrow; body 3.8–4.0 mm; cone 0.8–1.0 mm.

Known, in the British Isles, only from Scotland. The only spotted dandelion with red or orange achenes. V.cc. 77, 103, 108, 109, 111.

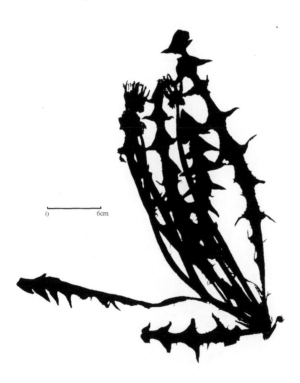

Closely allied to **23** and differing chiefly by the brick-red achenes and narrower exterior bracts (not exceeding 3.5 mm in width). Pollen is abundant. There is some doubt as to whether Scottish material is identical to the Icelandic type.

0   6cm

24 T. euryphyllum (Dahlst.) Hjelt (1926)   Map 24

A robust medium-sized plant, with oblanceolate leaves 100–200 mm.

Leaves *pure green, with irregularly shaped spots, rough,* interlobes often with blotches, midrib coloured; lateral lobes 4–6, patent, acute, with a *sigmoid distal margin when well developed,* scarcely dentate or sometimes dentate on distal margins only; terminal lobe short, obtuse, with an occasional tooth; petiole *wide-winged,* purplish or green at base. Scapes 80–200 mm, erect, pale. Exterior bracts spreading to recurved or omni-directional, *9–12 × 2.8–3.7 mm, with a narrow, pale border, pruinose,* pale green on upper surface, blue-green on lower surface. Capitulum yellow, to 40 mm in diameter; ligules striped *red-purple,* with *purple* teeth; styles exserted, *discoloured*; pollen *very sparse,* in outer florets only, usually appearing to be absent. Achenes straw-coloured, spinulose above; body 3.5–4 mm; cone 0.7 mm. 2n=32.

Native. Frequent in wet, rather sheltered, somewhat base-rich sites throughout Great Britain but more frequent in the north and west; one record in eastern Ireland. V.cc. 1–4, 11, 12, 15, 18–20, 22, 23, 27–30, 34, 35, 37–43, 46, 48–51, 55–70, 72–78, 80–82, 85, 86, 89, 91–99, 101, 103–110, 112, H21.

Diagnosed by the broadly-winged petiole, the apparent absence of pollen and the sigmoid margins of the lateral lobes. The terminal lobe is scarcely bigger than the pairs of lobes below it, so distinguishing this species from **25** *T. maculosum.*

Section *Naevosa*   93

24a T. hirsutissimum C.C. Haw. in Dudman & A.J. Richards (1994)

A robust medium-sized plant, with leaves 50–200 mm.

Leaves *grey-green*, without or with very few faint spots, *very hairy*, interlobes without blotches, midrib faintly coloured; lateral lobes 4–7, patent to somewhat recurved, with linear, acute apex, with distal margin curved or angled, not or scarcely dentate; interlobes occasionally dentate; terminal lobe *sagittate with an acute, somewhat elongated apex*; petiole ± winged, purple. Scapes often purplish, somewhat arachnoid-hairy below capitulum. Exterior bracts recurved, about 12 × 2.5 mm, pale green on upper surface, blue-green on lower surface. Capitulum rather pale yellow, to 30 mm in diameter; styles exserted, *orange*; pollen *present*. Achenes straw-coloured; body 3.5 mm; cone 0.5 mm.

Endemic. Known only from the Shetland Islands. V.c. 112 only.

Similar to **24**, but with very hairy leaves so that the sparse spots tend to be hidden, with narrower acute lateral lobes and an elongated, sagittate terminal lobe, and orange styles bearing pollen; the ligule teeth are yellow.

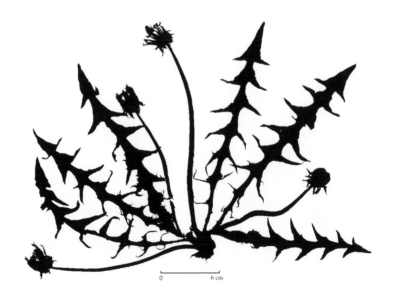

0   6 cm

Section *Naevosa*

25 T. maculosum A.J. Richards (1981)

Map 25

A medium-sized plant, with rather narrowly oblanceolate leaves 50–200 mm.

Leaves dull or dark green, with irregular spots, *rough*; midrib coloured; lateral lobes 2–4, often alternate, distant, patent to somewhat recurved, with acute apex, but broader proximally to form a *sigmoid distal margin when well developed*, sometimes dentate on proximal lobes; terminal lobe *to one quarter length of leaf or more, with acute apex*; petiole ± unwinged proximally, purple. Scapes 100–200 mm, decumbent to erect, pale. Exterior bracts spreading to suberect, 8–10 × 2.5–3.5 mm, scarcely bordered, *dark green, pruinose*. Capitulum yellow, 40 mm in diameter; ligules striped *purple*; styles exserted, *discoloured*; pollen *absent*. Achenes straw-coloured, with rather few acute spinules above; body 3.5 mm; cone 0.7 mm. 2n=32.

Native. Wet places, mainly in the north, especially wet wood-margins, cliff-faces etc.; not noticeably basicolous. Fairly common; perhaps introduced into the south-east. V.cc. 5, 7, 11, 12, 19, 23, 28, 29, 35, 37, 39, 41–46, 48, 50–52, 55–112, S, H9, H28, H32, H33, H36, H38–H40.

Diagnosed by the involucre with pruinose external bracts in two rows, the upper erect and the outer more spreading, by the hairy leaves with a rather long, narrow terminal lobe, and by the sigmoid margins to the distal side of the lateral lobes. *T. maculosum* always lacks pollen.

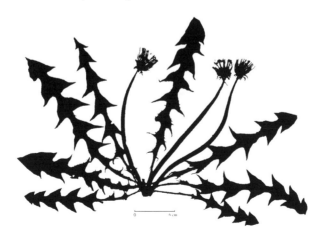

26 T. pseudolarssonii A.J. Richards (1972)

Map 26

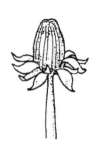

A medium-sized *very heterophyllous* plant, with leaves 100–200 mm.

Leaves *dark green, very heavily marked with purple or black spots, often coalesced into blotches on first emergence; uniquely, this pigment is water-soluble so that spots fade rapidly and are scarcely visible on late-season plants and old leaves*, leaves almost glabrous, midrib coloured; lateral lobes 3–5, sometimes very neat and regular in young leaves, patent to somewhat recurved, narrow, acute, becoming coarse and dentate on either margin and/or with dentate interlobes; terminal lobe at first subacute, sometimes helmet-shaped, later larger and dentate; petiole unwinged or winged, *bright purple at first, fading later.* Scapes 100–200 mm, erect, pale. Exterior bracts spreading to recurved, arcuate, about 9–11 × 2 mm, grey-green, *narrowly pale-bordered.* Capitulum deep yellow, to 45 mm in diameter; ligules striped grey-violet; styles exserted, discoloured; pollen *present.* Achenes straw-coloured, spinulose; body 3.5 mm; cone 0.5 mm. 2n=32.

Native. Mainly in Scotland and northern England, where it is an abundant species and in some meadows the dominant dandelion. It occurs equally commonly in country lanes and by moorland tracks; also common in sand-dunes. V.cc. 3, 25, 42, 50, 51, 57–62, 65–70, 72–74, 76–83, 85, 87, 89, 93, 94, 112.

Diagnosed early in the season by heavy spotting (though this disappears later, giving a distinctive, washed-out appearance). The spreading to recurved, arcuate bracts are rather small, pale on the upper surface and scarcely bordered. Pollen is abundant.

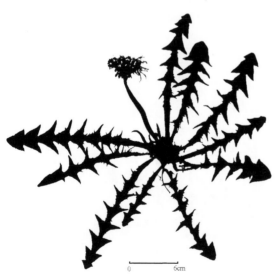

0 ———— 6cm

Section *Naevosa*

27 T. subnaevosum A.J. Richards (1981)   Map 27

A small to medium-sized, rather delicate plant, with suberect leaves to 140 mm.

Leaves dark green, *sparsely but regularly spotted with small black spots* on the upper side, almost glabrous, midrib green; lateral lobes 3–4, recurved to subpatent, acute, sub-convex, denticulate or more rarely entire on distal margin; interlobes denticulate; terminal lobe ± long, acute, entire or denticulate, with lateral apices *hamate*; petiole unwinged, ± dentate, greenish or purplish. Scapes usually exceeding leaves, thin, sparsely arachnoid-hairy. Exterior bracts *recurved, about 6–9 × 1.5–2.2 mm, scarcely bordered, pale green.* Capitulum rather pale yellow, to 30 mm in diameter; ligules striped *grey-purple*; styles exserted, *yellowish or occasionally darker*; pollen *absent*. Achenes straw-coloured, shortly spinulose above, otherwise ± smooth; body 3.1–3.3 mm; cone 0.6–0.9 mm.

Endemic. Frequent and widespread in some areas of northern England and Scotland. V.cc. 42, 50, 51, 57, 60, 67–70, 72–74, 77–79, 81–83, 85, 87–90, 92–97, 99, 101–109, 112.

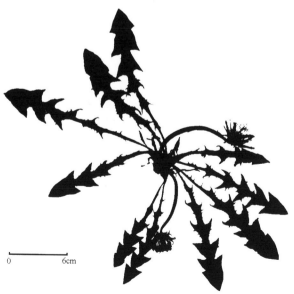

A tenuous plant, characterised by its rather large, hamate-based terminal lobe, small, punctate spots, usually yellowish stigmas, the absence of pollen, and the pale, narrow, recurved exterior bracts.

0   6cm

Section *Naevosa*   97

27a T. cornubiense A.J. Richards (1981)   Map 27a

A medium-sized, rather delicate plant, with suberect leaves 100–150 mm.

Leaves dull green, sparsely marked with small blackish spots on the upper side, interlobes without blotches, midrib green to faintly coloured; lateral lobes 4–5, recurved or subpatent, acute, subconvex and *strongly denticulate on the distal margin*; interlobes denticulate; terminal lobe short with an elongated apex, often divided into 2 acute lobules on one side only; petiole unwinged proximally, narrow, ± dentate, dull purplish. Scapes ± equalling leaves, thin, often purplish, arachnoid-hairy below capitulum. Exterior bracts spreading to recurved, *7–9 × 1.7–2.6 mm*, rather dark green on lower surface, with a rather indistinct pale border. Capitulum to 30 mm in diameter; styles exserted, *discoloured*; pollen *present*. Achenes straw-coloured, tuberculate to shortly spinulose above, otherwise ± smooth; body *3.6–3.8 mm*; cone 0.7–0.9 mm, subcylindrical. 2n=24.

Endemic. *T. cornubiense* has been recorded in 17 10-km squares in Cornwall. It occurs on old railway lines and in gardens. V.cc. 1, 2.

Similar to **27**, with the same punctate spots and small recurved exterior bracts, but diagnosed by the combination of large achenes (body 3.6–3.8 mm), the presence of pollen and the characteristic leaf-shape, with numerous teeth on the distal sides of the lateral lobes.

0   6cm

Section *Naevosa*

A small to medium-sized, delicate plant, with spathulate leaves 60–170 mm.

Leaves mid-green, usually with small, sparse spots, glabrous, interlobes without blotches, midrib green to faintly coloured; leaves sometimes unlobed and dentate, but more usually lobed with lateral lobes 2–5, broader proximally but apex acute, to form a *sinuate distal margin when well developed*; terminal lobe broad, entire, *rounded*; petiole unwinged or narrowly winged, green to dull purple. Scapes 100–200 mm, erect, pale. Involucre somewhat *pruinose*; exterior bracts erect to spreading, *about 8 × 2 mm, narrowly white-bordered, dark.* Capitulum yellow, to 40 mm in diameter; ligules striped *grey*; styles exserted, *discoloured*; pollen *present*. Achenes straw-coloured, *smooth*; body 3.0 mm; cone up to 0.5 mm. 2n=24.

Native. Rocks, cliff-ledges etc. at low altitudes in the west. Also in Spain and Portugal. V.cc. 1–3, 5, 9, 74, 75, 98–104, H6, H9, H16, H20, H21, H27.

Diagnosed by the combination of smooth, small achenes, pollen-rich, discoloured stigmas and erect to spreading, bordered, exterior bracts, usually with spotted leaves with sinuate-margined lateral lobes.

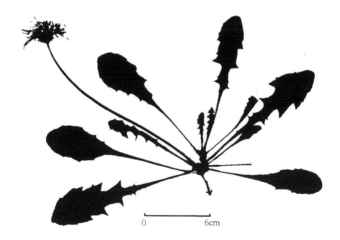

29 T. stictophyllum Dahlst. (1912)

Map 29

A small to medium-sized, squat plant, with obovate to oblanceolate leaves 80–250 mm, *usually prostrate in a tight rosette.*

Leaves *greyish-green*, with or rarely without scattered punctate spots, *roughly hairy*, interlobes without blotches, midrib coloured to bright red; lateral lobes *3–5*, recurved (sometimes extremely so), long, dentate, with linear and acute apex; terminal lobe broadly rounded to triangular, sometimes dentate; petiole broadly winged, pale or sometimes purple. Scapes short at first, pale, somewhat arachnoid-hairy below capitulum. Exterior bracts *many, crowded*, curved upwards to give a *rounded* involucre, *about 9 × 3 mm, faintly bordered*, dark green. Capitulum yellow, 25–40 mm in diameter; ligules striped red-purple; styles exserted, *discoloured*; pollen present. Achenes straw-coloured, very broad with broad-based cone, spinulose ± only at top; body 3.2 × 1.3 mm; cone 0.8–1.0 mm.

Native. Wet shaded rocky places at low altitudes. Scattered and locally frequent in the north and west of Great Britain; Norway. V.cc. 3, 42, 48, 50–52, 57, 60–62, 65–67, 69, 70, 72, 73, 75, 76, 78–80, 88, 89, 93–96, 98–104, 106, 109–111.

Diagnosed by the combination of prostrate, crowded, stiff, grey-green and hairy leaves, usually with small, sparse spots, and a most distinctive involucre. Pollen is rather sparsely present.

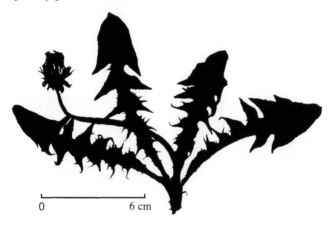

0   6 cm

Section *Naevosa*

A medium-sized, fairly robust plant, with leaves 150–200 mm.

Leaves *dark green*, with many scattered rather small purplish-black spots, rather hairy, midrib coloured; lateral lobes *6–8*, crowded, regular, triangular, with acute, backward-pointing apex, with distal margin ± straight but sometimes slightly sinuate and bearing a few subulate teeth; interlobes broad, slightly filiform-dentate; terminal lobe large, often with large teeth, with subacute apex; petiole unwinged or scarcely winged, purple. Scapes often purplish, somewhat arachnoid-hairy below capitulum. Exterior bracts suberect to spreading, 10–12 × 2–3 mm, somewhat arcuate, lanceolate, *with a distinct narrow white border*, pale green on upper surface, mid-green on lower surface. Capitulum 35–40 mm in diameter; ligules striped purple, central ones *tipped orange-red*; styles discoloured; pollen *absent* (rarely a few grains in outer florets). Achenes straw-coloured; body 3.2–3.7 mm, with broad-based spinules above; cone conical, 0.8 mm.

Endemic. Local but occasionally frequent in moist grasslands in Wales and northern England. In southern England confined to herb-rich meadows. V.cc. 3, 4, 11, 12, 19, 20, 22, 30, 31, 34, 35, 37, 41–43, 50, 51, 57, 58, 60, 61, 69, 70, 72, 73, 103.

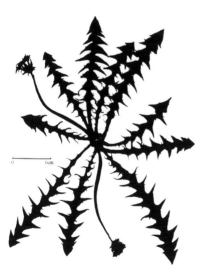

Related to **29**, with a similarly distinctive involucre and crowded, prostrate rosettes, but with 6–8-lobed, dark green leaves and nearly always lacking pollen. It is unusual in this section in having orange-red ends to the central florets.

Being without pollen, *T. richardsianum* could be confused with two other common pollenless dandelions of a similar size, **25** *T. maculosum* and **24** *T. euryphyllum*. Besides having a quite different involucre, not rounded at the base nor crowded, *T. maculosum* has long, narrow leaves with fewer lobes which are sigmoid on the distal margin. In *T. euryphyllum* the lateral lobes are more patent and less acute, and the petiole is more broadly winged.

Section CELTICA A.J. Richards (1985)

30 T. gelertii Raunk. (1903)

Map 30

A small to medium-sized plant, with ± oblong, flat leaves 50–200 mm.

Leaves dull green, *often somewhat bluish, without spots, smooth*; interlobes without blotches, midrib pinkish; lateral lobes 3–5, patent to somewhat recurved, *triangular to deltoid, with distal margin not toothed or sometimes with a single tooth on distal margin of distal lobes, convex to straight-sided*, proximal margin straight, patent; terminal lobe obtuse or subacute but sometimes slightly mucronate, entire or with a single blunt tooth; petiole narrowly winged, purple. Scapes usually equalling leaves, decumbent to erect. Exterior bracts *erect, ovate-lanceolate, 7 × 2 mm, with an indistinct white border, dark green*. Capitulum deep yellow, 30–45 mm in diameter; ligules *rather long*, striped *grey-violet*; styles exserted, *discoloured*; pollen usually present, sometimes absent. Achenes brownish, *rugose, spinulose*; body 3.2 mm; cone 0.5 mm. 2n=24.

Native. In grassy natural and semi-natural habitats, on well-drained to wet neutral to calcareous soils, often in species-rich grasslands; also not infrequently in man-made habitats such as walls, pavements, gardens and gravel-pits; on cliffs and ravines in the north and west. Common in the west. V.cc. 1–9, 11–17, 20, 22–24, 28–30, 34–37, 39, 41–52, 55, 57, 58, 60, 62–75, 77–83, 86, 88, 89, 93–104, 111–112, S, H1, H5, H9, H12, H15, H16, H19–H21, H33, H36, H38–H40.

The leaf-shape is variable, the achenes have many large spines and are rugose throughout, and the exterior bracts are characteristically erect, ovate-lanceolate and indistinctly bordered. See also **42d** *T. cambricum.*

102 Section *Celtica*

31 T. bracteatum Dahlst. (1925b)

Map 31

A medium-sized plant, with erect leaves 100–250 mm.

Leaves *dull, dark green*, without spots, interlobes sometimes with dark blotches, midrib *bright red or purple to apex*, leaves also usually with characteristic red lateral veining; lateral lobes *3–5*, slightly recurved, rather short, broadly triangular, with distal margin usually somewhat convex or sinuate, sometimes filiform-dentate; terminal lobe up to a quarter length of leaf, triangular to helmet-shaped, with sub-acute or mucronate apex; petiole unwinged proximally, narrow, *bright purple*. Scapes 50–200 mm, erect, often reddish, somewhat arachnoid-hairy below capitulum, sometimes with distinct isolated bracts. Involucre somewhat *pruinose*; exterior bracts ± erect, *about 10 × 3 mm, unbordered*, grey-green often suffused with purple on upper surface, *dark green on lower surface*. Capitulum

yellow, to 45 mm in diameter; ligules striped *purple*; styles exserted, *discoloured*; pollen present. Achenes straw-coloured; body 3–4 mm; cone 0.7–0.9 mm. 2n=24.

Native. Widespread, usually growing in damp habitats, throughout the British Isles. V.cc. 1–6, 9–20, 22, 23, 28–30, 33–35, 38–44, 46, 48, 50, 51, 54, 55, 57–62, 65–74, 76–78, 81, 83, 84, 88–91, 93–99, 101, 103, 109, 111–112, S, H12, H16, H33, H39.

The dark green leaves have contrasting brightly coloured petioles, midribs and veining. The exterior bracts are dark green on their lower surface, crowded and ± erect.

31a   T. orcadense Dahlst. (1926) Map 31a

A medium-sized plant, with spreading to erect leaves 50–200 mm.

Leaves *shining dark green*, without spots, interlobes without blotches, midrib glabrescent, deep pink to purple; lateral lobes *2–4*, patent to ± recurved, broad, short, acute, triangular at least on outer leaves, with margins straight, ± dentate; terminal lobe *about twice length of lateral lobes, broad, ± rounded*, usually mucronate, often divided and/or dentate; petiole unwinged or winged, *deep purple*. Scapes erect, often shorter than leaves. Exterior bracts spreading to erect, 10 × 2.5 mm, scarcely bordered, pale green on upper surface, *blackish green often suffused with purple on lower surface*. Capitulum mid-yellow, 50 mm in diameter; ligules striped brown-violet; styles exserted, discoloured; pollen present. Achenes straw-coloured; body 3.5 mm; cone 0.6 mm.

Endemic. Grassy places; known only from Mainland and Cava, Orkney, where it seems to be frequent. V.c. 111 only.

Closely related to **31** *T. bracteatum*, but with leaves of a shining dark green which have a large rounded terminal lobe and fewer lateral lobes. The exterior bracts are blackish green on their lower surface, often suffused with purple.

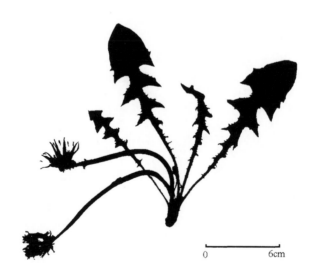

0   6cm

31b T. nietoi A.J. Richards (1992)

A medium-sized plant, with suberect to spreading, broadly oblanceolate leaves to 250 mm.

Leaves dark green, without spots, interlobes without blotches, midrib glabrescent, deep pink to purple; lateral lobes *2–3*, patent, broad, acute, with distal margin not or scarcely toothed, convex, sigmoid, straight-sided or concave-angled, proximal margin entire; terminal lobe broadly hastate, entire or with a solitary tooth or ± divided, subacute; petiole unwinged, purple; petiole and midrib with interwoven green strands. Scapes ± equalling leaves at flowering, glabrescent, bronze. Involucre large, dark green, with a rounded base; exterior bracts smooth, erect, *ovate, 8–10 × 4 mm, with a distinct white border* 0.5 mm wide. Capitulum mid-yellow, 35 mm in diameter; ligules striped *grey-purple*, with *purple* teeth; styles exserted, *yellowish*; pollen present. Achenes grey-brown, shortly spinulose at apex, otherwise smooth, with conical cone; body *3.8 mm*; cone 0.6 mm.

Native. Recorded in Britain only from a roadbank in Flint. Also occurs in Spain; links between the *Taraxacum* flora of Spain and western Britain are not unexpected, and at least four species are found in both places. V.c. 51.

T. nietoi is a characteristic member of Section *Celtica*. The leaf-shape is reminiscent of **42e** *T. lancastriense*, but the large ovate, beautifully white-bordered exterior bracts, the yellowish styles and the large achenes are distinctive. A relative of **31** *T. bracteatum*, but one which is immediately distinguished by its exterior bracts of 8–10 × 4 mm which have conspicuous white borders.

Section *Celtica*

32 T. britannicum Dahlst. (1927b)

Map 32

A small to medium-sized plant, with suberect flat leaves 50–200 mm.

Leaves bluish-green, without spots, glabrous, interlobes without blotches, midrib purple (or sometimes green); lateral lobes 4–6, patent, regular, *deltoid to strongly recurved or hamate*, only proximal ones filiform-dentate on distal margin; terminal lobe with an acute, somewhat elongated, entire apex; petiole unwinged proximally, narrow, purple. Scapes 70–200 mm, often purplish, somewhat arachnoid-hairy below capitulum. Involucre *neatly ovate*; exterior bracts erect to appressed, *7–10 × 2–3 mm, pruinose-blackish, distinctly but narrowly white-bordered*. Capitulum deep yellow, to 40 mm in diameter; ligules rather long, striped *grey-violet*; styles exserted, *blackish*; pollen present. Achenes brownish, *scarcely spined*; body 3.2–3.7 mm; cone 0.5–0.7 mm. 2n=24.

Native. On neutral to calcareous soils, often in species-rich grasslands, mainly in the west. V.cc. 1–6, 9, 23, 28, 34, 35, 38, 42, 44–46, 60, 70, 73, 74, 77, 83, 98, 101–103, S, H9, H16, H17, H19, H21, H36, H38–H40.

A typical member of Section *Celtica*, *T. britannicum* differs from **30** *T. gelertii* and **31** *T. bracteatum* by its leaf-shape, by the almost smooth achenes and by the neatly ovate, blackish involucre.

0   6cm

33 T. subbracteatum A.J. Richards in A.J. Richards & Map 33
C.C. Haw. (1984)

A small to medium-sized plant, with prostrate to ascending, narrowly oblanceolate, often *crisped* leaves 100–250 mm.

Leaves *dark green*, without spots, interlobes usually blotched on lower surface and occasionally on upper surface, midrib glabrescent, deep pink to purple, often becoming green distally; lateral lobes 4–6, somewhat recurved, rather short, with distal margin not toothed or with 1(–3) acuminate teeth, strongly *sigmoid*, often *double-lobed* distally; terminal lobe short, *helmet-shaped to weakly trilobate*, with subacute, mucronate apex, entire or with 1 tooth; petiole narrowly winged, a quarter to a third length of leaf, purple; petiole and midrib with interwoven green strands. Scapes usually shorter than leaves at flowering, arachnoid-hairy throughout, pinkish throughout or towards apex. Exterior bracts *spreading (to suberect), regular, not or scarcely overlapping, 8–11 × 3 mm, scarcely bordered, pale green or tinged purple on upper surface, dark green on lower surface, scarcely pruinose.* Capitulum deep yellow, 30–40 mm in diameter; ligules *flat*, striped *dark grey-violet*, with *purple* teeth; styles dark; pollen present. Achenes straw-coloured, shortly spinulose at apex, otherwise smooth, with conical cone; body *3.0–3.3 mm*; cone 0.3 mm.

Endemic. Throughout Great Britain, particularly in the north and west. Although only once recorded in Ireland, it appears to be principally an Atlantic species and it is locally abundant in areas such as west Argyll, Kintyre, South Wales, Pembrokeshire and Devon. However, it is one of the few species in Section *Celtica* which extend into south-eastern England. V.cc. 3–6, 9, 10, 12, 14–17, 19, 20, 23–25, 28, 30, 33–37, 39–44, 46, 49–51, 55–60, 62, 67–70, 72–75, 77, 81, 86, 88–90, 93–96, 98, 99–101, 104, 106, 109, S, H16.

Continued overleaf

T. subbracteatum is related to **32** *T. britannicum* and **31** *T. bracteatum*. The leaf-shape can be very similar to that of **32**, which, however, has very distinctive erect, blackish, white-bordered bracts and almost smooth achenes. **31** is a grosser plant with broader leaves with fewer lobes. The not or scarcely overlapping exterior bracts of *T. subbracteatum* are distinctive in living material.

33a   T. oellgaardii C.C. Haw. (1990)   Map 33a

A medium-sized plant, with oblong-lanceolate leaves 100–200 mm.

Leaves *pale green or yellow-green*, without spots, interlobes unblotched, midrib dull pink-purple with interwoven red and green strands; lateral lobes *4–6*, ± patent, deltoid, broad, acute, *lower lobes with many filiform teeth on distal margin*, which is frequently ± sigmoid; interlobes ± entire; terminal lobe medium-sized, triangular, entire, sometimes slightly mucronate, subacute; petiole to one third length of leaf, usually narrowly winged *with a sharp contrast between the green lamina and middle bright red portions.* Scapes usually ± equalling leaves, pale, glabrescent. Exterior bracts erect or suberect, 8–10 × 2–4 mm, ovate-lanceolate, scarcely to conspicuously bordered, pale green on upper surface, *darker green suffused with purple on lower surface.* Capitulum yellow, *30–40 mm in diameter*; ligules striped purple; styles exserted, discoloured; pollen present. Achenes straw-coloured, finely spinulose at apex, otherwise smooth; body *2.6–3.0 mm*; cone conical, 0.5–0.7 mm.

Endemic. Scattered. The species appears to be one of rich meadow habitats. V.cc. 23, 26, 34, 42, 44, 74, 86.

T. oellgaardii is a typical member of Section *Celtica* in ecology and morphology. It is an elegant species with pale, narrow, multilobed leaves. The many filiform teeth on the distal margin of the lower lateral leaf-lobes and the relatively small capitula are diagnostic. A relative of **33** *T. subbracteatum*, but with paler leaves and smaller achenes, the body not exceeding 3.0 mm.

0   6cm

34 T. duplidentifrons Dahlst. (1929)

Map 34

A medium-sized plant, with spreading to erect, often *crisped* leaves 50–200 mm.

Leaves *dull green*, without spots, shortly and sparsely hairy, interlobes without blotches, midrib *dark dull pinkish-red*; lateral lobes 3–5, patent to somewhat recurved, *rather short and broadly deltoid, tapering suddenly to an acute or acuminate tip*, with distal margin usually filiform- and triangular-dentate; terminal lobe triangular, acute, usually entire; petiole usually winged, sometimes broadly so, *dull pink to purple*. Scapes usually equalling leaves, arachnoid-hairy, ascending to erect. Exterior bracts *suberect to spreading, 9 × 2.5 mm, acute, faintly bordered, pale green on upper surface, darker green on lower surface*. Capitulum mid-yellow, 40–45 mm in diameter; ligules flat, striped *grey-violet*; teeth of inner ligules *blackish*; styles exserted, *darkly discoloured to blackish*; pollen present. Achenes olive-brown; body 3.0 mm; cone 0.4–0.7 mm. 2n=24.

Native. Grassy places everywhere, but especially on well-drained, base-rich soils. Locally common on sand-dunes, limestone grassland etc. This species can lay claim to being possibly our commonest dandelion, though, like most of this section, its distribution is concentrated in the north and west. V.cc. 1–7, 9, 11, 12, 14–17, 19–23, 25–31, 34, 35, 38–44, 46, 48–51, 53, 55–62, 64–91, 93–101, 103–106, 108–112, S, H13, H21, H22, H33, H38, H39.

It is most readily recognised by the often rather crispate foliage, which is dull and hairy, with triangular lobes ending in a wispy point. The small spreading exterior bracts and the dull ruby-pink colour of the petiole and midrib are also characteristic. *T. duplidentifrons* is the only one among its relatives, apart from **35** *T. celticum*, to have blackish ligule teeth and stigmas.

34a T. porteri C.C. Haw. (1990)

A medium-sized to tall, fairly robust plant, with ascending to erect, oblong to oblanceolate leaves to 300 mm.

Leaves *dull dark green*, without spots, interlobes sometimes with a slight dark blotch, midrib dull purple; lateral lobes 4–5, patent, *triangular or deltoid, with filiform acute apex, with distal margin often with a few filiform teeth*; interlobes entire or lightly filiform-dentate; terminal lobe medium-sized, *acutely triangular or trilobate*, with apex sometimes acuminate or mucronate; petiole to one third length of leaf, unwinged, dull purple; petiole and midrib with interwoven green strands. Scapes usually equalling leaves at flowering, moderately arachnoid-hairy, dull green or purple. Exterior bracts *erect, 8–12 × 2–4 mm*, ovate or lanceolate, bordered, green on upper surface, *dark green on lower surface*, suffused with anthocyanin towards tip, somewhat pruinose. Capitulum mid-yellow, 40–50 mm in diameter; ligules striped purple; styles discoloured; pollen present. Achenes straw-coloured, ± rugose throughout and with broad-based spinules at apex; body 3.0–3.2 mm; cone cylindrical to conical, 0.5–0.6 mm.

0   6cm

Endemic. Apparently confined to Wales and some Welsh border counties, where it can be frequent on grassy banks and along hedgerows. V.cc. 33–36, 42–44, 51, 58.

A handsome, robust species resembling **34** *T. duplidentifrons*, but with dark green leaves, and very characteristic terminal lobes which are strictly triangular or trilobate, often with a long acuminate apex. The exterior bracts are broader, to 4 mm in width. *T. porteri* is a striking member of Section *Celtica*, with its dark green, acute foliage, very deltoid or triangular leaf-lobation, and dark, erect external bracts. It cannot easily be confused with any other British dandelion.

35 T. celticum A.J. Richards in A.J. Richards & C.C. Haw. (1984)

Map 35

A medium-sized plant, with oblanceolate leaves 120–240 mm.

Leaves bright green, without spots, interlobes ± blotched on lower surface, midrib glabrescent, deep pink to purple often becoming green distally; lateral lobes 4–5, with a broad deltoid base *provided with 1(–3) large acute teeth or lobules on distal margin* and a patent, *forward-pointed* or irregularly directed, entire, acute, narrowly lanceolate, ± straight-sided process abruptly contracted from the base; terminal lobe *short, trilobate*, not toothed, the central process ± obtuse, mucronate, abruptly concave-angled to the short, subacute, often forward-pointing lateral processes; petiole winged, sometimes broadly so, purple; petiole and midrib with interwoven green strands. Scapes shorter than or equalling leaves at flowering, arachnoid-hairy below capitulum, green or suffused pink. Exterior bracts *spreading*, 9–12 × 3–4 mm, unbordered or scarcely bordered, suffused purple on upper surface, dark green suffused purple on lower surface, somewhat pruinose. Capitulum mid-yellow, 30–40 mm in diameter; ligules flat, striped *dark grey-violet*, with purple teeth; styles dark; pollen *absent* or sparsely present. Achenes pale brown, shortly spinulose at apex, otherwise smooth, with conical cone; body 3.5–3.8 mm; cone 0.4 mm.

Endemic. On light, well-drained neutral to calcareous soils, often in species-rich grasslands; also on walls, lane-banks etc. Scattered mainly in Wales and the south-west. V.cc. 3, 4, 34, 35, 37, 40, 42–44, 46, 48, 50, 51, 58, 60, 69, H1.

The narrow, often forward-pointing lateral leaf-lobes with large teeth or lobules and the trilobate terminal lobes are distinctive. The leaf-shape can resemble that of some forms of **42** *T. nordstedtii*, but that species has erect bracts and short ligules with brown stripes.

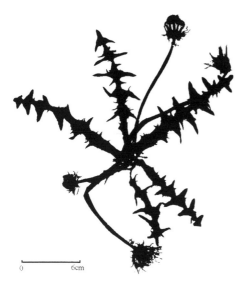

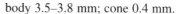
0   6cm

Often a robust plant, with erect, oblong, crispate leaves to 300 mm.

Leaves mid-green, without spots, *very conspicuously purple-blotched* on the interlobes on both surfaces, midrib bright purple but often with interwoven green strands; lateral lobes 5–6, *often irregularly and alternately arranged* along the axis, ± patent, with large subobtuse teeth which often divide the lobe, sometimes with a rather obtuse linear process at apex; interlobes narrow and long, usually strongly and irregularly toothed; terminal lobe medium-sized, obtuse or subobtuse, irregularly dentate; petiole to one quarter length of leaf, unwinged or scarcely winged, purple. Scapes usually equalling leaves, glabrescent, purple. Exterior bracts spreading, arcuate, *10–12 × 2–3 mm*, lanceolate, unbordered or scarcely bordered, pale green on upper surface, *darker green on lower surface, often with some purple coloration, pruinose.* Capitulum bright yellow, 35–45 mm in diameter; ligules striped purple, with bright purple teeth; styles exserted, discoloured; pollen present but sometimes rather sparse. Achenes olive-brown, spinulose above; body 2.8–3.0 mm; cone conical, not clearly demarcated, 0.3–0.4 mm.

Endemic. This species lies morphologically between Sections *Celtica* and *Hamata* and is only placed in the former section on grounds of distribution, since it occurs, as its name suggests, mainly in the west of Britain. It is however known in some eastern counties, although only from 'good' habitats.

0   6cm

V.cc. 3, 4, 6, 19, 22, 30, 34–36, 40–44, 47, 50, 51, 58, 60, 70, 77, 99.

T. hesperium has some resemblance to **55** *T. lamprophyllum*, which is placed in Section *Hamata*, but it is much more irregular in leaf lobation (the lateral lobes often alternating along the axis) and the dentation is less uniform (the teeth being fewer and much larger). In *T. lamprophyllum* the exterior bracts are larger and more ovate. See also **37** *T. excellens*.

36a   T. 'cestrense' T. Edmondson ined. Map 36a

Although **36** *T. hesperium*, **37** *T. excellens* and **55** *T. lamprophyllum* are typically well separated, morphologically intermediate plants do occur. These are multi-lobate plants with the narrowly lanceolate leaf-shape of *T. excellens*, but with leaves which are more dentate, approaching *T. hesperium*, but less strongly blotched than in either species, thus resembling *T. lamprophyllum*. Such plants are informally described as *T. 'cestrense'*.

V.cc. 6, 39, 50, 51, 58, 59.

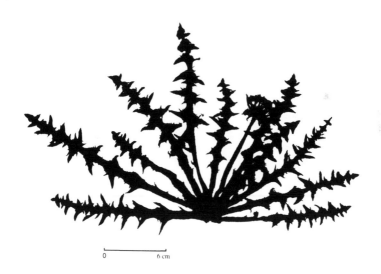

0 ———— 6 cm

37 T. excellens Dahlst. (1935)

Map 37

A medium-sized plant, with prostrate to ascending, narrowly lanceolate, flat leaves in a dense rosette, 50–200 mm.

Leaves green, without spots, interlobes *with conspicuous purple blotches* or with dark borders, midrib glabrescent, deep red to purple; lateral lobes *regular*, 4–6, patent to somewhat recurved, short, broad, obtuse, with distal margin sometimes bluntly large-toothed, convex, sigmoid, straight-sided or concave-angled, the proximal margin convex or ± concave; terminal lobe small and neat, about as long as broad or sometimes up to twice as long, obtuse but sometimes slightly mucronate, sometimes divided and/or with a solitary tooth; petiole winged and parallel-sided, sometimes broadly so, pink. Scapes usually equalling leaves. Exterior bracts spreading, 10 × 3.5 mm, scarcely bordered, *dark green suffused with pink on upper surface, blackish green and ± pruinose on lower surface*. Capitulum mid-yellow, 30–45 mm in diameter; ligules flat, striped dark grey-violet; styles exserted, discoloured; pollen present. Achenes straw-coloured, spinulose at apex; body 3.5 mm; cone 0.5 mm. 2n ± 24.

Native. Scattered, mainly through the western side of Great Britain, with one record in eastern Ireland. V.cc. 3, 6, 12, 14, 19, 20, 30, 34, 35, 39, 42–44, 46, 50, 51, 55, 57–60, 67, 69, 70, 72, 74, 88, 89, 93, 99, H21.

A variable taxon, which lies on the border between three sections, *Celtica*, *Hamata* and *Ruderalia*. As in **36** *T. hesperium*, the multi-coloured green, purple and red leaves are very distinctive; it is effectively a more regularly lobed, less dentate version of the former. See also **36a** *T. 'cestrense'*.

A medium-sized plant, with erect leaves 150–250 mm.

Leaves dull dark green, without spots, interlobes often somewhat blotched, midrib dull purple; lateral lobes 3–5, patent to recurved, broad at base, tapering to a narrow acuminate apex with up to 7 long, filiform teeth on distal margin; terminal lobe medium-sized, about as long as broad or somewhat longer, hastate to sagittate or *helmet-shaped*, entire; petiole *winged, shining purple.* Scapes usually equalling leaves, erect. Exterior bracts *spreading to recurved*, 10 × 3 mm, scarcely bordered, pale green often lightly suffused purple on upper surface, dark green on lower surface. Capitulum mid-yellow, 40–45 mm in diameter; ligules striped *grey-purple*, with purple teeth; styles exserted or ± inserted, discoloured; pollen *absent* (or present in one site in v.c. 44). Achenes straw-coloured, spinulose; body 2.8–3.0 mm; cone 0.4 mm.

Endemic. Locally frequent in Scotland and northern England and extending to South Wales, with one Irish record. V.cc. 42, 44, 51, 60, 65, 67–70, 72, 74, 79, 81, 88, 89, 93, 94, 101, 112, H12.

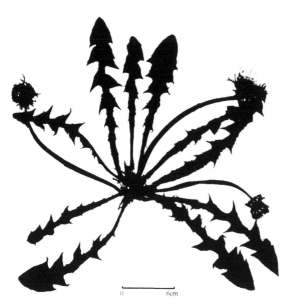

The lack of pollen is a useful character, as are the broad, shining purple petioles. For a member of Section *Celtica*, this species can have a complicated dentate and variable leaf-shape, and the external bracts are unusually long and spreading. In some ways *T. inane* resembles members of Section *Hamata*, but none of these lack pollen.

39 T. fulgidum G.E. Haglund (1938)

Map 39

A medium-sized plant, with spreading to erect, broad, flat leaves 80–200 mm.

Leaves *pale, pure green*, sometimes with scattered small dark spots and always with marked *purple blotches* on the interlobes, midrib shining purple; lateral lobes *2–3*, patent, rather short, triangular, *with distal margin strongly toothed*; terminal lobe *large, rounded, entire*; petiole a quarter to half length of leaf, *winged, shining bright purple.* Scapes usually exceeding leaves, erect, purple, at least at base and below capitulum. Exterior bracts spreading to erect, 10 × 3 mm, *unbordered*, pale green on upper surface, *dark green on lower surface,* often purple-tipped. Capitulum deep yellow, 40–50 mm in diameter; ligules striped brown-purple, *the inner with purple tips*; styles exserted, darkly *discoloured*; pollen present. Achenes olive to straw-coloured; body 3.5 mm; cone 0.4 mm.

Native. Damp hay-meadows. Scattered, mainly in the south and east, throughout the English chalklands, and north to Lancashire and Yorkshire; one record from Ireland. V.cc. 1, 4, 7, 11–13, 19–23, 25, 28, 30, 34, 50, 55, 58, 60, 61, S, H39.

T. fulgidum is the only species with both rounded terminal lobes and dark, spreading to erect exterior bracts. The leaf-spots (when present) and very bright purple petioles are also diagnostic.

0   6cm

Section *Celtica*

39a T. tamesense A.J. Richards (1972)

A small to medium-sized plant, with erect, *oblanceolate-spathulate* leaves 40–150 mm.

Leaves *dark green, with irregular purple blotches*, especially on the interlobes, midrib glabrescent, deep pink to purple; lateral lobes *(0–)2–3, patent to recurved, very short, wide, acute or ± obtuse, with distal margin on upper lobes not toothed*, convex, sigmoid, straight-sided or concave-angled, but distal margin on lower lobes denticulate or occasionally provided with a single large tooth; terminal lobe medium-sized, about as long as broad, hastate or triangular, entire; petiole *unwinged, a third to half length of leaf, bright purple.* Scapes usually exceeding leaves, erect, slender. Exterior bracts spreading to erect, 8 × 2 mm, *unbordered*, dark green *suffused with purple*. Capitulum deep yellow, 35 mm in diameter; ligules striped (but *not tipped*) purple; styles exserted, *discoloured*; pollen present. Achenes straw-coloured; body 3.0 mm; cone 0.6 mm.

Native. Water-meadows mown for hay (meads); scattered mainly in central southern England. V.cc. 6, 12, 19, 20, 23, 24, 30, 33, 42, 55, 70.

This is a most attractive little species with purple-marked leaves, bright purple petioles and spreading to erect purplish exterior bracts. A close relative of **39**, with which it often grows, but smaller and more delicate, with oblanceolate-spathulate leaves. The terminal lobe is rounded but more elongated, and the denticulation of the lateral lobes is regular. The bright purple petioles are unwinged and the inner ligule tips are yellow.

0   6cm

T. texelense Hagend., Soest & Zevenb. (1976)

A small plant, with *broadly oblanceolate* leaves 50–120 mm.

Leaves mid to dark green, *without spots,* interlobes *without blotches*, midrib pink to purple; lateral lobes 2–4, patent to recurved, broad, acute, with distal margin ± dentate, convex; terminal lobe a quarter to a third length of leaf, *obtuse but with ± elongated apex*; petiole unwinged, purple. Scapes usually exceeding leaves. Exterior bracts spreading, 10 × 3.5 mm, *bordered*, pale green on upper surface, *dark green and pruinose on lower surface*. Capitulum deep yellow, 20–30 mm in diameter; ligules striped *reddish-violet*; styles exserted, discoloured; pollen present. 2n ± 24.

Native? Recorded only from an estuarine saltmarsh in Lancashire. V.c. 60 only.

Very similar to **39a** *T. tamesense*, but leaves unblotched, broader, with an obtuse, ± elongated, but not rounded, terminal lobe. The exterior bracts are distinctly bordered and are not suffused with purple.

0   6cm

39c T. hygrophilum Soest (1956)

A small to medium-sized plant, with erect leaves 50–100 mm.

Leaves *pure green, without spots*, smooth, interlobes *without blotches*, midrib green; lateral lobes 3–4, *crowded*, recurved, short and broad, entire, sometimes dentate on distal margin; terminal lobe short, medium-sized, about as long as broad, obtuse or somewhat mucronate to lingulate, entire; petiole winged, sometimes broadly so, *whitish*. Scapes 50–80 mm, erect, narrow. Exterior bracts erect, 5 × 2 mm, *with a clear white or rose border*, pale green on upper surface, *darker green on lower surface*. Capitulum deep yellow, 30 mm in diameter; ligules short, striped grey-violet; styles exserted, discoloured; pollen present. Achenes brown, spinulose above; body 3.0 mm; cone 0.3 mm; rostrum *very short, 4–5 mm*.

Native. Water-meadows in Kent and the Netherlands. Rare. V.c. 15 only.

A distinctive little relative of **39b**, with bright green leaves lacking blotches, and with 3–4 crowded, recurved, short and broad lateral leaf-lobes. The winged petioles are whitish. Unlike any other species, *T. hygrophilum* is best known by the small, bright green leaves of a characteristic shape, and the small brown achenes with a very short rostrum. In the Netherlands, this species grows to a considerably larger size than any of the specimens so far recorded in Britain.

0   6cm

40 T. haematicum G.E. Haglund ex H. Øllg. & Wittzell (1995)   Map 40

A medium-sized plant, with spreading to erect leaves 80–150 mm. Leaves dark, pure green, interlobes usually with dark blotches, midrib deep pink to bright purple; lateral lobes *4–5*, patent to somewhat recurved, *narrowly triangular*, with distal margin *concave or sigmoid*, entire or filiform-dentate only on proximal lobes; terminal lobe triangular to lingulate or narrowly *trilobate, with narrow but obtuse apex*; petiole *a quarter to half length of leaf, unwinged, bright purple*. Scapes usually exceeding leaves, arachnoid-hairy below capitulum, often purplish at base. Exterior bracts spreading to erect, regular, scarcely overlapping one another, 10 × 3–4 mm, *dark shining green on lower surface*, pale green on upper surface, often suffused purplish, especially at tips and margins, with a distinct, often reddish, border. Capitulum deep yellow, 40 mm in diameter; ligules striped dark brown-purple; styles exserted, *discoloured*; pollen present. Achenes olive-brown; body 3.2 mm; cone 0.4 mm. 2n=24.

Native. In rich, damp, basic grassland throughout Great Britain, with one Irish record. V.cc. 6, 20, 22, 23, 30, 33, 34, 42, 51, 55, 60–62, 61, 70, 71, 75, 93, H21.

This species is the most widespread of the 'mead species', both in Britain and elsewhere. It is characterised by the long, narrow, bright purple petioles and leaf-lobes with a concave or sigmoid distal margin. The sectional position of *T. haematicum* is problematical: it appears to lie on the difficult border between Sections *Celtica* and *Ruderalia*. The purple petioles and midribs, the purplish scapes and its frequent occurrence in meadows suggest the former; the not, or only weakly, striatulate midribs and the complex leaf-lobation perhaps suggest the latter. Øllgaard & Wittzell (1995) place it in *Ruderalia*; we have for the present preferred to retain it in *Celtica*.

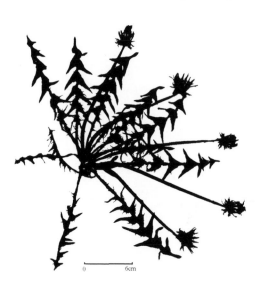

0 ____ 6cm

Section *Celtica*

40a T. akteum Hagend., Soest & Zevenb. (1974)   Map 40a

A close relative of **40**, chiefly distinguished by having fewer (2–3) lateral leaf-lobes which are shortly subobtuse-deltoid, a triangular to helmet-shaped terminal

leaf-lobe, a whitish to brownish-rose petiole and a brownish midrib to the leaf, and slightly narrower exterior bracts (not exceeding 3.5 mm in width).

Apparently native. So far recorded only from a single site in North Hants; wet meadows. Otherwise known from slightly saline maritime meadows in the Netherlands. V.c. 12.

40b T. beeftinkii Hagend., Soest & Zevenb. (1972)   Map 40b

Differs from **40** by the fewer (usually 3), claw-shaped to hamate lateral leaf-lobes, the distal ones entire or often with a single tooth, the proximal regularly denticulate on the distal margin, and the bluntly helmet-shaped terminal lobe. The exterior bracts are slightly narrower (to 3.5 mm wide) and are clearly pale-bordered. Differs from **40a** by the wine-red petiole and the distinctive leaf-shape.

Apparently native. Known only from saltmarsh grassland and road-verges subject to maritime flooding in Essex. Otherwise known only from similar localities in the south-west Netherlands. V.c. 19.

Section *Celtica*

41 T. landmarkii Dahlst. (1925a)

Map 41

A medium-sized but delicate plant, with leaves 50–120 mm, outer prostrate, inner suberect.

Leaves dull green, without spots, smooth, interlobes without blotches, midrib *green*; lateral lobes 4–5, patent, *narrow*, acute, usually entire, sometimes abruptly narrowing to a long, forward-pointing process, with distal margin entire, concave, straight-sided or concave-angled, the proximal margin straight; interlobes sometimes dentate; terminal lobe small and trilobate or medium-sized and hastate, entire, usually with a narrow, acute, elongated apex; petiole unwinged, *purple*. Scapes usually exceeding leaves, erect, green. Exterior bracts spreading to erect, 8–10 × 2–3 mm, *unbordered*, dark green suffused purple. Capitulum mid-yellow, 35 mm in diameter, convex; ligules striped *purple*; styles exserted, *discoloured*; pollen *absent*. Achenes warm straw-brown, spinulose above; body 3–3.4 mm; cone rather narrow, 0.6 mm. 2n=32.

Native. Streamsides, ravines, wet cliffs, pathsides etc. Local; scattered, mainly in the north and west of Britain; perhaps commonest in the Scottish Highlands.

0 ——— 6cm

V.cc. 3, 4, 28, 29, 35, 40–42, 46, 48, 50, 57, 62, 66–76, 78–80, 83–86, 88, 91–93, 95–105, 107–112, H1, H6, H16, H26, H38–H40.

T. landmarkii is related to **42** *T. nordstedtii*, but it has narrower lateral lobes which give a distinctive, pretty leaf-shape. The exterior bracts are not pruinose, and the ligules are relatively longer, with purple stripes. Pollen is always missing.

Section *Celtica*

42 T. nordstedtii Dahlst. (1911b)

Map 42

A small to robust plant, with *very variable* leaves 40–160 mm. A quite exceptionally variable species.

Leaves mid-green (sometimes suffused with purple), usually without spots but sometimes spotted, usually smooth, interlobes without blotches, midrib usually green but sometimes pink to purple; lateral lobes 4–5, triangular, patent to somewhat recurved, obtuse, with distal margin not toothed, sigmoid and usually and characteristically *concave-angled*, the proximal margin straight or convex; terminal lobe *medium-sized*, obtuse or subacute, triangular, trilobate or hastate, entire, usually slightly narrower than rest of blade of leaf; petiole usually winged, purple or green. Scapes decumbent to erect, pale green or purplish. Exterior bracts *erect, imbricate*, 10 × 3 mm, dark green, *scarcely bordered, ciliate, pruinose*. Capitulum deep yellow, 30–40 mm in diameter; ligules *short*, striped *brown or puce*; styles exserted, *discoloured*; pollen usually present. Achenes olive-brown, spinulose above; body *3.2–3.5 mm*; cone 0.4 mm. 2n=48.

Native. Common in wet places throughout the British Isles below 450 m (1,500 ft). In the south-east mostly confined to wet meadows, but very catholic in the west, occurring on walls, banks, cliffs, roadsides and waste ground. V.cc. 1–6, 8–25, 27–30, 32–52, 55, 57–74, 76–83, 85–91, 93–103, 105–109, 112, S, H1, H8, H9, H12–H16, H20, H23, H25–H27, H33, H36, H38–H40.

T. nordstedtii is one of the most interesting and puzzling of all dandelion species. It is very variable for character states which are generally reliable in *Taraxacum*, such as the presence of anthocyanin in the petioles, midribs and scapes, leaf-shape and the presence of pollen. It is best recognised by the erect, imbricate, ciliate, dark, pruinose, ± unbordered exterior bracts, the short ligules with

Section *Celtica*

brown or puce stripes, and, in non-laciniate forms, the concave-angled distal margin to the lateral lobes. Although itself variable, it takes a central position in a complex of related species which do not share the distinctive involucre and capitulum of *T. nordstedtii*. This is the only hexaploid dandelion in the British Isles.

42a T. pseudonordstedtii A.J. Richards (1972)   Map 42a

A small to medium-sized prostrate plant, with decumbent, crowded leaves 50–130 mm.

Leaves green or dark green, often *suffused purple*, usually smooth, midrib *purple*; lateral lobes 4–6, *regular, triangular, patent to somewhat recurved, very short, usually entire*; interlobes *very narrow, often reduced to the midrib*; terminal lobe *medium-sized or small*, obtuse or subacute, triangular, sagittate or rhomboidal, entire, usually slightly narrower than rest of blade of leaf; petiole usually narrowly winged, purple. Scapes erect, purplish. Exterior bracts erect,

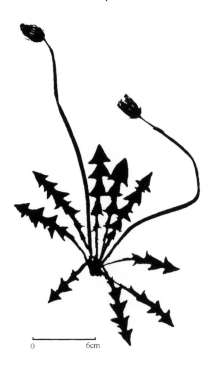

9 × 3 mm, scarcely bordered, dark green. Capitulum deep yellow, to 35 mm in diameter, *convex*; ligules *short,* striped purple; styles exserted, discoloured; pollen *present.* Achenes grey-brown, shortly tuberculate above; body *3 mm*; cone 0.3 mm. 2n=32 (counts made on British material).

Endemic. Calcareous flushes in Upper Teesdale, west Cumberland and north and west Lancs. V.cc. 60, 65, 66, 69, 70.

A very close relative of **42** *T. nordstedtii*, but retaining its distinctive features after cultivation. It is a low plant, with prostrate crowded rosettes of dark purplish leaves dissected ± to the midrib into 4–6 short, acute, somewhat recurved lateral lobes which are not concave-angled on the distal margin. Pollen is always present. See also **44** *T. caledonicum.*

0   6cm

42b T. berthae C.C. Haw. in A.J. Richards & C.C. Haw. (1984) Map 42b

A small to medium-sized plant, with leaves 50–140 mm.

Leaves *dull dark green, with black spots*, almost glabrous, midrib purple; lateral lobes 2–4, subpatent to recurved, triangular, with distal margin subconvex to straight or sigmoid, entire or with sparse filiform teeth; interlobes entire to filiform-denticulate or occasionally with a larger tooth; terminal lobe *usually large*, up to one third of leaf length, subsagittate, subobtuse, mucronate, entire or divided at base; petiole unwinged or narrowly winged, purple.

Scapes equalling leaves at flowering, often purplish, subglabrous or arachnoid-hairy. Involucre somewhat pruinose; exterior bracts erect to appressed, ovate, 7–9 × 1.5–4 mm, mostly unbordered, pale green on upper surface, dark green on lower surface, *often suffused with purple at apex*, somewhat pruinose, somewhat corniculate. Capitulum rather pale yellow, to 30 mm in diameter; ligules striped dark purple; styles exserted, discoloured; pollen *absent.* Achenes straw-coloured, with broad-based spinules above, otherwise smooth; body *3.6–3.9 mm*; cone conical, 0.5–0.6 mm.

Endemic. Known only from south-west Scotland, north-west England and South Wales. V.cc. 42, 44, 60, 65, 69, 70, 73, 101.

Diagnosed by the combination of small size, dark, robust, erect bracts, dark green spotted leaves with a large terminal lobe, and absence of pollen. Differs from **42** as follows: leaves dull dark green, with black spots; distal margin of lateral lobes not concave-angled, often sigmoid and ± convex; terminal lobe

large, up to one third of leaf length, subsagittate; exterior bracts slightly shorter, to 9 mm, often suffused purple. Pollen is always absent.

42c   T. olgae A.J. Richards (1981)

A small to medium-sized plant, with erect or patent leaves to 120 mm.

Leaves green to *yellow-green*, rather sparsely marked with blackish spots on upper side, midrib dull pink-purple to green; lateral lobes 3–4, recurved, acute, subconvex on distal margin, entire or somewhat denticulate; interlobes dentate or often with a single large tooth; terminal lobe *short*, entire, with a slightly elongated apex; petiole unwinged, sometimes dentate distally, pink to purple. Scapes ascending, usually ± equalling leaves, arachnoid-hairy, purplish. Exterior bracts erect, 6–9 × 2–4 mm, pruinose, green, *conspicuously white-bordered.* Capitulum yellow, 30 mm in diameter; ligules striped purple; styles exserted, *dark or even blackish*; pollen *absent.* Achenes straw-grey, with broad-based spines above, otherwise smooth; body *2.6–3.0 mm*; cone conical, 0.5–0.8 mm.

Endemic. Known so far only from Kirkcudbrightshire and west Cumberland. V.cc. 70, 73.

Like **42a**, a rather small relative of **42** *T. nordstedtii* with spotted leaves of a similar shape, but leaves yellow-green, with terminal lobe rather short and exterior bracts conspicuously white-bordered. The achenes are small; with the body only 2.6–3.0 mm, and the stigmas are blackish. Pollen is absent. The leaf shape, colour and spotting, as well as the small size of the achenes, are very similar to those of **27** *T. subnaevosum*, which also lacks pollen; however, the involucres of the two species are quite different, as is the style colour. The exterior bracts of *T. olgae* closely resemble those of **47** *T. unguilobum*, an unspotted species with reddish achenes, which also lacks pollen. The dark style colour of *T. olgae* is distinctive.

0   6cm

42d T. cambricum A.J. Richards in A.J. Richards & C.C. Haw. (1984)

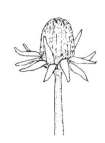

A medium-sized plant, with broadly oblanceolate leaves 100–250 mm.

Leaves bright green, without spots, interlobes without blotches, midrib glabrescent, deep pink to purple; lateral lobes (2–)3–4, patent to somewhat recurved, broad, obtuse, with distal margin not toothed, convex, sigmoid, straight-sided or concave-angled, the proximal margin convex, occasionally provided with a single large tooth; terminal lobe medium-sized, about as long as broad, obtuse but slightly mucronate, *helmet-shaped*, entire, slightly narrower than rest of blade of leaf; petiole winged, sometimes broadly so, purple; petiole and midrib with interwoven green strands. Scapes usually exceeding leaves, arachnoid-hairy at first, glabrescent, pale green but pinkish below capitulum. Exterior bracts mostly erect, the lowest ± spreading, 8–13 × 2–3.5 mm, scarcely bordered, pale green on upper surface, *blackish green and heavily pruinose on lower surface.* Capitulum mid-yellow, 40–45 mm in diameter; ligules flat, striped *dark grey*, with *yellow* teeth; styles exserted, discoloured; pollen present or, rarely, absent. Achenes fulvous to straw-coloured, somewhat rugose at apex, otherwise smooth; body *3.8–4.0 mm*; cone conical, 0.6 mm.

Endemic. On light, well-drained neutral to calcareous soils, often in species-rich grasslands; also on walls, lane-banks etc.; scattered, mainly in the west. V.cc. 3, 4, 35, 40, 42–44, 50, 51, 70, 73, 109, H21.

Differs from **42** by the broad leaves, the helmet-shaped terminal leaf-lobe, the longer ligules with grey stripes, and the longer achenes.

Continued overleaf

Section *Celtica*

T. cambricum is close to the more widespread **30** *T. gelertii*, but has paler leaves and is more robust generally. The achenes are also diagnostic: in common with those of **32** *T. britannicum*, the achenes of *T. cambricum* are nearly smooth, even at the apex, but they are much longer than those of *T. britannicum*.

The name *T. cambricum* should not be confused with the now obsolete name *T. cambriense* A.J. Richards (1972, p. 98), referring to a species for which the correct name is *T. lancastriense* A.J. Richards (**42e**).

42e T. lancastriense A.J. Richards (1981)   Map 42e

A medium-sized plant, with leaves 80–170 mm.

Leaves *pale green*, usually unspotted but sometimes ± spottted, interlobes without blotches, midrib green; lateral lobes 4–5, patent, narrow, acute, entire or slightly denticulate, with distal margin sigmoid, straight-sided or concave-angled, the proximal margin straight; terminal lobe *large, a quarter to a third length of leaf, subacute, hastate, entire*; petiole unwinged, purple. Scapes usually exceeding leaves, erect, green. Exterior bracts *appressed, erect, 9 × 4 mm, dark green, glaucous, with a clear white border*. Capitulum mid-yellow, 40 mm in diameter; ligules short, striped *grey-violet*; styles exserted, discoloured; pollen *absent*. Achenes pale brown, shortly spinulose at apex, otherwise rugose; body *2.8–3.0 mm*; cone conical, 0.4 mm.

Endemic. On neutral to calcareous soils, often in species-rich grasslands; also on walls, lane-banks etc.; scattered, mainly in the west of Britain. V.cc. 35, 41, 42, 44, 59, 60, 64, 67, 68, 70.

Differs from **42** by the long, hastate terminal lobes to the pale green leaves, the clear white border to the exterior bracts, and the grey-violet ligule stripes. Pollen is absent, and the achene body is short (2.8–3.0 mm). Part of the *T. nordstedtii* problem!

0   6cm

42f   T. palustrisquameum A.J. Richards (1981)   Map 42f

A rather dwarf to tall plant, with narrowly oblanceolate leaves 100–250 mm.

Leaves entire with remote teeth or shortly lobate, green, with small, sparse, blackish spots on upper surface, midrib green; lateral lobes, if present, 2–3, patent, subdeltoid, acute, short, entire, *concave on distal margin*; interlobes entire; terminal lobe acute, entire; petiole unwinged, narrow, entire, *white*, half length of leaf or more. Scapes usually exceeding leaves, green, glabrous. Exterior bracts erect to subappressed, 6–9 × 3–5 mm, rather dark green with a rather pale, broad, white or rose-coloured border. Capitulum yellow, 35 mm in diameter; ligules striped purple; styles exserted, discoloured; pollen *absent.* Achenes straw-coloured, shortly spinulose at apex, otherwise smooth; body *3.1–3.5 mm*; cone conical, 0.5 mm.

Apparently endemic. Scattered; it appears to be mainly restricted to grass-fens, where it may be locally frequent. V.cc. 27, 28, 59, 82, 89.

Most likely to be confused with **17** *T. anglicum*, but that species has pollen and purple petioles. *T. palustrisquameum* is intermediate between **42** *T. nordstedtii* and **17** *T. anglicum*, and thus in some sense it lies between Sections *Celtica* and *Palustria*. The black spots and the relatively plump achene shape (untypical for Section *Palustria*) suggest that it is better placed here.

0   6cm

A small to medium-sized plant, with rather narrow leaves 50–180 mm.

Leaves dull, rather dark green, without spots, interlobes without blotches, midrib green or pinkish; lateral lobes 3–5, patent to somewhat recurved, triangular, *acute*, with distal margin *convex, often with 1 tooth*; terminal lobe usually small, triangular, with a slightly elongated apex; petiole *unwinged, purple*. Scapes usually exceeding leaves, ascending to erect. Exterior bracts spreading to recurved, 9 × 2 mm, unbordered, pale green, often pruinose on upper surface, dark green on lower surface. Capitulum deep yellow, *25–30 mm in diameter*; ligules *short*, striped grey-violet; styles exserted, *yellow in fresh and dried condition*; pollen *absent*. Achenes brown, body *2.8 mm*; cone 0.6 mm. 2n=24.

Probably native. Waste places, gardens, walls, paths etc. Scattered throughout Great Britain, but not recorded from Ireland. V.cc. 1, 3, 4, 12, 15, 23–31, 41, 42, 45, 60–62, 67–70, 72, 80, 86, 90, 94–96, 98, 99, 101, 104, 108, 109, S.

Distinguished by the yellow styles, the absence of pollen and the small capitula with short, crowded florets.

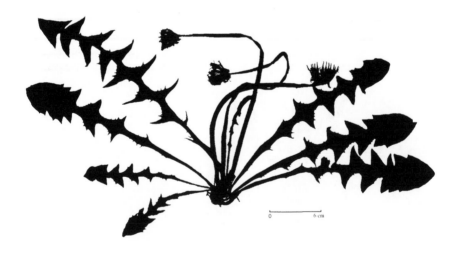

43a T. breconense C.C. Haw. in Dudman & A.J. Richards (1994)

A small to medium-sized plant, with leaves 80–150 mm. Leaves mid-green, without spots, ± glabrous, interlobes without blotches, midrib green; lateral lobes 2–4, recurved, with linear and acute apex but broader proximally to form a *convex or sigmoid distal margin when well developed*, ± denticulate on distal margin; terminal lobe to one quarter length of leaf, *subsagittate*, often *heavily divided, ± dentate*, with an acute apex; petiole *unwinged, green*. Scapes 80–100 mm, often purplish, somewhat arachnoid-hairy below capitulum. Exterior bracts spreading to recurved, 7–10 × 2.5 mm, grey-green often suffused with purple on upper surface, dark green on lower surface, sometimes with white or pink borders. Capitulum rather pale yellow, *to 20 mm in diameter*; ligules *involute*; styles inserted, *yellow*; pollen *absent*. Achenes straw-coloured, spinulose; body *3.5 mm*; cone 0.7 mm.

Endemic. Known only from limestone cliffs, walls, lane-banks etc. in Breconshire. V.c. 42.

0   6cm

A close relative of **43**, also with yellow styles without pollen and with small capitula with crowded ligules, but with ligules involute and with a character-istic leaf-shape with a large, subsagittate, heavily divided and dentate terminal lobe; the narrow petiole is green, and the achene body is larger.

A small to medium-sized plant, with prostrate leaves 40–100 mm, in a tight rosette.

Leaves dark green, without spots, *almost glabrous*, interlobes without blotches, midrib green to pink; lateral lobes 4–6, recurved, short, ± entire, *with distal margin convex*; internodes sometimes denticulate; terminal lobe short or sometimes a quarter to a third length of leaf, subacute *with a mucronate tip*; petiole *unwinged, purple*. Scapes 20–150 mm, ascending to erect, pale. Exterior bracts erect, *11 × 3 mm, very dark purplish-green, pruinose*, red-tipped, unbordered. Capitulum *convex or closed*, deep yellow, to 20 mm in diameter; ligules *short, flat or some-times involute*, striped *purple*; styles *inserted, discoloured*; pollen *absent*. Achenes *grey-brown, slightly spinulose above*; body *4.0 mm*; cone *0.2 mm*. 2n=40.

Endemic. Montane, usually base-rich localities in the Scottish Highlands. V.cc. 88, 90, 93–96.

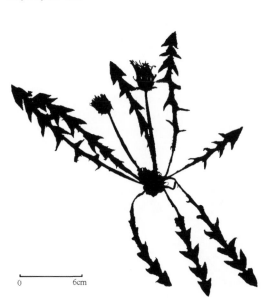

The characteristic leaf-shape, very dark involucre, short and sometimes involute ligules, lack of pollen, and grey-brown achenes are diagnostic. This is an endemic alpine of species-rich sites in the Scottish Highlands. It is related to **42a** *T. pseudo-nordstedtii*, but pollen is absent and the achenes are much longer.

0   6cm

45 T. fulvicarpum Dahlst. (1927a)

Map 45

A medium-sized plant, with erect leaves 100–200 mm.

Leaves *pale green*, without spots or lightly spotted near midrib, interlobes without blotches, midrib green; lateral lobes 3–5, recurved, narrow, straight-sided or sigmoid, *coarsely dentate*; terminal lobe sagittate or trilobate, divided and/or dentate; petiole unwinged, pink to purple. Scapes 30–100 mm, decumbent to erect. Exterior bracts erect to spreading, 9 × 2–3 mm, ± bordered, *pale green suffused with purple and pruinose throughout*. Capitulum mid-yellow, 40 mm in diameter; ligules striped violet; styles exserted, *discoloured*; pollen absent. Achenes *cinnamon* (oxidising to brown); body 3.4 mm; cone 0.7 mm. 2n=32

Endemic. Ecologically very catholic, occurring in wet grassland, wood-borders and dune-slacks. Local; commonest in west Scotland, especially on the islands, and the commonest dandelion in the Outer Hebrides. V.cc. 41–43, 45, 46, 49, 57, 67, 73, 81, 86, 89, 90, 94, 97, 99–101, 103, 104, 106, 108, 110–112, H9, H16, H40.

Distinguished by its coarsely dentate leaves, concolorous bracts and cinnamon achenes, becoming brown. *T. fulvicarpum* has no close relatives, but it has links with robust species in Section *Erythrosperma* and is possibly better placed there.

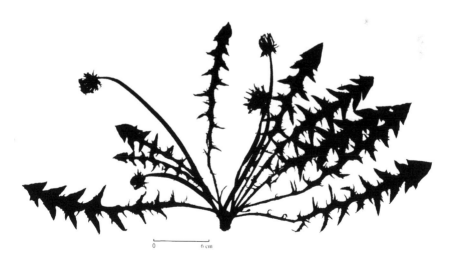

A small to medium-sized plant, with narrowly to broadly oblanceolate leaves 50–200 mm, prostrate or becoming erect later in the season.

Leaves mid-green to yellow-green, without spots, interlobes without blotches, midrib pink; lateral lobes *4–6, recurved, sometimes extremely so*, acute, proximal ones filiform-dentate on distal margin; terminal lobe sagittate, *with convex distal margins and strongly recurved basal projections*, entire; petiole winged or unwinged, *pink.* Scapes usually exceeding leaves, decumbent to erect, green or pink. Exterior bracts spreading to erect, 8 × 2 mm, *pruinose, pale glaucous green on upper surface, dark green on lower surface, pink-tipped with a clear white border.* Capitulum *pale yellow*, 35 mm in diameter; ligules striped *pink*; *styles inserted, yellow*; pollen *absent.* Achenes *rust-coloured*, slightly spinulose at apex; body 3.2 mm; cone 0.5 mm. 2n=32.

Native. Wet paths, rock-faces, roadsides and flushes in hilly districts. Common in the north and west; rare and perhaps introduced in the south and east. V.cc. 1–4, 6, 14, 23, 26, 32, 34–36, 38, 39, 41, 42, 44–46, 48–52, 57, 58, 60, 62, 64–83, 85–91, 93–99, 100–112, H1–H3, H9, H12–H14, H16, H21, H26–H28, H36, H38.

The highly recurved leaf-lobes, the glaucous, pink-tipped and white-bordered, usually erect exterior bracts, the absence of pollen, and the small, rust-coloured achenes are all diagnostic. One of the commonest and most easily identified native dandelions away from the south-east.

0   6cm

46a T. luteum C.C. Haw. & A.J. Richards Map 46a
in A.J. Richards & C.C. Haw. (1984)

A medium-sized plant, with ascending to erect, *narrowly oblong* leaves to 200 mm.

Leaves *dull grey-green*, without spots, *arachnoid-hairy on upper surface*, inter-lobes without blotches, midrib purple; lateral lobes 4–5, rather distant, *frequently alternate*, recurved, narrowly triangular and tapering to a filiform apex, with distal margin sigmoid or straight and entire or with a few filiform teeth; interlobes somewhat crisped, entire or with filiform teeth or occasionally with a single long narrow tooth; terminal lobe either medium-sized and triangular or large and divided with a few narrow, recurved teeth towards base; petiole to one third length of leaf, *unwinged, shining purple*. Scapes ± equalling leaf length at flowering, arachnoid-hairy below capitulum, otherwise sparsely clothed, green and pink. Exterior bracts erect to appressed, lanceolate or ovate, 8–10 × 2–4 mm, scarcely bordered, pale green on upper surface, *glossy and green on lower surface*, suffused with anthocyanin towards the obtuse tip. Capitulum *bright yellow*, 35–40 mm in diameter; ligules *unstriped*; styles exserted, *discoloured*; pollen present. Achenes straw-coloured, with a few narrow recurved spinules at apex, otherwise smooth; body 3.5–3.8 mm; cone broadly based, conical, 0.4 mm.

Endemic. In damp grasslands, and also on walls, lane-banks etc.; apparently centred in Cumbria, but with scattered records elsewhere.V.cc. 42, 60, 67, 69, 70, 94, 99, 103, 112, H21, H36, H40.

A relative of **46**, but immediately recognised by its luminous yellow flowers without ligule stripes. The unwinged petiole is purple and shining. The erect exterior bracts are a dark, glossy green, lacking pruinosity or obvious borders. *T. luteum* is unique among British and Irish dandelions in lacking a ligule stripe, a feature which renders it both striking and instantly recognisable. It is a most beautiful species.

Section HAMATA H. Øllg. (1983)

47 T. hamatum Raunk. (1906)

Map 47

A medium-sized plant, with decumbent to erect leaves 80–300 mm.

Leaves dark olive green, sometimes suffused purple, inter-lobes sometimes blotched, midrib coloured pink to purple in exposed sites, greenish in shadier locations; lateral lobes 3–5, *regular, forming pairs, recurved, hamate*, rather short, acute or sometimes obtuse, with distal margin convex, entire or filiform-dentate, the proximal margin straight or concave; terminal lobe usually entire, rather small and triangular to sagittate; petiole unwinged, at least below, purple; petiole and midrib with interwoven green strands. Scapes usually equalling leaves. Involucre distinctly conical at base; exterior bracts mostly erect, the lowest ± spreading, 8–11 × 2–3.5 mm, acute, forming a stellate involucre in bud, unbordered, pale green on upper surface, *very dark, blackish green and pruinose on lower surface, outermost not noticeably narrower*; involucre of inner bracts *inky-black at apex when in bud.* Capitulum deep yellow, 40–45 mm in diameter; ligules striped *grey-violet*; styles exserted, *discoloured*; pollen present. Achenes straw-coloured; body *3.5 mm*; cone 0.6 mm. 2n=24.

Native. Mature woodland (often subnatural), grassy places, roadsides, scrub, wasteland, gardens, rocky places etc., usually in partial shade. Widespread throughout Great Britain; locally common in the south; very common in lowland northern England and Scotland; scattered throughout Ireland. Often the only dandelion in woodland habitats.

0   6 cm

Section *Hamata*

V.cc. 1–9, 11–26, 28–30, 32–46, 48–62, 64–78, 80–83, 85–91, 93–99, 101–104, 106, 109, 111–112, S, H4, H5, H12, H13, H16, H19, H21, H23, H33, H36–H39.

T. hamatum is characterised by the regular, recurved, symmetrically opposed lateral lobes, the erect, dark, glaucous exterior bracts, the interior bracts, which are inky-black in bud, at least at the apex, and the large achenes.

47a   T. hamatulum Hagend., Soest & Zevenb. (1973)   Map 47a

A medium-sized plant, with leaves 100–200 mm.

Leaves dull dark green, without spots, interlobes sometimes blotched, midrib glabrescent, deep pink to purple; lateral lobes of inner leaves 2–3, of outer leaves to 5, *regular, recurved*, deltoid, rather short, acute or sometimes obtuse, with distal margin convex, entire or filiform-dentate, the proximal margin straight or concave; terminal lobe medium-sized, triangular or helmet-shaped, blunt, entire or sometimes ± divided; petiole unwinged, purple; petiole and midrib with interwoven green strands. Scapes usually equalling leaves. Involucre faintly conical at base; exterior bracts spreading, 11 × 3.5 mm, *with very distinct, white, often ciliate, border*, pale green on upper surface, *blackish-green and heavily pruinose on lower surface.* Capitulum mid-yellow, 30–40 mm in diameter; styles exserted, *yellowish*; pollen present. Achenes straw-coloured; body *3.8–4.0 mm*; cone 0.3 mm. 2n ± 24.

Native? Scattered in Great Britain, mainly in England and Wales. V.cc. 6, 8, 14, 20, 26, 30, 35, 42, 43, 50, 51, 58, 60, 67, 68, 74, 99, 112.

A close relative of **47** *T. hamatum*, differing chiefly by the distinctly white-bordered, ciliate exterior bracts, the yellowish stigmas and the apices of the lateral lobes often forming a line parallel to the midrib. Generally a more slender plant.

48 T. subhamatum M.P. Christ. (1936)

Map 48

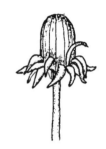

A medium-sized plant, with decumbent to erect leaves 100–300 mm.

Leaves dull, olive green, interlobes sometimes blotched, midrib green to faintly coloured; lateral lobes 4–7, patent to recurved, obtuse or narrowing to a long (to 40 mm) acute apex, with distal margin convex, straight, sinuate or concave, slightly dentate proximally, the proximal margin concave, straight or convex; interlobes ± dentate; terminal lobe usually rather small and triangular or sagittate, *usually with an elongated apex or mucronate*; petiole narrowly winged, purple; petiole and midrib with interwoven green strands. Scapes usually equalling leaves. Exterior bracts spreading to recurved, 10–11 × 2.5–3.5 mm, lanceolate with distinct tip, slightly *bordered, pale green* often lightly suffused with purple on upper surface, *dark green and strongly pruinose on lower surface.* Capitulum deep yellow, 50 mm in diameter; ligules striped *grey-violet*, with *orange* teeth; styles exserted, *discoloured*; pollen present. Achenes straw-coloured; body 3.1 mm; cone 0.5 mm. 2n ± 24.

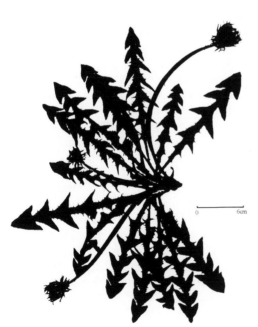

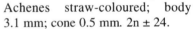

Native. Grassy places, roadsides, scrub, wasteland, gardens, rocky places etc. Scattered throughout Great Britain, perhaps commoner in the west, and recorded from two vice-counties in eastern Ireland. V.cc. 2–4, 6, 9, 11, 12, 17–22, 25, 30, 33–35, 37–39, 41–44, 46–48, 50, 51, 55, 57–62, 67–70, 72–74, 77, 81, 82, 88, 89, 91, 93, 94, 96, 97, 99, 112, H19, H21.

T. subhamatum is characterised by the elongated or mucronate tip of the terminal lobe and the strongly pruinose involucre. It is not an easy species to identify, being rather lacking in distinctive characters and plastic in leaf morphology.

48a   T. marklundii Palmgr. (1910a)

Map 48a

A medium-sized plant, with decumbent to erect leaves 50–200 mm.

Leaves dull, often dark green, midrib coloured light brown, mauve or purple; lateral lobes 3–5, *regular*, usually *recurved, sometimes acutely so*, or patent at base and abruptly recurved at acute apex, usually narrow, with distal margin convex, *usually filiform-dentate throughout and often with 1 or 2 large teeth*, the proximal margin concave; terminal lobe usually rather small, sagittate, often dentate, with elongated apex; petiole unwinged, purple; petiole and midrib with interwoven green strands. Scapes usually equalling leaves. Exterior bracts spreading to recurved, 10 × 2.5 mm, unbordered, *purple* on upper surface, dark green suffused with purple on lower surface. Capitulum yellow, 45 mm in diameter; ligules striped *grey-violet*, with orange teeth; styles exserted, discoloured; pollen present. Achenes straw-coloured; body 3.0 mm; cone 0.5 mm. 2n=24 (counts made on British material).

Native. Grassy places, roadsides, wasteland etc. Scattered throughout Great Britain, mainly in the south and west, with one Irish record. V.cc. 2, 5, 6, 20, 22, 24, 28, 30, 33–35, 37, 39, 41–44, 50, 51, 54, 55, 57, 58, 60–62, 67–70, 83, 95, 96, H12.

Closely related to **48** *T. subhamatum* and sometimes included within it. Differs chiefly by the highly recurved, regular, strongly dentate leaf-lobes. Distinctive in extreme forms, but connected to **48** by a range of intermediates.

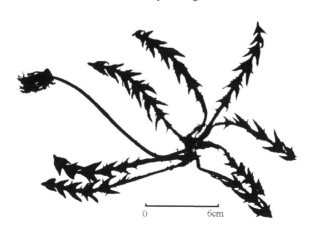

0   6cm

49 T. hamiferum Dahlst. (1929)

Map 49

A medium-sized plant, with leaves 100–200 mm.

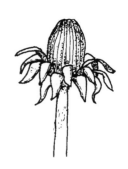

Leaves *dark green*, without spots, interlobes sometimes blotched, midrib glabrescent, deep pink to purple; lateral lobes of inner leaves 2–3, of outer leaves to 5, *regular, recurved, hamate*, rather short, acute or sometimes somewhat obtuse, with distal margin convex, entire or filiform-dentate, the proximal margin straight or concave; terminal lobe medium-sized, triangular or *helmet-shaped*, blunt, entire; petiole unwinged proximally, purple; petiole and midrib with interwoven green strands. Scapes usually equalling leaves. Exterior bracts spreading, 9–10 × 2–2.5 mm, slightly bordered, pale green on upper surface, *blackish green and pruinose on lower surface*; inner bracts *not equally broad and usually irregularly connate*. Capitulum deep yellow, 30–40 mm in diameter; styles exserted, *discoloured*; pollen present. Achenes straw-coloured; body 3.0–3.5 mm; cone 0.5–0.6 mm. 2n ± 24.

Doubtfully native. Scattered throughout Great Britain, with one Irish record. V.cc. 1–4, 6, 14–23, 25, 26, 30, 31, 33–36, 39, 40–44, 46, 50, 51, 54, 55, 57, 58, 60, 66–70, 72–74, 76, 81, 83, 90, 93, 94, 97–99, H23.

T. hamiferum is best characterised by the irregular splitting of the inner bracts as the capitulum opens. Morphologically at the interface between **47** *T. hamatum* and **48** *T. subhamatum*; also closely related to **49a** *T. quadrans*. See also **52b** *T. pruinatum*.

0   6cm

Section *Hamata*

49a T. quadrans H. Øllg. (1978)

A medium-sized plant, with erect, ± oblong, rather fleshy leaves 50–250 mm.

Leaves dull dark *bluish-green*, without spots, interlobes sometimes blotched, midrib glabrescent, deep pink to purple; lateral lobes 3–5, *regular, recurved*, deltoid, rather short, acute or sometimes obtuse, with distal margin *frequently and characteristically very obtusely angled* or at least convex, entire or filiform-dentate, the proximal margin straight or concave; terminal lobe medium-sized, triangular or *helmet-shaped*, blunt, sometimes mucronate, entire or with 1–2 teeth; petiole unwinged, purple; petiole and midrib with interwoven green strands. Scapes usually equalling leaves. Exterior bracts spreading, 11 × 3.5 mm, distinctly narrow-bordered, pale green on upper surface, *blackish green and heavily pruinose on lower surface*; inner bracts ± equally broad. Capitulum mid-yellow, 30–40 mm in diameter; ligules striped grey-violet; styles exserted, faintly discoloured; pollen present. Achenes straw-coloured; body *3.8–4.0 mm*; cone 0.3 mm.

Probably not native. Scattered throughout the British Isles. V.cc. 1–4, 6, 9, 13–26, 28, 30, 34–36, 39–44, 46, 48–51, 55, 57–62, 66–70, 72, 74, 76, 79, 84, 88, 89, 93, 97, 99, 112, S, H21.

A close relative of **49** *T. hamiferum*, but with bluish-green leaves of a thick, rather fleshy texture and lateral lobes with a characteristic very obtuse angle on the distal margin. The achenes are among the longest in this group. This is the neatest of the *Hamata* species. Its blue-green foliage grows very erect and the leaves have regular, 'squared-off' lobes with the outer half of the distal margin parallel with the midrib.

50 T. pseudohamatum Dahlst. (1932)

Map 50

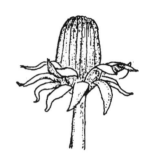

A medium-sized to large plant, with decumbent to erect leaves *150–400 mm.*

Leaves dull, olive green, interlobes sometimes blotched, midrib purple; lateral lobes 3–6, patent to recurved, with distal margin ± convex, sometimes filiform-dentate, the proximal margin concave, straight or convex, with obtuse to subacute apex; interlobes ± dentate; terminal lobe triangular or sagittate, blunt or subacute; petiole ± winged proximally, purple; petiole and midrib with interwoven green strands. Scapes usually equalling leaves. Exterior bracts spreading to recurved, *10–12 × 3.5–5 mm*, lanceolate with distinct tip, distinctly bordered, pale green on upper surface, *dark green and strongly pruinose on lower surface.* Capitulum deep yellow, *50–55 mm in diameter*; ligules striped *grey-violet*, with *orange* teeth; styles exserted, *discoloured*; pollen present. Achenes straw-coloured; body 3.5 mm; cone 0.6 mm.

Native. Roadsides, grassy places, scrub, wasteland, gardens, rocky places etc. Common throughout the British Isles. V.cc. 1–7, 9–12, 14–26, 28–37, 39–44, 46–51, 54–62, 66–70, 72–74, 76–78, 80–83, 88, 89, 91, 93–95, 97, 99, 101, 103, 106, 112, S, H5, H19–H21, H25, H32, H33, H37–H40.

T. pseudohamatum is a very robust weed and is the commonest member of Section *Hamata* in the British Isles, and indeed one of our commonest dandelions. It seems almost confined to these islands, but, oddly, it is nevertheless more characteristic of roadsides than of native haunts. It has the largest capitula and widest bracts in this section, in which it most resembles a large **47** *T. hamatum.* It is normally our earliest-flowering dandelion and can, in favourable locations, be in flower by mid-March. Of the common *Hamata* species, it is the only one with bracts always exceeding 3.5 mm in width.

0   6 cm

50a   **T. fusciflorum** H. Øllg. (1983)   **Map 50a**

A medium-sized to large plant, with decumbent to erect leaves 300–400 mm.

Leaves dull grey-green, interlobes sometimes blotched, midrib purple; lateral lobes 5–6, triangular, patent to recurved, obtuse to subacute at apex, with distal margin convex, entire or, on inner leaves, dentate; interlobes ± dentate; terminal lobe of external leaves small, cordate-sagittate, often dentate, of the middle and internal leaves larger and also often dentate; petiole narrowly or not winged, purple; petiole and midrib with interwoven green strands. Scapes usually equalling leaves. Exterior bracts spreading to recurved, 12–14 × 4–5 mm, lance-olate with pink tip, *unbordered*, grey-green on upper surface, dark green and strongly pruinose on lower surface. Capitulum deep yellow, 50 mm in diameter; ligules striped *brown*; styles exserted, discoloured; pollen present. Achenes dark straw-coloured, *with strong recurved spines*; body *4.0–4.3 mm*; cone 0.7 mm.

Probably introduced. Uncommon. Scattered throughout Britain and Ireland. V.cc. 1, 4, 14, 16, 17, 21, 23, 25, 30, 34, 41, 42, 46, 50, 51, 55, 57, 58, 65, 67, 74, 76, 81, 101, H16.

Another robust *Hamata* species, *T. fusciflorum* differs from **50** *T. pseudohamatum* especially in its outer ligules, which are brown-striped for their entire width below, giving the closed capitulum a very dark appearance. Also, the exterior bracts are unbordered, and the achene body (4.0–4.3 mm) is very long and has long, recurved spines.

50b T. prionum Hagend., Soest & Zevenb. (1972)

A medium-sized plant, with decumbent to erect leaves 150–250 mm.

Leaves dull, dark green, *rather hairy*, interlobes sometimes blotched, midrib purple; lateral lobes 4–5, patent, broad, *deltoid* or triangular, acute to subacute at apex, with distal margin straight or convex, sometimes filiform-dentate, the proximal margin straight, sometimes dentate; interlobes ± dentate; terminal lobe small, triangular, subacute *with an obviously elongated apex*; petiole *narrowly winged*, purple; petiole and midrib with interwoven green strands. Scapes usually equalling leaves, *young ones thickly arachnoid-hairy*. Exterior bracts spreading to recurved, 11–13 × 3.5–4.5 mm, distinctly bordered, pale green on upper surface, *dark grey-green on lower surface*. Capitulum deep yellow, 50 mm in diameter; ligules striped grey-violet; styles exserted, discoloured; pollen present. Achenes straw-coloured; body 3.5 mm; cone 0.7 mm.

Probably introduced. Uncommon; a few scattered records from England, Wales and southern Scotland. V.cc. 4, 34, 55, 72, 73, 83.

Another rather robust relative of **50** *T. pseudohamatum*, but with rather hairy leaves, a distinctive leaf-shape with broad, rather deltoid lateral lobes and a small terminal lobe with a distinctive narrow, elongated apex. The young scapes are thickly arachnoid-hairy. The petioles are winged and the exterior bracts are a dark grey-green externally.

0   6 cm

Section *Hamata*

51 T. boekmanii Borgv. (1959)

Map 51

A medium-sized plant, with decumbent to erect leaves 150–250 mm.

Leaves dark green, slightly hairy, midrib *bright purple to apex, usually with red veining to leaf*; lateral lobes 3–5, *regular*, recurved or deltoid, hamate, rather short, *usually obtuse,* with distal margin convex or straight, usually entire or filiform-dentate, the proximal margin straight or usually concave; terminal lobe equalling or larger than pairs of lateral lobes, giving a spathulate character to the leaf, entire, *with obtuse to rounded apex*; petiole narrowly winged, *brilliant purple.* Scapes usually equalling leaves. Exterior bracts spreading to recurved, 10–12 × 2.5–3.5 mm, unbordered, pale green on upper surface, very dark, blackish green and grading to pruinose on lower surface.

Capitulum deep yellow, 40 mm in diameter; ligules striped grey-violet; styles exserted, discoloured; pollen present. Achenes straw-coloured; body 4 mm; cone 0.5 mm. 2n=?24.

Probably native. Grassy places, roadsides, waste land, gardens, open places in natural woodland etc. Widespread and scattered throughout Great Britain; also in eastern Ireland. V.cc. 1, 3–6, 11, 12, 14–23, 30, 33–37, 39, 41, 42, 44, 46, 48, 50, 51, 55, 57–62, 66–70, 76, 77, 82–84, 93, 99, 106, H21, H39.

T. boekmanii is characterised by the bright purple petiole and midrib coloured to the very apex, the red veining, the regular, symmetrically opposed, obtuse lateral lobes, and the rounded terminal lobe.

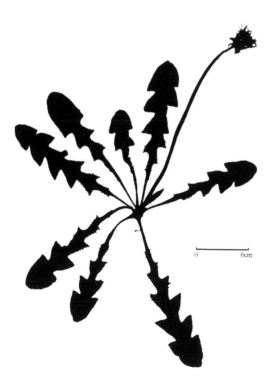

0   6cm

A small to medium-sized plant, with decumbent to erect leaves 50–200 mm.

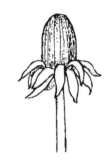

Leaves *rather dark, grey-green,* interlobes sometimes blotched, midrib greenish to faintly purple; lateral lobes 2–4, *short, regular, recurved, hamate,* acute to subacute, with distal margin straight or convex, filiform-dentate proximally, the proximal margin straight or concave; terminal lobe *large, ± obtuse, with 1 or 2 distinct teeth*; petiole *unwinged, at least below,* purple; petiole and midrib with interwoven green strands. Scapes usually equalling or exceeding leaves. Exterior bracts erect to spreading, *10–12 × 2–3 mm, ± unbordered, very dark green and grading to pruinose on lower surface, green to purplish on upper surface.* Capitulum mid-yellow, 30–40 mm in diameter; ligules striped *grey-violet*; styles exserted, *discoloured*; pollen present. Achenes straw-coloured; body 3.2–3.5 mm; cone 0.4–0.6 mm. 2n ± 24.

Possibly native in the south. Grassy places, roadsides, wasteland etc. Widespread throughout Great Britain and Ireland and locally common; distribution is uncertain because there has been confusion between this and the next species. V.cc. 1, 3, 6, 9, 11, 14–21, 25, 26, 28, 30, 33–37, 39–44, 46, 48–51, 55, 57–60, 62, 66–70, 72–74, 81, 85, 88, 89, 93, 97–99, 107, 110, 112, H17, H21, H28.

T. atactum is characterised by the large terminal lobe, which always has at least 1 and sometimes 2 distinct teeth, and by the rather narrow, ± unbordered bracts.

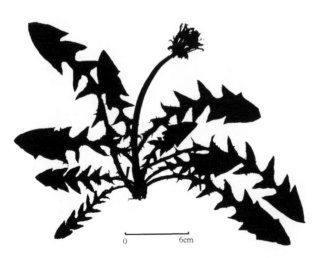

0   6cm

52a **T. sahlinianum** Dudman & A.J. Richards (1994)

A medium-sized plant, with broadly oblanceolate leaves to 200 mm.

Leaves *dark green*, without spots, interlobes without blotches, midrib deep pink to purple, glabrescent; lateral lobes 2–4, patent to somewhat recurved, broad, rather short, triangular, subacute, with distal margin dentate, ± convex or sometimes straight on lower lobes, which bear filiform teeth; terminal lobe medium-sized, about as long as broad to twice as long as broad, obtuse but slightly mucronate, *often with 1 or 2 large teeth*; petiole *distinctly winged*, purple, with filiform teeth; petiole and midrib with interwoven green strands. Scapes 80–200 mm, ascending to erect. Exterior bracts spreading, 10 × 3 mm, scarcely bordered, pale green on upper surface, darker green on lower surface. Capitulum mid-yellow, 40–45 mm in diameter; ligules striped dark grey-violet; styles exserted, discoloured; pollen present. Achenes fulvous to straw-coloured, rugose at apex, otherwise smooth; body 3.8–4.0 mm; cone conical, 0.6 mm.

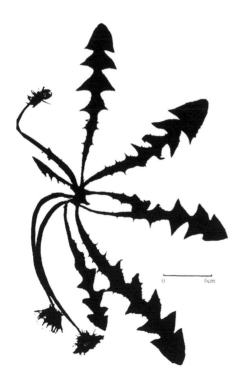

Endemic. V.cc. 3, 4, 9, 33–35, 39, 42, 44, 57, 58, 60, 62, 69, 70, 82, 91, 93, 97, H12.

A close relative of **52** *T. atactum*, with which it was confused until recently. Distinguished by the dirty green leaves which are broader, more dentate and have a distinctly winged petiole. Although it shares the large dentate terminal leaf-lobe of *T. atactum*, the plant is grosser and less 'tidy' in appearance. Until 1994 this species was given the workname of *T. 'British atactum'*.

Section *Hamata*

52b T. pruinatum M.P. Christ. (1936)

A medium-sized plant, with decumbent to erect leaves 150–300 mm.

Leaves *dull, blue-grey green*, midrib *green*; lateral lobes 3–5, regular, patent or recurved, triangular, rather long and narrow, acute, with distal margin straight or convex, entire or, on proximal lobes, filiform-dentate, the proximal margin straight or concave; terminal lobe subsagittate, *entire*; petiole unwinged, at least below, *very pale pink*; petiole and midrib with interwoven green strands. Scapes usually equalling leaves. Exterior bracts mostly erect, the lowest ± spreading, 10–11 × 1.5–3.5 mm, *pale green or whitish-green, heavily pruinose, with a white border.* Capitulum yellow, 40 mm in diameter; ligules striped grey-violet; styles exserted, discoloured; pollen present. Achenes straw-coloured; body 3.5 mm; cone *0.8 mm.*

0   6cm

Rare. Recorded only from the Chester district. V.cc. 50, 51, 58.

Quite similar in appearance to **52** *T. atactum*, but the subsagittate terminal lobes are entire, the midribs are green, and the exterior bracts are noticeably pale and heavily pruinose. *T. pruinatum* differs from **49** *T. hamiferum* by its hairier, lighter-coloured leaves, almost green petioles and broader outer involucral bracts with a distinct white border. In large specimens the leaf-lobes are much longer and narrower. The cone of the achene is longer (about 0.8 mm) than in *T. hami-ferum* (0.5–0.6 mm).

Section *Hamata*

53 T. hamatiforme Dahlst. in Lindm. (1926)

Map 53

A medium-sized plant, with spreading to erect, *irregularly and asymmetrically lobate* leaves 80–200 mm.

Leaves medium to dark bluish-green, interlobes often blotched, midrib purple; lateral lobes 3–5, patent or recurved, *narrowly triangular*, acute, with distal margin ± straight or concave, dentate or filiform-dentate, the proximal margin straight or concave; interlobes rectangular, often with a distinct tooth or teeth; terminal lobe triangular-sagittate with a ± elongated apex; petiole unwinged, at least below, *deep purple*; petiole and midrib with interwoven green strands. Scapes usually equalling leaves. Exterior bracts spreading to recurved, 10–11 × 2–3 mm, pale green to glaucous on upper surface, very dark shiny brown-green on lower surface, with an indistinct border, *lower ones often rudimentary or scaly.* Capitulum deep yellow, 45 mm in diameter; ligules striped *grey-violet*; styles exserted, *discoloured*; pollen present. Achenes pale straw-coloured; body 3.0 mm; cone 0.6 mm. 2n=23, 24, 25, 26, 27.

Native. Grassy places, roadsides, hedge-banks etc. Locally common throughout Great Britain and Ireland. V.cc. 1, 3–5, 12, 14, 15, 17, 19–23, 25, 26, 30, 31, 33–37, 39–44, 46, 50, 51, 55, 57–62, 66–70, 72–74, 77, 80–84, 88, 89, 93, 94, 96–99, 112, H5, H18, H19, H21, H36.

This species has brightly coloured petioles and rather narrow and unusually asymmetrical leaf-lobation; the rudimentary lowermost bracts are distinctive, although they are shared by **53a** *T. spiculatum.*

Section *Hamata*

149

53a T. spiculatum M.P. Christ. (1971)

A medium-sized plant, with spreading to erect, ± *regularly lobate* leaves 80–200 mm.

Leaves medium to dark bluish-green, interlobes often blotched, midrib purple to apex; lateral lobes 3–5, patent or recurved, sometimes strongly so, *triangular, long, very narrow, tapering, acute*, with distal margin straight, sinuate or convex, entire or filiform-dentate, the proximal margin ± straight; interlobes rectangular, with distinct tooth or teeth; terminal lobe *narrowly sagittate with elongated apex*; petiole unwinged, at least below, deep purple; petiole and midrib with interwoven green strands. Scapes usually equalling leaves. Exterior bracts spreading to recurved, 10–11 × 2–3 mm, pale green to glaucous on upper surface, very dark shiny brown-green on lower surface, with an indistinct border, *lower ones often rudimentary or scaly*. Capitulum deep yellow, 45 mm in diameter; ligules striped grey-violet; styles exserted, discoloured; pollen present. Achenes straw-coloured; body 3.0 mm; cone 0.6 mm.

Uncommon. Scattered in England, with two Scottish records. V.cc. 30, 33, 42, 51, 55, 58, 60, 72, 91.

Closely related to **53** *T. hamatiforme*, of which it resembles an extreme form, but with the terminal leaf-lobe narrowly and strikingly sagittate and with long, very narrow, usually highly recurved lateral lobes which are more regular and have tapering acute apices.

0 ⸻ 6cm

Section *Hamata*

53b T. lancidens Hagend., Soest & Zevenb. (1976)

A medium-sized plant, with spreading to erect leaves 80–250 mm.

Leaves *mid-green*, interlobes often blotched, midrib purple; lateral lobes 3–5, patent or recurved, *long*, narrow, deltoid, with distal margin straight or concave, frequently *with at least 1 large tooth*, the proximal margin straight or concave, sometimes dentate, with acute or acuminate apex; interlobes rectangular, *often dentate*; terminal lobe sagittate, with elongated apex; petiole unwinged, at least below, deep purple; petiole and midrib with interwoven green strands. Scapes usually equalling leaves. Exterior bracts spreading to recurved, 10–11 × 3 mm, light grey-green on upper surface, dark olive-green on lower surface, unbordered or slightly bordered. Capitulum deep yellow, 45 mm in diameter; ligules striped *dark brown*, inner ones with purple teeth; styles exserted, discoloured; pollen present. Achenes pale straw-coloured; body *3.0 mm*; cone *0.7 mm*.

0   6cm

Introduced. Rare. V.cc. 9, 14, 50, 51, 58.

A relative of **53** *T. hamatiforme*, but a more robust species with mid-green leaves and long acute lateral lobes which often carry a long tooth. Rudimentary outer bracts are absent and the ligules are striped brown, the inner ligule ends being purple. The cone (0.7 mm) is rather long in comparison with the achene body (3.0 mm). *T. lancidens* is best characterised by the large teeth on the distal margins of the lateral lobes and often on the interlobes.

A medium-sized plant, with spreading to erect, *irregularly lobed* leaves 80–200 mm.

Leaves *mid-green*, interlobes blotched, midrib purple; lateral lobes 3–5, patent or recurved, long, ± *linear*, rapidly narrowing from a broad base, strongly toothed, often divided, sometimes deeply so, with distal margin straight or sinuate, entire or dentate, the proximal margin straight or concave, with acute or acuminate apex, *often on a long linear process*; terminal lobe trilobate, with elongated apex, frequently divided; petiole unwinged, deep purple; petiole and midrib with interwoven green strands. Scapes usually equalling leaves. Exterior bracts spreading to recurved, 10–11 × 3–4 mm, dark green, unbordered. Capitulum deep yellow, 45 mm in diameter; ligules striped *dark violet*; styles exserted, *discoloured*; pollen ± present. Achenes pale straw-coloured; body 3.0 mm; cone 0.5 mm. 2n ± 24.

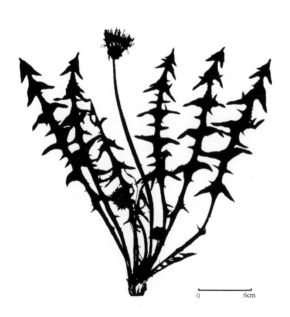

0 ————— 6cm

Introduced. Uncommon. Scattered throughout Great Britain; not recorded from Ireland. V.cc. 1, 12, 15, 18–20, 23, 34–36, 42, 50, 51, 55, 58, 61, 66–68, 70, 73, 81, 97, 101.

T. kernianum is perhaps the least characteristic member of Section *Hamata*: the lobation is highly irregular and cannot be described as hamate, the lateral lobes in the inner and middle leaves being characterised by a long linear apical process.

A medium-sized to large, *robust* plant, with spreading to erect leaves 180–400 mm.

Leaves dark-green, interlobes *usually heavily blotched*, midrib coloured; lateral lobes 5–6, patent or recurved, hamate, with distal margin straight, concave, or angled, *usually strongly dentate, frequently with at least 1 large tooth*, the proximal margin straight or concave, sometimes dentate, with apex acute to acuminate or obtuse (when the lobe is entire); interlobes ± dentate; terminal lobe sagittate with elongated apex or obtusely triangular, often dentate; petiole unwinged, at least

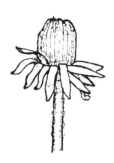

below, purple; petiole and midrib with interwoven green strands. Scapes usually equalling leaves. Exterior bracts spreading to recurved, *11–13 × 3–5 mm*, pruinose, suffused purplish on upper surface, dark olive green on lower surface, with pink tip, narrowly white-bordered. Capitulum deep yellow, 50 mm in diameter; ligules striped *dark brown*; styles exserted, *discoloured*; pollen present. Achenes pale straw-coloured; body 3.0 mm; cone 0.5 mm. 2n ± 24.

Perhaps introduced. Scattered throughout the British Isles, sometimes common. V.cc. 1, 3, 5, 6, 9, 11, 12, 14–17, 19–23, 28, 30, 31, 34, 35, 37, 39–42, 44–47, 49–51, 55, 57, 58, 60–62, 66–74, 76, 81, 86, 93, 97, 99, 101, 102, 104, 109, 112, S, H21, H33, H38, H39.

One of the largest and perhaps the most distinct species in Section *Hamata*, *T. lamprophyllum* is distinguished by its large size, usually heavily blotched interlobes, strongly dentate lateral lobes and rather broad exterior bracts. See also **36** *T. hesperium* and **36a** *T. 'cestrense'*.

0   6cm

Section RUDERALIA Kirschner, H. Øllg. & Štěpánek in Kirschner & Štěpánek (1987)

56 T. laeticolor Dahlst. (1906)

Map 56

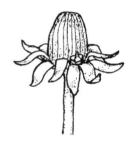

A medium-sized plant, with erect, broadly oblong-spathulate, *flat* leaves 80–200 mm.

Leaves mid-green, often pale, unblotched, midrib green or brownish; lateral lobes 4–6, *rather broad*, patent, subdeltoid to *triangular*, or narrower and *omnidirectional*, usually subentire or with a few large teeth, acute at apex, with distal margin straight or slightly concave or sigmoid, the proximal margin ± straight; interlobes entire or dentate, ± dark-bordered; terminal lobe *large, especially on inner leaves*, helmet-shaped, entire or once or twice shallowly dissected, subacute to obtuse, that of outer leaves triangular and less obviously larger than pair of lobes below it; petiole unwinged or (usually) *narrowly winged, green*. Scapes usually equalling leaves, green. Exterior bracts *suberect*

to spreading, *10–11 × 3–4 mm, dark green, usually suffused purplish on lower surface*, pink-tipped, scarcely bordered. Capitulum yellow, about 40 mm in diameter; ligules striped grey-violet; styles exserted, discoloured; pollen sparsely present. Achenes straw-coloured, spinulose above, otherwise smooth; body 4.0 mm; cone 0.6–0.8 mm.

Probably introduced. Scattered throughout Great Britain. Grassy places, roadsides etc. V.cc. 3, 6, 12, 14, 15, 17–19, 21, 23, 25, 28, 30, 33–35, 39, 42–44, 46, 50, 51, 55, 57, 58, 60, 67, 68, 70, 72, 81, 93, 99.

T. laeticolor is characterised by the broad, suberect, often purplish bracts, by the large terminal lobe of the inner leaves, by the tendency of at least some lateral lobes to be triangular, and by the green, usually winged, petiole.

56a T. macrolobum Dahlst. (1911b)

A medium-sized to large plant, with erect, broadly elliptical, *crisped* leaves 100–300 mm.

Leaves mid-green, often pale, midrib green or brownish; lateral lobes 4–6, entire or divided, *abruptly narrowed into linear processes (often with swollen, subobtuse apices) from a broad base*, patent or forward-pointing, deltoid, proximal ones dentate, sometimes with a few large teeth, and acute at apex, all with distal margin sigmoid, the proximal margin ± straight; interlobes entire or dentate, ± dark-bordered; terminal lobe of outer leaves *trilobate* with obtuse lateral lobes, *often lingulate*, entire or divided, subacute to obtuse, that of inner leaves *large*, helmet-shaped, acute to mucronate; petiole narrowly winged, green. Scapes usually equalling leaves, green. Exterior bracts *erect* to spreading, 10–14 × 3–4 mm, dark green, usually suffused purplish on lower surface, pink-tipped, scarcely bordered. Capitulum yellow, 50–55 mm in diameter; ligules striped grey-violet; styles exserted, discoloured; pollen present. Achenes straw-coloured, spinulose above, otherwise smooth; body 3.0 mm; cone 0.3 mm.

Probably introduced. Scattered throughout Great Britain, with one record from Northern Ireland. Grassy places, roadsides etc. V.cc. 2, 11, 12, 15, 17, 20, 21, 23, 24, 29, 30, 34, 55, 56, 60, 69, 70, 99, 112, H39.

A close relative of **56** *T. laeticolor*, differing principally in leaf-shape, having much narrower lateral lobes which form linear processes, often with swollen, subobtuse apices; linear lobules and large narrow teeth are also often formed at the lobe base; the term-inal lobe of outer leaves is trilobate, often with an expanded, narrowly ling-ulate apex. Resembles **57** *T. pannucium* in many ways, but heterophyllous, with large terminal lobes to inner (later) leaves. Compare also with **57a** *T. subexpallidum*, which has more obtuse lobe apices.

0 |——————| 6cm

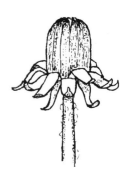

A medium-sized to large plant, with erect, oblanceolate, *flat* leaves 150–300 mm.

Leaves *pale green*, interlobes unblotched, midrib green or faintly coloured; lateral lobes 4–6, somewhat recurved, abruptly narrowed from a broad base, acute, with distal margin concave or angled, denticulate, the proximal margin straight or convex; terminal lobe *narrow, elongated, sometimes divided*; petiole *usually long, a third to half length of leaf, green, narrowly winged to ± unwinged, at least below*. Scapes usually equalling leaves. Exterior bracts erect to spreading, *12 × 3–4 mm*, unbordered, dark green, sometimes violet-tipped. Capitulum deep yellow, 45 mm in diameter; ligules striped brown-purple; styles exserted, *discoloured*; pollen present. Achenes straw-coloured; body 2.8 mm; cone 0.8 mm. 2n=24.

Probably introduced. Grassy places, roadsides, scrub, wasteland etc. Widespread throughout Great Britain, locally common; scattered in Ireland. V.cc. 1, 3, 8, 9, 11, 12, 15–17, 19–4, 26, 28, 29, 32, 34–36, 39–43, 46, 50, 51, 54–62, 64, 66–74, 76, 77, 80–82, 84, 88, 89, 91, 95, 96, 101, 106, 109, 112, S, H16, H40.

T. pannucium is characterised by its long green petiole, the rather large, green, erect to spreading bracts, and the narrow, elongated terminal lobe.

There is a single record from South Northumberland (v.c. 67) for a variant with a striking involucre, in which the exterior bracts are strictly erect distally but are recurved proximally, strongly so in the outermost, which are also wider than the remainder. Outer leaves have a lingulate tip to the terminal lobe; in inner leaves this lobe is broader and more dentate-incised. The achene cone is longer (0.8–1.0 mm) and almost cylindrical. This variant, which has not been formally described, has been given the workname *T. 'distendens'* by H. Øllgaard.

57a T. subexpallidum Dahlst. (1929)

A medium-sized to large plant, with erect, oblong-spathulate, *somewhat crisped* leaves 100–300 mm.

Leaves *mid-green*, interlobes not obviously blotched, midrib green to slightly coloured; lateral lobes 4–7, regular, patent to slightly recurved, long, narrow, deltoid or triangular, subacute to obtuse at apex, with both margins ± straight or angled, sometimes to give a hooked shape but sometimes with a forward-pointing process, the distal margin dentate (to filiform-dentate) or, rarely, entire, the proximal margin entire; terminal lobe of outer leaves triangular and elongated, sometimes divided, somewhat waisted, *with lingulate, obtuse tip*, those of inner leaves usually large, triangular, cordate or helmet-shaped, entire or dentate, *obtuse but frequently mucronate*, sometimes divided; petiole *unwinged, at least below*, pallid or somewhat pink on inner leaves. Scapes usually exceeding leaves. Exterior bracts recurved to spreading, 11–14 × 2.5–4.5 mm, unbordered, green on upper surface, darker on lower surface. Capitulum deep yellow, 50 mm in diameter; ligules striped grey-violet; styles exserted, *discoloured*; pollen present. Achenes *dark straw-brown*; body 3.0 mm; cone to 1.0 mm.

Probably introduced. Grassy places, roadsides, scrub, wasteland etc. Widespread and locally common. Many British records were made under the synonym *T. linguatum* Dahlst. ex M.P. Christ. & Wiinst. in Raunk. (1934). V.cc. 3–6, 9, 10, 12, 15–17, 19–24, 28–30, 32–37, 39–44, 46, 50, 51, 55–58, 60, 62–64, 67–70, 72–74, 79, 82, 83, 85, 95, 101, 105, 106, S, H39.

A close relative of **57** *T. pannucium*, differing chiefly by the distinctive shape of the ends of the lateral and terminal leaf-lobes, which are generally (except for terminal lobes of inner leaves) narrowly lingulate and obtuse to rounded. Variable in leaf-shape, but readily identified.

58 T. corynodes G.E. Haglund (1943)

Map 58

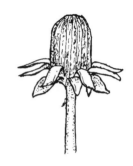

A medium-sized to robust, squat plant, with decumbent to erect, oblanceolate, *highly crisped* leaves *100–200 mm.*

Leaves *mid-green*, interlobes unblotched, midrib green; lateral lobes *4–8, crowded, short, sometimes divided*, narrowing from a broad base, *with a narrower, often forward-pointing process*, subacute to obtuse at apex, with distal margin *convex or sigmoid, often strongly humped*, entire or dentate, the proximal margin *concave, convex or (often) sigmoid*; interlobes *shallow, giving a broad central core to the leaf*; terminal lobe usually *small*, triangular, often divided, with apex obtuse to acute without a distinct elongated tip; petiole *broadly winged*, green. Scapes usually equalling leaves. Exterior bracts spreading to *recurved*, 11–15 × 4–5 mm, ± *unbordered*, grey-green on upper surface. Capitulum mid-yellow, 50 mm in diameter; ligules striped grey-violet; styles exserted, discoloured; pollen present. Achenes straw-coloured; body 3.5 mm; cone 0.5 mm.

Introduced. Grassy places, roadsides, wasteland etc. Known mainly from Wales and the Welsh border. V.cc. 3, 14, 33–35, 42, 43, 50, 51, 57, 58, 60, 62.

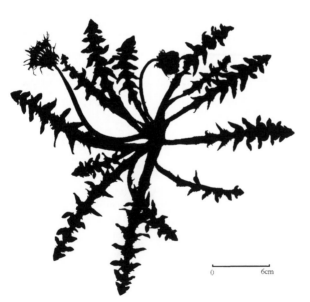

0 ———— 6cm

T. corynodes is characterised by the crowded, ± obtuse, short, multi-directional lateral lobes with the distal lobe-bases often strongly 'humped'. It has a highly characteristic leaf-shape.

Section *Ruderalia*

A medium-sized to robust, squat plant, with erect, broadly oblanceolate, *highly crisped, waxy, fleshy* leaves 100–300 mm.

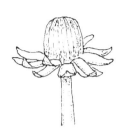

Leaves dark green, interlobes unblotched, midrib green; lateral lobes 4–6, *crowded, regular, recurved*, narrowing from a broad base, *frequently giving the effect of a high shoulder*, acute or subacute at apex, with distal margin convex, entire or dentate, the proximal margin concave; terminal lobe medium-sized to large, triangular, often subdivided, with apex obtuse to acute without a distinct elongated tip; petiole *broadly winged*, green. Scapes usually equalling leaves, thickly arachnoid-hairy, especially when young. Exterior bracts *erect* to spreading, 11–15 × 4–5 mm, narrowly bordered, grey-green on upper surface. Capitulum mid-yellow, 50 mm in diameter; ligules striped grey-violet; styles exserted, discoloured; pollen present. Achenes straw-coloured; body 3.5 mm; cone 0.5 mm. 2n=24.

Probably native. Grassy places, roadsides, wasteland etc. Scattered throughout Great Britain; also recorded from Dublin. V.cc. 17, 19, 26, 33–35, 37, 40, 42–44, 50, 51, 57, 58, 60, 67, 74, H21.

Amongst green-petioled species, *T. undulatum* is characterised by the highly crisped, waxy, fleshy leaves, with crowded, regular, arched lateral lobes, and by the large, ± erect exterior bracts.

Section *Ruderalia*

A medium-sized plant, with erect, broadly oblong to oblanceolate, *highly crisped* leaves 100–200 mm.

Leaves brilliantly *shiny mid-green*, interlobes unblotched, midrib green; lateral lobes 4–6, *often divided*, deltoid or triangular, narrowing from a broad base, patent or *forward-pointing*, acute at apex, with distal margin convex or straight, entire or dentate, the proximal margin ± straight; terminal lobe usually medium-sized to small, ± triangular, with apex acute without a distinct elongated tip; petiole *unwinged*, green. Scapes equalling or (often) exceeding leaves. Exterior bracts *erect to appressed*, 11–15 × 4–5 mm, narrowly bordered or unbordered, green on upper surface. Capitulum mid-yellow, 50 mm in diameter; ligules striped grey-violet; styles exserted, discoloured; pollen present. Achenes straw-coloured; body 3.5 mm; cone 0.5 mm.

Introduced. Grassy places, roadsides etc. Uncommon and scattered through Great Britain. V.cc. 6, 14, 19, 21, 34, 37, 42, 44, 54, 58, 83, 99, 112.

In effect, a small, condensed, highly crisped, brilliantly shiny-green version of **59** *T. undulatum*, but with erect to appressed exterior bracts, unwinged petioles, and lateral lobe processes which are often forward-pointing.

0   6cm

59b T. dilaceratum M.P. Christ. (1936)

Map 59b

A medium-sized to robust plant, with erect, broadly oblong to oblanceolate, *crisped* leaves 100–250 mm.

Leaves mid-green, interlobes unblotched, midrib green; lateral lobes 4–6, *divided*, narrowing from a broad base, *with a narrower, often forward-pointing process, subacute to obtuse at apex*, with distal margin convex or sigmoid, entire or dentate, the proximal margin concave, convex or (often) sigmoid; interlobes *usually bearing single lobules*; terminal lobe usually medium-sized, triangular or tripartite, often divided, entire or dentate, with acute apex; petiole *narrowly or broadly winged, parallel-sided*, green. Scapes usually equalling leaves. Exterior bracts ± *spreading*, 11–15 × 4–5 mm, narrowly bordered, grey-green on upper surface. Capitulum mid-yellow, 50 mm in diameter; ligules striped grey-violet; styles exserted, discoloured; pollen present. Achenes straw-coloured; body 3.5 mm; cone 0.5 mm.

Probably introduced. Grassy places, roadsides etc. Scattered through Great Britain. V.cc. 9, 19, 21, 25, 26, 33–37, 42, 43, 51, 57, 58, 60, 67, 69, 70, 77, 81, 112.

0   6cm

Intermediate between **59** *T. undulatum* and **59a** *T. tenebricans*, but characterised by lateral lobes bearing broadly linear processes which are often forward-pointing and subacute to obtuse at the apex; well-marked small single lobes are usually present at the interlobes. Differs from **59a** by having winged petioles and ± spreading exterior bracts.

A medium-sized plant, with erect, often very narrowly oblong, *flat* leaves 80–250 mm.

Leaves bright mid-green, *glabrous*, interlobes unblotched, midrib green; lateral lobes 3–5, regular, patent or slightly recurved, deltoid, *short, acute or subacute*, with distal margin ± convex, entire or with 1 to a few denticulations or with 1 tooth, the proximal margin straight or concave; terminal lobe triangular or helmet-shaped, often divided; petiole *long, a third to half length of leaf*, green, *with characteristic, narrow, parallel, entire wings*. Scapes usually equalling or exceeding leaves. Exterior bracts *oblong, recurved but abruptly spreading at apex, 12 × 3–4 mm*, unbordered, *glaucous on upper surface, pink-tipped, obtuse-mucronate*. Capitulum deep yellow, 45–50 mm in diameter; ligules striped *grey-violet*; styles exserted, *discoloured*; pollen present. Achenes olive-brown; body 3.0 mm; cone 0.5 mm. 2n=24.

Native. Grassy places, roadsides, wasteland etc. Widespread throughout Great Britain, locally very common; also in Northern Ireland and the Channel Isles. V.cc. 1, 2, 6, 7, 9, 11, 12, 14–17, 19–24, 26, 28–30, 32–38, 40–44, 48, 50, 51, 53–55, 57–62, 66–74, 76, 79–83, 85, 88, 89, 95, 99, 101, 102, 110, 112, S, H38, H40.

0   6 cm

T. alatum is characterised by the long, green, narrowly winged, entire petioles and the glaucous, oblong, pink-tipped bracts of a characteristic posture. The leaf-shape, however, can be very variable.

Section *Ruderalia*

60a   T. horridifrons Rail. (1967)

A medium-sized plant, with narrowly oblong to oblance-olate-spathulate, flat leaves to 80–250 mm.

Leaves erect, mid to dark *greyish green, usually hairy or at least matt*, interlobes sometimes blotched, midrib green; lateral lobes 3–7, *sometimes divided or even laciniate*, deltoid, patent or slightly recurved, *long, acute*, with distal margin ± convex, entire or dentate, the proximal margin straight or concave; interlobes sometimes dentate; terminal lobe on older (outer) leaves small, triangular, on inner leaves larger, sometimes divided, lingulate or helmet-shaped; petiole long, green, ± *broadly winged.* Scapes usually equalling or exceeding leaves. Exterior bracts *recurved or reflexed*, 12–15 × 3.5–5 mm, bordered or unbordered, *grey-white on upper surface.* Capitulum yellow, 45–50 mm in diameter; ligules striped grey-violet; styles exserted, *blackish*; pollen present. Achenes straw-coloured; body *4.0 mm*; cone *0.8 mm.*

Introduced. Roadsides; very local in England and Wales, but occasionally abundant. V.cc. 22, 30, 34, 37, 40, 43, 50, 51, 55, 58, 60, 66–68, 70.

Related to **60** *T. alatum*, and structurally similar, but with leaves usually evenly short-haired, giving the leaf a greyish, matt appearance, and with less regular, some-times even laciniate lobing. Exterior bracts evenly grey-white on upper surface; styles blackish; achenes paler and longer.

60b T. densilobum Dahlst. (1935)

A medium-sized plant, with erect, narrowly oblong to oblanceolate, flat leaves to 80–200 mm.

Leaves bright mid-green, *glabrous*, interlobes unblotched, midrib green; lateral lobes 3–6, *often divided*, regular, patent or slightly recurved, deltoid, *longer and narrower* than in **60** and *often double*, acute or subacute, with distal margin ± convex, entire or with 1 to a few denticulations or (frequently) with 1 tooth, the proximal margin straight or concave; interlobes ± dentate; terminal lobe *small*, triangular to hastate, sometimes divided; petiole *short*, green, *narrowly to ± broadly winged*. Scapes usually equalling or exceeding leaves. Exterior bracts oblong, *recurved to ± reflexed, often abruptly spreading at apex*, 12 × 3–4 mm, unbordered, pale green on upper surface. Capitulum deep yellow, 45–50 mm in diameter; ligules striped grey-violet; styles exserted, discoloured; pollen present. Achenes olive-brown; body 3.0 mm; cone 0.5 mm.

Introduced. Road-verges; uncommon and scattered, especially in the south-east. V.cc. 12, 13, 19, 20, 22, 26, 34, 37, 42, 70, H40.

0 ———— 6cm

Structurally similar to **60** *T. alatum*, with the same distinctive involucre, but with crowded, 'fussier' leaf-lobes more resembling **59b** *T. dilaceratum*, although the leaf has longer, narrow, often double processes to the lateral lobes and a short, winged petiole. The terminal lobe is small, triangular as in **60**, but often more hastate than helmet-shaped; the leaves are not hairy (as they are in **60a**).

164

61 T. insigne Ekman ex M.P. Christ. & Wiinst. in Raunk. (1934)

Map 61

A medium-sized plant, with ascending, narrowly oblong to oblanceolate, nearly flat leaves 70–200 mm.

Leaves bright mid-green, *with a broad pale undivided central region*, interlobes *unblotched*, midrib green to faintly coloured; lateral lobes 4–7, *regular*, crowded, triangular, rather short, patent or ± *pointing forward*, subacute to obtuse at apex, entire or with 1–2 large teeth; interlobes *lobulate*; terminal lobe *usually rather small, triangular to tripartite*, often divided; petiole about one third length of leaf, green or, on inner leaves, faintly pink, winged. Scapes equalling or exceeding leaves. Exterior bracts *spreading, somewhat twisted in the horizontal plane, spaced, narrowly parallel-sided, 12–14 × 2–2.5 mm,* unbordered, *pale green, often suffused purple and violet-tipped on upper surface, dark green on lower surface.* Capitulum yellow, 45 mm in diameter; ligules striped *grey-violet*; styles exserted, *discoloured*; pollen present. Achenes straw-coloured; body 3.5 mm; cone 0.8 mm. 2n ± 24.

Native. Dry open grassy places, roadsides, wasteland etc. Widespread throughout Great Britain and locally common; also recorded from two Irish vice-counties. V.cc. 1, 3, 9, 11, 12, 14–23, 26, 28–30, 33–35, 37, 39, 40, 42–45, 48, 50–52, 55–61, 66–70, 72–75, 80, 81, 84, 85, 88, 89, 91, 93, 94, 97, 99, 101, 103, 104, 106, 109, 112, H14, H16.

T. insigne is characterised by the bright green leaves with a broad pale undivided central region and a wide pale petiole; the narrow purplish bracts spread horizontally and are spaced out and parallel-sided, forming a 'narrowly cogged wheel' when viewed from above.

61a T. laciniosum Dahlst. (1910)

A medium-sized to large plant, with leaves 150–300 mm.

Differs from **61** in being a taller plant having narrower leaves with parallel-sided, dark-blotched interlobes, distant, short, obtuse, sublinear lateral lobes, often accompanied by 1–2 lobules, and a protracted terminal lobe. The spreading to recurved exterior bracts are wider (3.5 mm) and are dark green. Unlike those of **61** and **61b**, the inner ligule tips are yellow.

Introduced. Only three confirmed records, from v.cc. 70 and 98.

61b T. atonolobum Hagend., Soest & Zevenb. (1972)

A medium-sized to *robust* plant, with ascending, ± oblong, nearly flat leaves 70–250 mm.

Leaves mid-green, interlobes unblotched, midrib green to faintly coloured; lateral lobes 4–6, regular, deltoid, *often recurved*, acute at apex, with distal margin ± straight or sigmoid, on lowest lobes sometimes dentate or denticulate, the proximal margins entire; interlobes often with 1 tooth or denticulate; terminal lobe *medium-sized, sagittate*; petiole about a quarter to a third length of leaf, green, winged.

Introduced. Two records only, from v.cc. 37 and 50.

An altogether heavier-looking plant than **61**, with regular, larger, often recurved lateral lobes and a larger, sagittate terminal lobe.

Section *Ruderalia*

62 T. pannulatiforme Dahlst. (1932)

Map 62

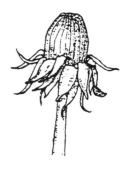

A robust plant, with decumbent to erect, lanceolate, ± *crisped* leaves 150–300 mm.

Leaves *mid-green*, interlobes *blotched*, midrib *white or slightly coloured*; lateral lobes 5–8, *often divided, crowded*, patent to *recurved*, triangular to lingulate, sometimes narrowing abruptly from a broad base to give a convex angle to distal margin, acute or sometimes obtuse, with proximal margin straight or concave, sometimes with 1 tooth, the distal margin usually dentate, *sometimes with 1 or 2 large teeth*; interlobes ± *dentate*; terminal lobe *triangular-sagittate*, tripartite or divided; petiole ± broadly winged, white or, on inner leaves, pink. Scapes usually exceeding leaves. Exterior bracts *spreading to recurved*, 11–15 × 2–4 mm, unbordered, *green, with pink tips*, paler green on upper surface. Capitulum yellow, 40–50 mm in diameter; ligules striped *grey-violet*; styles exserted, *discoloured*; pollen present. Achenes straw-coloured; body 3.0 mm; cone *0.4 mm*. 2n ± 24.

Native. Grassy places, roadsides, wasteland etc. Scattered throughout Great Britain, locally common. Rare outside Britain. V.cc. 3–6, 12, 20, 21, 23, 33–35, 42–44, 50, 51, 57, 58, 60, 62, 66, 69, 70, 72, 74, 93, H21.

T. pannulatiforme is characterised by the many, crowded, usually recurved lateral lobes, some of which have large teeth, by the tar-coloured, ± dentate interlobes, and by the distinctive terminal lobe.

62a T. nigridentatum T. Edmondson in Dudman & A.J. Richards (1994)

Map 62a

A robust, medium-sized to large plant, with elliptical leaves 150–250 mm.

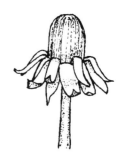

Leaves *dark green* without spots, interlobes *with dark blotches, ± plicate*, midrib *pink*; lateral lobes 5–8, patent to somewhat recurved, long and rather narrow, acute, *with distal margin with ± many dark or black teeth*, occasionally with a single large tooth, convex or sigmoid; terminal lobe slightly narrower than rest of blade of leaf, hastate or sagittate, ± divided or often with 1 or 2 teeth, with an elongated apex; petiole winged, sometimes broadly so, pink, sometimes white at base. Scapes usually equalling leaves at flowering, pink. Exterior bracts *mostly spreading*, the lowest ± recurved, 11–14 × 2–3.5 mm, unbordered, pale green on upper surface, darker green on lower surface. Capitulum mid-yellow, 40–50 mm in diameter; ligules striped grey-brown, with *dark* teeth; styles exserted, discoloured; pollen present. Achenes straw-coloured to grey-brown, spinulose, with no or very slight cone; body 2.0–2.2 mm; cone *to 0.2 mm.*

Native and probably endemic. Scattered in the west of England and in Wales in grassy places and on walls, cliffs etc. V.cc. 6, 33–35, 39, 42, 51, 58, 70.

Differs from *62 T. pannulatiforme* mostly in having darker leaves with pink midribs and copiously blackened interlobes and teeth; the lateral lobes tend to be narrower and less well defined, the exterior bracts are mostly spreading, and the very small achenes almost lack a cone.

0   6cm

A medium-sized plant, with *decumbent* to erect, *broadly oblanceolate,* nearly flat leaves 100–200 mm.

Leaves mid-green, interlobes unblotched, midrib green; lateral lobes 4–7, *regular, crowded, ± overlapping,* rather short and *broad*, patent to *recurved, subacute at apex*, with distal margin *convex*, entire or filiform-dentate, the proximal margin ± straight; terminal lobe triangular, often divided, *subacute, often mucronate at apex*; petiole ± *broadly winged*, green. Scapes usually equalling leaves. Exterior bracts *recurved,* 11–13 × 3.5–4.5 mm, unbordered, green, paler green on upper surface. Capitulum yellow, 50 mm in diameter; ligules striped grey-violet; styles exserted, discoloured; pollen present. Achenes straw-coloured; body 4.0 mm; cone *0.8 mm.*

Native. Grassy places, road-sides, wasteland etc. Wide-spread throughout Great Britain, locally common; a few records from eastern Ireland. V.cc. 1, 3, 6, 14–23, 25, 26, 30, 33–37, 42–44, 46, 55, 58, 60, 62, 66, 67, 69, 70, 72–78, 81, 82, 84, 88, 89, 91, 93, 99, 101, 103, 106, 112, H21.

T. laticordatum is characterised by its crowded, regular, broad, recurved lateral lobes, its broadly winged green petiole and its often decumbent habit.

0   6cm

63a   T. pallescens Dahlst. (1910)

A medium-sized plant, with decumbent to erect, *broadly elliptical*, nearly flat leaves to 100–200 mm.

Leaves mid-green, interlobes unblotched, midrib green; lateral lobes 4–7, *regular, crowded so as to form acute interlobes*, deltoid, *narrow*, patent to recurved, *acute (or sometimes rounded) at apex*, with distal margin convex, entire or filiform-dentate, the proximal margin ± straight, sometimes with 1 tooth; terminal lobe triangular or hastate, sometimes divided, *acute at apex*; petiole *broadly winged*, green or white, *pale pink on inner leaves*. Scapes usually equalling leaves. Exterior bracts *spreading*, 11–13 × 3.5–4.5 mm, unbordered, green, paler green on upper surface.

Probably introduced. Scarce and scattered on road-verges and occasionally in old meadows. V.cc. 4, 6, 11–13, 17, 19–21, 23, 28, 30, 34, 36, 42, 61, 66–68, 89, 99, 112.

Generally a smaller plant, but closely related to **63** *T. laticordatum*, differing chiefly by the narrower, more crowded and more acute leaf-lobes forming acute interlobes. However, occasional lateral lobes have rounded apices, a feature which is never seen in **63**. The inner leaves have pale pink petioles and the exterior bracts are spreading.

0   6 cm

Section *Ruderalia*

63b T. subhuelphersianum M.P. Christ. (1971)

A medium-sized to tall plant, with erect, *broadly spathulate,* ± flat leaves 150–300 mm.

Leaves *light, rather greyish green,* interlobes unblotched, midrib green to slightly coloured; lateral lobes 5–6, broad, patent to recurved, deltoid, acute at apex, with distal margin straight to convex, dentate to filiform-dentate (especially on lower lobes), the proximal margin straight or concave, entire; terminal lobe *larger* than pair of lobes below it, *broadly triangular or hastate,* rarely divided, entire to (often) *with 1 tooth, with acute apex;* petiole unwinged or *narrowly winged distally,* green to faintly coloured. Scapes usually equalling leaves. Exterior bracts *recurved to reflexed, 12–16 × 3.5–4.5 mm, bordered,* pale green suffused with violet on upper surface, darker green on lower surface. Capitulum deep yellow, 50 mm in diameter; ligules striped grey-violet; styles exserted, yellow when fresh, discoloured when dry; pollen *absent.* Achenes straw-coloured; body 3.5 mm; cone *0.5–0.8 mm.*

Introduced and casual. A Danish species recorded infrequently and, at least in the Newcastle area, not persisting. Despite its name, it has no obvious resemblance to *T. huelphersianum.* V.cc. 34, 50, 58, 67.

Superficially similar to **63** *T. laticordatum,* but with distinctly pale, slightly greyish leaves with a large, broad, obtuse, often single-toothed terminal lobe and a narrowly winged petiole. The exterior bracts are larger, more reflexed and bordered, and, diagnostically, there is no pollen.

63c   T. necessarium H. Øllg. (1978)

Map 63c

A medium-sized plant, with decumbent to erect, *narrowly oblanceolate to elliptical*, flat leaves to 80–300 mm.

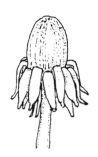

Leaves bright *dark green*, interlobes usually blotched, midrib green; lateral lobes 5–7, *regular, rather short, rather crowded, ± overlapping*, deltoid, recurved, acute to subacute at apex, with distal margin straight to subconvex, entire to regularly dentate, the proximal margin straight or concave; terminal lobe usually entire or once-divided, cordate to sagittate at base, *subacute to obtuse at apex*; petiole *with ± parallel-sided wings*, green. Scapes usually equalling leaves. Exterior bracts *recurved to reflexed, about 14 × 4 mm*, unbordered, green, paler green on upper surface. Capitulum yellow, *40–45 mm in diameter*; ligules striped grey-violet, *outer ones often smudged blackish at apex*; styles exserted, discoloured; pollen present. Achenes straw-coloured; body *short, 2.5–3.0 mm*; cone *0.5 mm*.

Possibly introduced. Grassy places and roadsides; scattered and rather uncommon. V.cc. 3, 4, 19, 23, 26, 30, 34, 35, 39, 42–44, 58, 60, 70, 72, 74, 93.

Differs from **63** *T. laticordatum* by its darker green, more narrowly oblanceolate to elliptical leaves with rather short, neat, regular lobing and with petioles of which the wings are more parallel-sided; the subacute to obtuse, entire to once-divided terminal lobe is often cordate at the base, and the achenes are small. The apex to the outer ligules tends to be smudged blackish. The neat regular lobing of the leaves gives them something of the appearance of a barbed arrow.

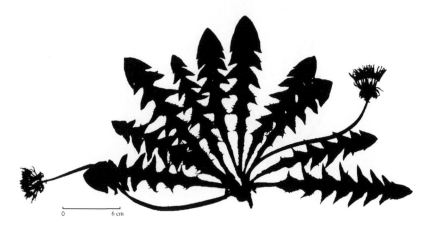

0 ⊢————⊣ 6 cm

Section *Ruderalia*

63d T. margettsii C.C. Haw. (1990)

A medium-sized to large plant, with erect, *oblong-spathulate*, flat, *fleshy* leaves to 200 mm.

Leaves mid-green, *shiny*, interlobes unblotched; lateral lobes of outer leaves 3–4, *irregularly divided, with broad-based, obtuse to subacute teeth*, those of inner leaves 1–3, very broad, triangular, patent to recurved, acute; terminal lobe of outer leaves *rather large*, with up to three blunt teeth, *rounded at apex*, that of inner leaves *very large, rounded at apex*; interlobes long, with several medium-sized teeth; petiole of outer leaves green at base, *unwinged, but becoming winged above*, merging into decurrent margin of lowest lobe, that of inner leaves sometimes faintly pink. Scapes green or pink, glabrous, usually equalling leaves. Exterior bracts spreading, *9–11 × 4–5 mm*, bordered, grey-pink, pruinose on upper surface, dull green on lower surface. Capitulum deep yellow, about 40 mm in diameter; ligules striped grey-violet; styles exserted, discoloured; pollen present. Achenes straw-coloured, shortly spinulose; body 3.0–3.5 mm; cone *long, 0.8–1.0 mm*.

0   6cm

Native and endemic to Cornwall and Devon, mostly on the Lizard Peninsula, where it is plentiful. V.cc. 1, 3.

A distinctive local endemic of uncertain affinity not closely related to **63**, **63a**, **63b** or **63c**. Immediately recognised by its shiny, fleshy leaves with a distinctive shape including a rounded terminal lobe, the outer leaves having irregularly divided lateral lobes with large, broadly based, obtuse to subacute apices and teeth. The spreading exterior bracts are short and broad, and the achene has a long cone.

A medium-sized plant, with erect, ± spathulate, ± flat leaves 50–200 mm.

Leaves mid-green, interlobes often blotched, midrib green; lateral lobes 3–5, ± regular, patent or ± recurved, triangular or deltoid, rather short, acute or subacute at apex, with distal margin convex, *entire or denticulate*, the proximal margin ± straight, entire; interlobes *dentate or with small lobes*; terminal lobe short, wide, often divided, subacute at apex; petiole narrowly winged below, green, sometimes rose at base. Scapes equalling or exceeding leaves. Exterior bracts mostly *suberect to spreading*, 8–11 × 3.5 mm, unbordered, green suffused with pink on upper surface, *darker*, shiny green on lower surface. Capitulum deep yellow, *40 mm in diameter*; ligules striped grey-violet; styles exserted, discoloured; pollen present. Achenes straw-coloured; body 3.2 mm; cone 0.7 mm.

0   6cm

Native. Grassy places, water-meadows, road-sides, wasteland etc. Scattered throughout Great Britain. V.cc. 3, 6, 12, 17–19, 21–23, 28, 30, 34–37, 42, 43, 55, 58–61, 66, 70, 74, 88, 89, 96, 99.

T. sublaeticolor is characterised by the narrow green petioles, small capitula, and rather dark, suberect to spreading exterior bracts.

64a T. lepidum M.P. Christ. (1936)

A medium-sized plant, with erect, oblanceolate, ± flat leaves to 50–250 mm.

Leaves dark green, interlobes sometimes blotched, midrib green; lateral lobes 3–5, ± regular, patent or ± recurved, triangular or deltoid, rather short, acute at apex, with distal margin convex, *dentate*, the proximal margin ± straight, entire or denticulate; interlobes *dentate or with small lobes*; terminal lobe triangular or hastate, *often dentate* or denticulate, sometimes divided, subacute at apex; petiole ± unwinged, at least below, green, sometimes rose at base. Scapes usually equalling or exceeding leaves. Exterior bracts *few, recurved, 10–13 × 2–3 mm*, unbordered, green suffused with pink, *pruinose on upper surface, darker, shiny green on lower surface.*

Possibly native. Road-verges, old meadows etc. Scattered and uncommon, chiefly in the west of Britain. V.cc. 9, 19, 21, 30, 34–37, 40, 42, 44, 47, 50, 51, 58–60, 70, 76, 82, 88.

Related to **64** but with distinctive rather small very dark green, pruinose involucres with few, recurved, narrow exterior bracts. The leaves are in general more dentate than in **64**, often even the terminal lobe and proximal margin of the lateral lobes bearing some large teeth. British material was previously often described as *T. subpraticola* G.E. Haglund (1934).

65   T. expallidiforme Dahlst. (1910)

Map 65

A medium-sized plant, with erect, broadly elliptical-spathulate, ± flat leaves 80–250 mm.

Leaves rather pale green, interlobes unblotched, midrib green; lateral lobes 3–5, *rather crowded*, patent to slightly recurved, deltoid, *not reaching to midrib*, rather short, subacute to *blunt at apex*, with distal margin slightly convex, entire, denticulate or dentate, the proximal margin straight or concave; length of proximal margin of a lateral lobe usually *equalling width of lobe at its base*; interlobes acute, shallow; terminal lobe short, broad, triangular, *with a shortly elongated tip*, sometimes divided; petiole *rather short, pale green or white, broadly winged*. Scapes usually exceeding leaves. Exterior bracts *spreading to recurved, 9 × 2.5–3.5 mm*, unbordered, *pale green*, often lightly suffused with violet, *on upper surface*, darker green on lower surface. Capitulum deep yellow, 45 mm in diameter; ligules striped purple-brown; styles exserted, discoloured; pollen present. Achenes olive-brown; body 3.5 mm; cone 0.5–0.7 mm.

Native or possibly introduced. Grassy places, roadsides, wasteland etc. Widespread through the British Isles, locally common. V.cc. 1, 3, 5, 6, 11, 12, 14–26, 28–31, 33–36, 38–44, 49–51, 54–62, 64–74, 77, 81–89, 91, 92, 96, 97, 101, 106, 109, 112, S, H21, H38.

T. expallidiforme is characterised by the broad central undissected portion of the leaf, the broadly winged, pale petiole and the small ± recurved exterior bracts. It is a common plant lacking obvious distinguishing marks; the short broad terminal lobe and rounded lateral lobes give the leaf a 'high-shouldered' look.

0 ——— 6cm

Section *Ruderalia*

65a T. subcyanolepis M.P. Christ. in Raunk. (1934) Map 65a

A medium-sized plant, with erect, broadly oblong-spathulate leaves 80–250 mm.

Leaves mid-green, interlobes unblotched, midrib green; lateral lobes 3–5, recurved, straight-sided or with distal margin ± convex, filiform-dentate, with apex usually subacute (but *some quite rounded*); petiole green, narrowly winged. Scapes usually equalling leaves. Exterior bracts 10 × 2 mm, recurved, *commonly suffused reddish-purple*. Capitulum yellow, 45 mm in diameter; ligules striped grey-purple; styles exserted, discoloured; pollen present. Achenes straw-coloured; body 3.2 mm.

Probably native and frequently found in old grasslands etc., but much less common and widespread than **65**, except perhaps in Ireland, and probably over-recorded. V.cc. 5, 6, 9, 15–17, 22, 23, 25, 26, 28, 29, 34, 39, 41, 46, 48–52, 54, 55, 57–62, 66–71, 73, 82, 85, 89, 90, 91, 93, 99, 100–102, 106, 107, 109, 110, S, H5, H9, H15–H17, H21, H23, H37–H39.

Very similar to **65**, but distinguished with care by using the following characters: terminal leaf-lobe *without an elongated tip*; interlobes *more rounded*; lateral leaf-lobes *narrower*, so that length of proximal margin *exceeds width of lobe at its base*; characteristically, occasional lateral lobes have a rounded apex; exterior bracts more commonly suffused with purple, especially in well-lit locations.

0   6cm

65b T. pallidipes Markl. (1938)

A medium-sized to tall plant, with erect, broadly oblong-spathulate, ± flat leaves to 80–250 mm.

Leaves rather pale green, sometimes hairy, interlobes unblotched, midrib green; lateral lobes 3–5, rather crowded, patent to slightly recurved, deltoid or triangular, *not reaching to midrib*, rather short, subacute to blunt at apex, with distal margin slightly convex, entire, denticulate or dentate, the proximal margin straight or concave, entire or sometimes with 1 tooth; interlobes long; terminal lobe as large as or larger than pair of lateral lobes below it, triangular or hastate, without an elongated tip, rarely divided; petiole *whitish, narrowly winged.* Scapes usually exceeding leaves. Exterior bracts *strongly recurved, 12–15 × 4–5 mm*, unbordered or bordered, *pruinose grey-white on upper surface*, darker green on lower surface.

Probably introduced. Scattered on road-verges etc., often in rather shady sites, but only fairly recently recognised and perhaps under-recorded. V.cc. 14, 19–22, 25, 26, 33–35, 39, 42, 50, 51, 60, 62, 67, 69, 70, 74.

Generally a taller and more elegant plant than **65** *T. expallidiforme*, with larger, narrowly hastate terminal leaf-lobes lacking an elongated tip; diagnostically the much longer and more recurved exterior bracts are pruinose grey-white on the upper surface, and the narrowly winged petiole is whitish. *T. pallidipes* also closely resembles *T. 'opertum'* (see under **66** *T. croceiflorum* for distinctions).

A medium-sized to robust plant, with ascending, oblong, somewhat crisped leaves 100–300 mm.

Leaves mid-green, interlobes unblotched, midrib green; lateral lobes 5–7, *pointing forward, patent or somewhat recurved*, triangular to deltoid, rather short, often divided with 1–2 lobules, acute to subacute at apex, *with distal margin ± straight, obviously dentate*, the proximal margin sometimes with a conspicuous tooth; terminal lobe *small, triangular, divided or tripartite*; petiole *green, ± broadly winged*. Scapes usually equalling leaves. Exterior bracts spreading to recurved, *9–12 × 2.5–3.5 mm*, unbordered, green ± suffused with purple at least at tips. Capitulum 40–45 mm in diameter, *orange-yellow owing to ligule teeth and inner florets being tipped orange-red*; ligules *striped red-purple*; styles exserted, discoloured; pollen present. Achenes brown; body 3.0 mm; cone 0.7 mm. 2n=24.

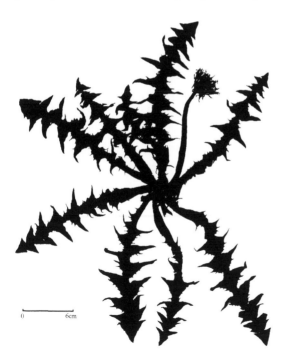

Native. Grassy places, roadsides, wasteland etc. Widespread throughout the British Isles, locally common. V.cc. 1–6, 8, 9, 11–30, 33–37, 42–44, 46, 48–51, 54–61, 64–73, 75–77, 79–85, 88, 89, 98, 99, 101, 108, 109, 112, S, H9, H16, H18, H38, H39.

T. croceiflorum is characterised by the orange-yellow heads, the broad central undissected portion of the leaf, the omni-directional, dentate lateral lobes, and the small, triangular terminal lobe.

Plants with the same small head and red-purple ligule stripes as **66** *T. crocei-florum* but with darker green leaves with less dissected lateral lobes, which *never point forwards* and are usually somewhat *recurved*, and with the terminal lobe relatively *larger* and somewhat *sagittate* in shape, have been called *T. 'opertum'* H. Øllg. ined. and have been recorded only from four sites in West Gloucestershire (v.c. 34). Superficially *T. 'opertum'* closely resembles **65b** *T. pallidipes*, but it has a much smaller flowering head with red-purple ligule stripes and the lower leaf-lobes lack large teeth.

66a   T. lacerifolium G.E. Haglund (1946)   Map 66a

A medium-sized to robust plant, with ascending, oblong, somewhat crisped leaves 100–300 mm.

Leaves mid-green, interlobes unblotched, midrib green; lateral lobes 5–7, point-ing forward, patent or somewhat recurved, triangular to deltoid, rather short, often divided with 1–2 lobules, acute to subacute at apex, with distal margin ± straight, ± dentate, the proximal margin sometimes with a conspicuous tooth; terminal lobe small, triangular, divided or tripartite; petiole green or *somewhat pink*, ± winged. Scapes usually equalling leaves. Exterior bracts spreading to recurved, *13–15 × 3–4.5 mm*, unbordered, green ± suffused with purple at least at tips. Capitulum *mid-yellow*, 45–50 mm in diameter; ligules striped *grey-brown, inner ones with yellow teeth*; styles exserted, discoloured; pollen present. Achenes grey-brown; body 3.0 mm; cone less than 0.3 mm.

Probably introduced. Scattered on road-verges and other grassy places, locally frequent in the south of Great Britain. V.cc. 3, 4, 6, 9, 17, 19, 20, 23, 26, 30, 33–37, 40, 42, 44, 50, 51, 56, 58, 60, 72.

Superficially very similar to 66 *T. crocei-florum*, especially in the herbarium, but differing by the mid-yellow capitula with grey-brown ligule stripes. Use of a lens in the herbarium shows that the teeth of the inner ligules are yellow, not orange-red. Also, the bracts are longer and the petioles of inner leaves are faintly pink.

67 T. stenacrum Dahlst. (1929) Map 67

A robust plant, with erect, narrowly oblong-spathulate, crisped leaves 150–300 mm.

Leaves pale to mid-green, *hairy*, interlobes not obviously blotched, midrib green to slightly coloured; lateral lobes 5–8, *usually strictly patent* but sometimes forward-pointing or occasionally slightly recurved, *long, broadly linear, long-dentate at base*, upper lobes *typically divided to form a large lobule, acute to subacute at apex*, ± club-shaped, with distal margin *sometimes narrowing sharply from a broad base, forming a 'shoulder'*, the proximal margin straight; terminal lobe usually *narrow*, ± divided or tripartite *with a lingulate tip*; petiole ± unwinged, narrow, *green*. Scapes usually equalling leaves, *arachnoid-hairy throughout*. Exterior bracts recurved, *12–16 × 2.5–3.5 mm*, unbordered, pale green, somewhat suffused with pink. Capitulum yellow, 50 mm in diameter; ligules striped olive-brown; styles exserted, *discoloured*; pollen *present*. Achenes straw-coloured; body 3.0 mm; cone 0.6 mm.

Endemic. Grassy places, roadsides, wasteland etc. Widely scattered through Great Britain and Northern Ireland, locally common. V.cc. 1–3, 7, 9, 10, 12, 15–17, 19–24, 27–29, 33–36, 39, 41, 42, 46, 50, 55–58, 61, 67, 68, 70, 72, 79, 98, H38, H40.

T. stenacrum is characterised by the deep bilobation of the usually strictly patent upper leaf-lobes and by the narrowly lingulate terminal lobe. It is one of the very few endemic species in Section *Ruderalia*.

0   6cm

Section *Ruderalia* 181

67a T. cherwellense A.J. Richards (1972)

A rather small plant, with erect, oblong, *deeply dissected, skeletal*, crisped leaves 150–200 mm.

Leaves pale to mid-green, ± *glabrous*, interlobes not obviously blotched, midrib green to slightly coloured; lateral lobes 3–6, patent or forward-pointing, *linear, often double*, long, *acute to subacute at apex*, ± club-shaped, the proximal margin straight; terminal lobe very narrow, triangular or tripartite, with elongated, lingulate tip; petiole ± unwinged, short, narrow, *green.* Scapes usually equalling leaves. Exterior bracts recurved, *10 × 2.0 mm*, unbordered, pale green. Capitulum yellow, 45 mm in diameter; ligules striped grey-purple; styles exserted, *discoloured*; pollen *absent.* Achenes brown; body 2.8 mm.

Endemic. A little known plant of grassland, gardens, paths etc. in central southern England; best known from its type locality in the Oxford Parks, where it was first collected in 1928 and where it can still be found sparingly. V.cc. 7, 12, 17, 23, 34.

Very similar to a slender and depauperate version of **67** *T. stenacrum*, with the leaves skeletal in outline and the strictly linear (and often double) lateral lobes dissected virtually to the midrib; diagnostically, pollen is absent and the exterior bracts are small.

0   6cm

67b T. porrigens Markl. ex Puol. (1933)

A robust plant, with erect, broadly spathulate, crisped leaves 150–300 mm.

Leaves pale to mid-green, *glabrous*, interlobes not obviously blotched, midrib green to slightly coloured; lateral lobes 5–8, *usually strictly patent* but sometimes forward-pointing or occasionally slightly recurved, *long, linear, long-dentate at base*, upper lobes *typically divided to form a large lobule, narrowly acute at apex*, ± club-shaped, with distal margin sometimes *narrowing sharply from a very broad base, forming a conspicuous and characteristic 'hump'*, the proximal margin straight; terminal lobe narrowly tripartite or, *on inner leaves, broadly triangular*; petiole ± unwinged or narrowly winged, narrow, *green or, on inner leaves, pinkish*. Scapes usually equalling leaves, *glabrous except below involucre*. Exterior bracts recurved or ± *straight and reflexed, 10–15 × 3.5–4.5 mm*, unbordered, pale green, somewhat suffused with pink. Capitulum yellow, 50 mm in diameter; ligules striped olive-brown; styles exserted, *yellow to faintly discoloured*; pollen *present*. Achenes straw-coloured; body 3.0 mm; cone 0.6 mm.

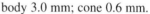

Probably introduced. Only recently recorded and possibly under-recorded, being mistaken for **67**. V.cc. 6, 34, 40, 50.

Closely related to **67** *T. stenacrum* and differing by the distal margins to the lateral lobes, which are often strongly humped, by the narrowly acute apex to the these lobes, by the variation in the terminal lobes, which become broadly triangular on inner leaves (which also usually have faintly pink petioles), by the usually more strongly reflexed exterior bracts, and by the yellowish stigmas.

67c T. 'broddesonii' G.E. Haglund ined.

A *huge*, robust plant, to 600 mm, perhaps the
largest dandelion recorded in the British Isles.
Leaves fleshy, dark *shining* green, narrowly
oblong; leaf-lobes 2–5, rather regular, short,
shallow, triangular to deltoid, with large teeth.
Capitula *very large*, over 70 mm in diameter.
Unmistakable.

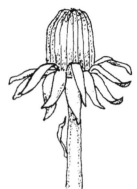

Introduced. A few casual records from waste
places, most recently in a pub car-park. V.cc. 51,
57, 60.

Section *Ruderalia*

68 T. leucopodum G.E. Haglund (1943)

A medium-sized plant, with decumbent to erect, broadly oblong-spathulate, ± flat leaves 80–200 mm.

Leaves clear, rather dark green, interlobes not obviously blotched, midrib green; lateral lobes 4–5, broad, recurved, ± *hamate*, acute to subacute at apex, with distal margin convex, entire to denticulate, the proximal margin straight or concave, often with a single large tooth towards the interlobe; interlobes ± dentate, *often with 1 conspicuous tooth*; terminal lobe *small and rounded, with a markedly acute elongated tip*, thus characteristically the shape of a 'German helmet'; petiole winged, *white*. Scapes usually equalling leaves. Exterior bracts spreading to somewhat recurved, irregularly arranged to somewhat twisted, lanceolate, *15–16 × 3–4 mm*, unbordered, pale green to *whitish-pruinose* on upper surface. Capitulum deep yellow, 40 mm in diameter; ligules striped grey-violet; styles exserted, discoloured; pollen present. Achenes straw-coloured; cone 0.4–0.7 mm.

0   6cm

Probably introduced. Grassy places, roadsides, wasteland etc. Very local in southern England and Wales, with one record in eastern Ireland. V.cc. 18, 19, 22, 26, 34, 35, 37, 42, 43, H21.

T. leucopodum is characterised by the white petioles, by the pale, whitish exterior bracts and, especially, by the distinctive shape of the terminal leaf-lobes.

68a   T. obtusilobum Dahlst. ex G.E. Haglund (1935a)

Not closely related to **68** *T. leucopodum* or indeed to any other British dandelion, this is a much smaller plant which is totally unmistakable, with *fleshy grey-green* leaves, the outer of which have rather small *regular, rounded, denticulate* lateral lobes. The inner leaves are usually oblanceolate-spathulate and *subentire* but dentate, the petiole and midrib *chalk-white*; and the exterior bracts *very small, 8 × 2 mm, spreading to erect* and *dark purple*. 2n=16, 17.

Native to an area of southern Sweden. Introduced to Great Britain on several occasions, but not persisting. V.cc. 15, 34, 66, 83, 106.

Of very considerable interest as the only fully sexual dandelion ever recorded from Britain (or indeed Scandinavia). Usually accompanied by confusing hybrids with surrounding apomictic dandelions (for instance in the County Durham site chiefly with *T. polyodon*), which are themselves usually sexual and sometimes persist after *T. obtusilobum* has disappeared (although not for much longer). Being sexual and self-incompatible, *T. obtusilobum* and its hybrids are often distinguished by their very poor seed-set.

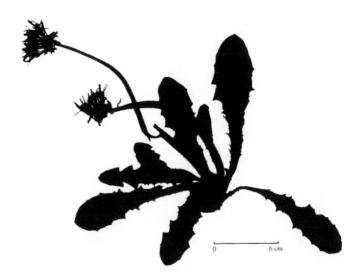

0   6 cm

Section *Ruderalia*

A medium-sized to tall plant, with erect, narrowly elliptical (some inner ones broadly spathulate in outline), ± flat leaves 150–300 mm.

Leaves *dull, rather dark green*, interlobes *blotched blackish*, midrib green to slightly coloured; lateral lobes 5–6, *long, narrowly deltoid to linear*, patent to recurved or sometimes forward-pointing, *acute at apex*, with distal margin straight to convex, dentate to filiform-dentate, the proximal margin straight or concave, *entire or filiform-dentate*; terminal lobe broadly triangular or, *on inner leaves, larger and hastate*, sometimes divided, with acute apex with ± elongated tip; petiole unwinged or narrowly winged distally, green to faintly coloured. Scapes usually equalling leaves. Exterior bracts recurved, 12–14 × 2.5–4.0 mm, unbordered, pale green suffused with violet on upper surface, darker green on lower surface. Capitulum deep yellow, 50 mm in diameter; ligules striped grey-violet; styles exserted, yellow when fresh, discoloured when dry; pollen present. Achenes straw-coloured; body 3.5 mm; cone 0.5 mm.

Probably introduced. Roadsides, wasteland etc. Widespread and common on roadsides throughout Great Britain, with several records around Dublin. V.cc. 3, 5, 6, 9, 12–16, 18–24, 28, 30, 33–40, 42–44, 46, 50, 51, 55, 57–61, 66–70, 75, 81, 86, 89, 94, H21.

T. undulatiflorum is not a very characterful species; it is perhaps best characterised by the dull colour, by the large, hastate terminal lobe of the inner leaves, and by the rather slender build of the leaves.

69a T. chloroticum Dahlst. (1935)

A medium-sized to tall plant, with erect, narrowly elliptical, ± flat leaves 150–300 mm.

Leaves *dull, mid-green to slightly coloured*; lateral lobes 5–6, crowded, patent to recurved, *narrow, deltate, very acute at apex*, with distal margin straight to convex, dentate to filiform-dentate, the proximal margin straight or concave, *entire or filiform-dentate*; terminal lobe *triangular or tripartite, with elongated acuminate apex* and elongated basal projections; petiole unwinged or narrowly winged distally, green to faintly coloured. Scapes usually equalling leaves. Exterior bracts recurved, 12–14 × 2.5–4.0 mm, unbordered, pale green suffused with violet on upper surface, darker green on lower surface. Capitulum yellow, 40 mm in diameter; ligules striped grey-brown; styles exserted, yellow when fresh, discoloured when dry; pollen present. Achenes straw-coloured; body 3.0 mm; cone 0.8 mm.

Introduced to a few roadsides etc., mainly in the south-east of England. V.cc. 17, 19, 21, 22, 34, 39, 60.

Closely related to **69** *T. undulatiflorum*, but with paler, neater, more spiky leaves with more acute, narrow lateral lobes and a distinctive terminal lobe which is triangular to tripartite and very acuminate.

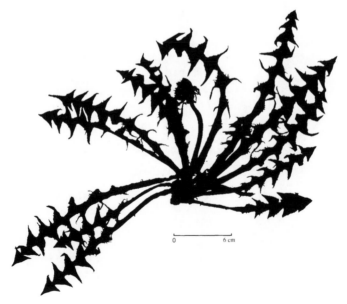

Section *Ruderalia*

69b T. speciosum Raunk. (1903)

A *large* plant, with erect, narrowly elliptical (some inner ones broadly spathulate in outline), ± flat leaves to 300 mm.

Leaves *dark green*, interlobes blotched, midrib green to slightly coloured; lateral lobes 5–6, patent to recurved, deltoid or triangular, acute at apex, with distal margin straight to convex, dentate to filiform-dentate (especially the lower lobes), the proximal margin straight or concave, entire; terminal lobe broadly triangular or hastate, rarely divided, *entire or (often) with 1 tooth*, acute at apex with an obviously elongated tip, that *of inner leaves larger than pair of lobes below it*; petiole unwinged or narrowly winged distally, green to faintly coloured. Scapes usually equalling leaves. Exterior bracts recurved to reflexed, 12–16 × 3.5–4.5 mm, unbordered, pale green suffused with violet on upper surface, darker green on lower surface. Capitulum *deep yellow to orange, 50–70 mm in diameter*; ligules striped grey-violet; styles exserted, yellow when fresh, discoloured when dry; pollen *absent*. Achenes straw-coloured; body 3.5 mm; cone 0.5–0.8 mm.

Introduced and casual; single individuals recorded on three occasions, not persisting, at least in Newcastle upon Tyne. V.cc. 17, 42, 67.

A massive plant of uncertain affinity, with somewhat similar leaf shape and colour to **69** *T. undulatiflorum*, but immediately recognised by its very large (to 70 mm in diameter) orange capitula which lack pollen.

Section *Ruderalia*

A medium-sized *heterophyllous* plant, with decumbent to erect, oblong to oblanceolate, ± *crisped* leaves 80–200 mm.

Leaves *dark green*, interlobes *dark-blotched*, midrib *green towards base but characteristically coloured towards apex*; lateral lobes 3–5, deltoid or triangular, patent to recurved, *short, acute to subacute at apex*, with *distal margin straight to concave-angled*, entire or dentate, the proximal margin ± straight; interlobes *strongly plicate*; terminal lobe *variable*, that of outer leaves small, subsagittate, *with a short lingulate tip*, sometimes divided, sometimes with a single tooth, that of inner leaves usually large, subacute or obtuse at apex; petiole narrowly winged, *on outer leaves white (to green), on inner leaves pale but ± reddish*. Scapes usually equalling leaves. Exterior bracts *mostly spreading*, oblong, 11–12 × 3–4 mm, unbordered, *leaden-violet*. Capitulum dark yellow, *35 mm in diameter*; ligules striped *grey-violet, with yellowish tips*; styles exserted, discoloured; pollen present. Achenes olive-brown; body 3.5 mm; cone 0.6 mm. 2n=24.

Probably introduced. Roadsides, wasteland etc. Widespread throughout Great Britain and locally common. V.cc. 1, 3, 4, 6, 15, 16, 19–23, 25, 29, 30, 32–36, 39, 42–44, 46, 50, 51, 54, 55, 57–60, 62, 67, 69, 70, 72, 73, 77, 81, 85, 93, 99.

T. piceatum has a very variable leaf-shape, but the leaden-violet, mostly spreading bracts and the combination of white (to green) petioles and coloured midribs are distinctive.

0   6cm

Section *Ruderalia*

70a T. cyanolepis Dahlst. (1911b)

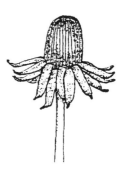

A medium-sized plant, with decumbent to erect, oblong to oblanceolate leaves 80–200(–250) mm.

Leaves *light bluish-green*, interlobes *blotched*, midrib green, sometimes faintly coloured towards apex; lateral lobes 3–5, deltoid or triangular, patent to recurved, short, *shallowly cup-shaped at obtuse to subacute apex, with distal margin straight to convex*, entire or denticulate to dentate, the proximal margin ± straight; interlobes *long and rounded, not strongly plicate*; terminal lobe subacute or obtuse at apex, that of outer leaves small, subsagittate, *shallowly cup-shaped at apex without a lingulate tip*, sometimes divided, sometimes with a single tooth; petiole narrowly winged, *white* (or green). Scapes usually equalling leaves. Exterior bracts spreading, *12 × 3 mm*, unbordered, *blue-purple*. Capitulum deep yellow, *55 mm in diameter*; ligules striped *red-purple, with purplish tips*; styles exserted, discoloured; pollen present. Achenes olive-brown; body 3.0 mm. 2n=24.

Native, at least in Scotland. Humid grasslands, including species-rich sites; also walls, cliffs etc. Abundant very locally, especially in north-east Scotland, but with a curiously scattered distribution through much of the British Isles and

absent from large areas. It has apparently become much less common since about 1970. V.cc. 1, 6, 15–17, 20, 22–24, 28–30, 34, 37, 42, 45, 49, 50, 55, 57–60, 64, 66–68, 70, 72–74, 79, 81–85, 88, 89, 91, 93–98, 101, 103, 106, 108, 109, 111, 112, S, H9, H20, H21, H38, H39.

Similar to **70** *T. piceatum*, but with the interlobes not strongly plicate and the inner ligules with purplish ends. Differs also in leaf-shape, with the terminal lobe less obviously variable and lacking a lingulate tip and with notably obtuse lateral lobes with ± convex distal margins. The ends of the lobes are three-dimensional, with a raised edge forming a shallow cup. The exterior bracts are consistently a beautiful blue-purple colour.

70b T. curtifrons H. Øllg. (1978)

A medium-sized *heterophyllous* plant, with erect leaves 150–200 mm.

Leaves *bright green*, interlobes *unblotched*, midrib greenish or brownish; lateral lobes of outer leaves 3–5, regular, deltoid, rather short, *shallowly cup-shaped at acute apex*, with *distal margin ± straight or convex*, entire or filiform-dentate, the proximal margin ± straight or convex, those *of rather hairy inner leaves incompletely developed*; interlobes *long and rounded, particularly on inner leaves*; terminal lobe of outer leaves small and *shallowly cup-shaped at apex*, that of inner leaves rather large and sagittate to hastate; petiole winged, *white* (or green). Scapes usually exceeding leaves. Exterior bracts slightly recurved with erect tips, *12 × 4 mm*, unbordered, *clearly violet-coloured on upper surface, dark green on lower surface*. Capitulum deep yellow, 40–45 mm in diameter; ligules striped *grey-violet*; styles exserted, discoloured; pollen present. Achenes straw-coloured, shortly spinulose; body 3.5 mm; cone 0.4 mm.

Introduced. A few scattered records, mainly from southern England and Wales. V.cc. 22, 23, 33, 34, 35, 50, 55.

Another close relative of **70** and **70a**, heterophyllous, with bright green leaves of a distinctive shape. *T. curtifrons* can be confused with **70a** *T. cyanolepis*, which also has a cup-shaped end to the leaf-lobes, white (or green) petioles and violet outer bracts. However, *T. cyanolepis* has more obtuse lateral lobes to the leaves, with more convex distal margins to these lobes, and longer, even more rounded, interlobes. The inner leaves of *T. curtifrons* are quite different from those of *T. cyanolepis* and the latter species has narrower exterior bracts.

0 ____ 6cm

70c T. acutifrons Markl. (1940)

A medium-sized to robust plant, with decumbent to erect, oblong leaves 80–220 mm.

Leaves *very light green,* interlobes *not obviously blotched,* midrib green to slightly coloured; lateral lobes 4–6, regular, deltoid, ± patent, *abruptly narrowing to a patent linear process with acute to very acute apex,* with distal margin angled, entire or filiform-dentate, the proximal margin ± straight or convex, entire; terminal lobe ± narrowly triangular or hastate, *sometimes waisted and often with 1 characteristically rounded basal projection, acute at apex;* petiole unwinged, *white to faintly pink.* Scapes usually exceeding leaves. Exterior bracts ± *horizontally spreading,* 10–15 × 3.5–5.0 mm, ± bordered, *very deep violet on upper surface,* pruinose. Capitulum yellow, 50 mm in diameter; ligules striped grey-purple; styles exserted, discoloured; pollen present. Achenes straw-coloured; body 3.5 mm; cone 0.6 mm.

0   6cm

Introduced. Road-verges etc. in the west of England and in Wales. V.cc. 6, 33–36, 42, 50, 58, 60.

Probably related to **70**, with similar broad, horizontally spreading, pruinose-violet exterior bracts and whitish petioles, and with a similar terminal lobe to the leaves, but with ± unblotched, very pale green leaves of a characteristic shape, the regular deltoid lateral lobes being abruptly contracted into acute patent processes.

70d T. chrysophaenum Rail. (1957)

A medium-sized to large plant, with erect, oblong, somewhat crisped leaves 100–250 mm.

Leaves *pale to mid-green*, interlobes *not obviously blotched*, midrib green to slightly coloured; lateral lobes 6–8, *regular, crowded*, patent to slightly recurved, deltoid or triangular, acute to subacute at apex, with distal margin ± straight or convex, or angled, to give a claw-shaped lobe, upper lobes entire, lower lobes dentate to filiform-dentate, the proximal margin ± straight; terminal lobe usually not larger, triangular, cordate or helmet-shaped, sometimes divided, entire, acute to subacute at apex, sometimes mucronate; terminal lobe of inner (later) leaves sometimes larger, helmet-shaped; petiole narrowly winged, white. Scapes usually exceeding leaves. Exterior bracts recurved, 14–17 × 2–4 mm, unbordered, *green*, pruinose, paler green on upper surface. Capitulum deep yellow, 35–40 mm in diameter; ligules striped *grey-violet, inner ones with reddish-orange tips*; styles exserted, discoloured; pollen present. Achenes straw-coloured; body 3.5 mm; cone 1.0 mm.

Introduced. V.cc. 3, 23, 34, 35, 44.

Differs from **70** by the paler, ± unblotched leaves, more regular, crowded leaf-lobes, and especially by the pale green, uncoloured exterior bracts; the inner ligules have reddish-orange apices.

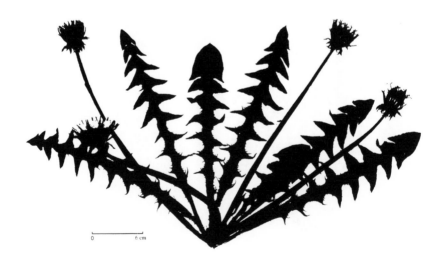

0   6 cm

Section *Ruderalia*

71 T. tumentilobum Markl. ex Puol. (1933)   Map 71

A medium-sized plant, with decumbent to erect, narrowly elliptical, ± crisped leaves 100–250 mm.

Leaves mid-green, interlobes *dark-blotched*, midrib green to slightly coloured; lateral lobes 5–7, regular, *triangular, patent, rather short*, subacute to *subobtuse*, with distal margin ± straight to convex, entire or filiform-dentate (*often with a single tooth at base*), the proximal margin ± straight; interlobes *characteristically with a single large tooth or small lobe*; terminal lobe usually rather small, *on outer leaves hastate*, on inner (later) leaves often larger, divided or with 1 or 2 teeth; petiole unwinged below, pink. Scapes usually equalling leaves. Exterior bracts *spreading to recurved, 10–15 × 3–4 mm*, unbordered, green on upper surface, darker green on lower surface. Capitulum yellow, 50 mm in diameter; ligules striped grey-violet; styles exserted, discoloured; pollen present. Achenes straw-coloured; body 3.5 mm; cone 0.6 mm.

Probably introduced. Grassy places, roadsides, wasteland etc. Scattered through Great Britain. V.cc. 6, 17, 18, 20, 21, 23, 36, 37, 39, 42, 44, 50, 57, 58, 60, 67, 70, 88.

Not easily identified, this species is best known by its blotched leaves, rather short, patent, lateral lobes (which often bear a single distal tooth), interlobes also often bearing a single tooth, and its relatively large, ± spreading exterior bracts.

0   6cm

Section *Ruderalia*

72 T. intumescens G.E. Haglund (1934)

A medium-sized plant, with erect, oblanceolate, ± crisped leaves 80–200 mm.

Leaves mid-green, interlobes dark-blotched, midrib green to slightly coloured; lateral lobes 4–6, *regular, triangular to deltoid, patent, short*, acute to subacute at apex, with distal margin straight to convex, *upper lobes dentate, lower lobes filiform-dentate*, the proximal margin straight or *convex*; interlobes *often with a single large distinct tooth*; terminal lobe usually rather *small*, triangular to subsagittate; petiole unwinged to narrowly winged, *green*. Scapes equalling or exceeding leaves. Exterior bracts spreading to recurved, *10–14 × 2–4.5 mm*, unbordered, *grey-green to lead-coloured on upper surface*, dark green on lower surface. Capitulum deep yellow, 40 mm in diameter; ligules striped grey-violet, *the inner with red tips*; styles exserted, discoloured; pollen present. Achenes straw-coloured; body 2.8–3.0 mm; cone 0.6 mm.

0   6cm

Introduced. Roadsides, wasteland etc. Uncommon. Scattered, mainly in southern England. V.cc. 6, 19, 23, 30, 34, 35, 39, 44, 57, 58, 70.

T. intumescens is characterised by the regular, patent, ± triangular and dentate leaf-lobes, with ± convex proximal margins, by the single interlobe tooth, by the small terminal lobe, and by the leaden-grey bracts. It can bear a superficial resemblance to **89d** *T. coartatum*, but that species has pink petioles and longer, more twisted exterior bracts. Compare also with the superficially very similar **92** *T. pachymerum*.

72a T. angulare Hagend., Soest & Zevenb. (1976)

A medium-sized plant, with erect, oblong to oblanceolate, ± crisped leaves 80–200 mm.

Leaves mid-green, interlobes dark-blotched, midrib green to slightly coloured; lateral lobes 4–6, *patent, short*, acute to subacute at apex, with distal margin straight to convex, *upper lobes dentate, lower lobes filiform-dentate*, the proximal margin straight or *convex*; interlobes *often with a single large distinct tooth*; terminal lobe on inner (later) leaves often larger than pair of lobes below it, rounded-triangular to subsagittate, entire or *with 1–2 broad, short, subobtuse teeth*; petiole unwinged to narrowly winged, *green*. Scapes equalling or exceeding leaves. Exterior bracts spreading to recurved, *10–16 × 3–4.5 mm*, unbordered, *green on upper surface*, dark green on lower surface. Capitulum deep yellow, 40 mm in diameter; ligules striped grey-violet; styles exserted, discoloured; pollen present. Achenes straw-coloured; body 2.8–3.0 mm; cone 0.6 mm.

Introduced. A few recent records. V.cc. 33, 34, 72.

Closely related to **72** *T. intumescens*, but with terminal lobes, especially on inner leaves, which are characteristically large and rounded but rendered angular by 1–2 broad, short, subobtuse teeth; the exterior bracts are green on the upper surface and slightly larger.

73 T. ancistrolobum Dahlst. (1925a)

Map 73

A *very robust, squat* plant, with usually decumbent, *narrowly obovate*, flat leaves 100–250 mm.

Leaves dull, dark green, interlobes not obviously blotched, midrib green proximally but *slightly coloured distally*; lateral lobes *2–3(–4)*, regular, recurved, *large and broad, subacute to obtuse at apex, with distal margin convex*, entire to filiform-dentate, the proximal margin straight or concave, entire; terminal lobe *large, with base contiguous to or over-lapping uppermost lateral lobes, subacute to obtuse at apex*; petiole winged, *green*. Scapes usually equalling or exceeding leaves. Exterior bracts spreading to recurved, 11 × 2.5–4.0 mm, unbordered, pale grey-green ± suffused with purple. Capitulum mid-yellow, 50 mm in diameter; ligules striped red-purple; styles exserted, discoloured; pollen present. Achenes straw-coloured; body very wide, 3.5 × 1.4 mm; cone 0.6 mm.

0 ⊢——————⊣ 6cm

Native. Grassy places, roadsides, wasteland etc. Widespread through-out Great Britain, locally common in the south and very common in lowland northern England and Scotland; Channel Isles; rare in Ireland. V.cc. 1, 2, 5–9, 12–14, 16–18, 21–24, 28, 29, 31, 33–37, 39–44, 46, 47, 50, 51, 55–63, 65–71, 73, 81, 86, 88, 89, 96, 99, 106, 108, 112, S, H21.

T. ancistrolobum is usually a quite unmistakable species, one of the few rapidly learnt by beginners. The broad, squat, few-lobed, round-ed leaves with green petioles but slightly coloured midribs are highly distinctive.

Section *Ruderalia*

A *robust* plant, with spreading to erect, oblanceolate, slightly crisped leaves 100–250 mm.

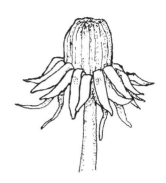

Leaves dull, mid to dark green, interlobes not
obviously blotched, midrib *dirty-coloured, often
bordered by black lines*; lateral lobes 3–6, patent
to recurved, triangular or deltoid, acute to subacute at apex, with distal margin convex or
angled, upper lobes entire or *with large teeth*,
lower ones *with large teeth*, the proximal margin
straight or concave, *angled margins frequently
producing characteristically arching lobes*;
terminal lobe ± triangular, often divided; petiole winged, green. Scapes usually
exceeding leaves. Exterior bracts *stiff and arching*, spreading to recurved, *10–14
× 3.5–6 mm*, unbordered, *dull green, pruinose, leaden or somewhat violet*, pink-
tipped on upper surface, darker green on lower surface. Capitulum mid-yellow,
50 mm in diameter; ligules striped grey-purple; styles exserted, discoloured;
pollen present. Achenes straw-coloured; body 3.0–3.5 mm; cone 0.7 mm.
2n=24, 26, 28.

Native. Grassy places, roadsides, wasteland etc. Widespread throughout Great
Britain and one of the commonest dandelions; also in Ireland. V.cc. 1, 2, 4–6,
9–11, 14, 16–22, 25, 26, 29, 30, 32–44, 46, 50, 51, 55, 57–62, 67–70, 72, 73, 76,
77, 79, 80, 82–84, 86, 88, 89, 96, 97, 99, 104, 112, H21, H36–H38, H40.

T. sellandii is a vari-
able plant charac-
terised by its heavy
build, the often arch-
ing lateral lobes to the
leaf, many with large
teeth, the stiff, acute,
usually wide, ± leaden
exterior bracts, and the
characteristically dirty
colour of the middle of
the leaf.

75 T. altissimum H. Lindb. (1907)

Map 75

A notably *tall* plant, with *erect*, oblanceolate-spathulate, slightly crisped leaves (80–)200–300 mm.

Leaves dark to mid-green, interlobes *dark-blotched*, midrib green to slightly coloured; lateral lobes 3–5, *regular*, patent to recurved, triangular to deltoid, acute at apex, with distal margin convex, *dentate*, the proximal margin straight or concave; terminal lobe *usually long, helmet-shaped, divided, dentate, with ± acute apex*; petiole long, unwinged below, green. Scapes usually exceeding leaves, very long. Exterior bracts spreading, *11–15 × 4–5 mm*, bordered, green. Capitulum yellow, 50–60 mm in diameter; ligules striped grey-violet; styles exserted, discoloured; pollen present. Achenes *olive-brown*; body 2.5 mm; cone 0.7 mm.

0   6cm

Probably introduced. Grassy places, roadsides, wasteland etc. Scattered through Great Britain, but uncommon, except perhaps in north-east England. V.cc. 3, 18, 21, 25, 26, 34, 40, 60, 67, 68, 70, 72, 77, 89, 112.

T. altissimum is characterised by the long terminal lobe, which is often divided and ± dentate, and by the regular, dentate lateral lobes, with dark-blotched interlobes. It is invariably the tallest dandelion in a community, standing well clear of its competitors, and is thus easily spotted.

Section *Ruderalia*

A medium-sized to robust plant, with decumbent to erect, elliptical to oblanceolate, somewhat crisped leaves 80–220 mm, *usually lobed ± to the base.*

Leaves dull, *dark green*, interlobes blotched, midrib green to slightly coloured; lateral lobes *5–8*, regular, patent to recurved, deltoid, *acute to very acute at apex*, with distal margin straight to convex, *dentate, sometimes with 1 or more large teeth*, or filiform-dentate, the proximal margin straight or concave, entire; terminal lobe *rather narrow, ± attenuate, often divided*, acute or mucronate at apex; petiole winged, green to faintly pink, or absent. Scapes usually exceeding leaves. Exterior bracts *recurved, 11–14 × 2–3.5 mm*, ± slightly bordered, green with pink tips on upper surface, darker green on lower surface. Capitulum yellow, 50 mm in diameter; ligules striped grey-purple; styles exserted, *yellowish*; pollen present. Achenes straw-coloured; body 3.5 mm; cone 0.6 mm.

Probably introduced. Grassy places, roadsides, wasteland etc. Scattered throughout Great Britain, rather uncommon. V.cc. 3, 15, 18, 19, 27, 28, 34–36, 42, 50, 51, 67, 72, 78, 93, 99.

T. aequisectum is characterised by its multilobate, elliptical to oblanceolate, dark green leaves, lobed more or less to the base, the acute, ± attenuate, often divided terminal lobe, and the rather narrow, recurved bracts.

A medium-sized plant, with spreading to erect, *narrowly oblanceolate*, flat to slightly crisped leaves 80–200 mm, *often lobed almost to the base.*

Leaves dull, mid to dark green, *somewhat hairy,* interlobes sometimes blotched, midrib brown; lateral lobes 4–8, *regular, deltoid, recurved, acute to acuminate at apex, with distal margin sigmoid,* entire or filiform-dentate, the proximal margin straight or concave; terminal lobe either long and helmet-shaped or rather small and sagittate, *acute or very acute at apex*; petiole *unwinged* or narrowly winged, *pink.* Scapes usually equalling leaves. Exterior bracts mostly recurved, 10–15 × 4–5 mm, unbordered, pale green on upper surface, darker green on lower surface. Capitulum yellow, 40 mm in diameter; ligules striped grey-violet; styles exserted, discoloured; pollen present. Achenes straw-coloured; body 3.5 mm; cone 0.6 mm.

0   6cm

Probably introduced. Grassy places, roadsides, wasteland etc. Scattered throughout Great Britain; locally abundant in cities such as London, Edinburgh and Glasgow; very scarce elsewhere. V.cc. 3, 6, 14, 16, 17, 19, 21, 25, 30, 36, 39, 42, 44, 51, 52, 58, 60, 61, 67, 70, 76, 77, 81, 83.

T. interveniens is characterised by the distinctive narrow leaf-shape and the sigmoid-margined lobes almost to the base of the leaf.

Section *Ruderalia*

78　T. angustisquameum Dahlst. ex H. Lindb. (1907)　Map 78

A medium-sized plant, with decumbent to ascending, oblanceolate, somewhat crisped leaves 80–200 mm.

Leaves *dark to mid-green, glabrous*, interlobes usually dark-blotched, midrib green to slightly coloured; lateral lobes *4–8, regular, recurved*, deltoid, *rather short, acute to mucronate at apex,* with distal margin straight to convex or somewhat sigmoid, entire or *dentate*, the proximal margin straight or concave, entire or *dentate*; interlobes sometimes with a distinct acuminate tooth; terminal lobe *usually rather small and triangular or sagittate, often divided, acute, sometimes mucronate, at apex*; petiole unwinged below, pink. Scapes usually exceeding leaves. Exterior bracts *spreading and arcuate, becoming in time more recurved, 11–14 × 1.5–2.5 mm, unbordered*, green, paler green on upper surface, ± *pruinose*. Capitulum yellow, 40 mm in diameter; ligules striped grey-violet; styles exserted, discoloured; pollen present. Achenes straw-coloured; body *2.5 mm*; cone 0.5 mm.

0　　　6cm

Probably introduced. Grassy places, roadsides, wasteland etc. Scattered throughout Great Britain, rather uncommon; also in the Channel Isles. V.cc. 3, 6, 13, 17, 18, 20, 21, 30, 33–35, 39, 42, 55, 60, 67, 76, 81, 82, 88, 89, 93, S.

T. angustisquameum is characterised by the dark multilobate leaves with regular recurved lateral lobes, sometimes with a few large teeth, the narrow bracts and the distinctive, small, often divided terminal lobe. See also **79b** *T. semiglobosum.*

78a   T. mimulum Dahlst. ex H. Lindb. (1907)

A medium-sized plant, with decumbent to ascending, elliptical, somewhat crisped leaves 80–200 mm.

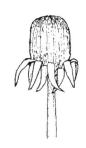

Leaves *mid-green*, glabrous, interlobes not obviously blotched, midrib green to slightly coloured; lateral lobes *3–6*, patent to recurved, deltoid, *very short, acute to very acute at apex*, with distal margin straight to concave or sigmoid, entire or dentate, the proximal margin straight or concave, entire or dentate; interlobes sometimes with a distinct acuminate tooth; terminal lobe usually rather small and triangular or sagittate, sometimes divided, *acuminate, sometimes mucronate, at apex*; petiole narrowly winged, pink. Scapes usually exceeding leaves. Exterior bracts *strongly reflexed or hanging vertically, 11–14 × 3–4 mm*, unbordered, green, paler green on upper surface, ± *pruinose*. Capitulum yellow, 40 mm in diameter; ligules striped grey-violet; styles exserted, discoloured; pollen present. Achenes straw-coloured; body *2.5 mm*; cone 0.5 mm, spinulose.

0   6cm

Introduced. A single record from improved chalk pasture in Oxfordshire (v.c. 23).

Differs from **78** by the sharply acute lateral lobes and by the somewhat wider (3.0–4.0 mm), strongly reflexed exterior bracts.

78b T. stereodes Ekman ex G.E. Haglund in T.A. Lange (1938)

A medium-sized plant, with decumbent to ascending, lanceolate, somewhat crisped leaves 80–200 mm.

Leaves *mid-green*, glabrous, interlobes not obviously blotched, midrib green to slightly coloured; lateral lobes *4–8, recurved*, deltoid, *rather short*, sometimes divided, acute to very acute at apex, with distal margin straight to convex or somewhat sigmoid, entire or dentate, the proximal margin straight or concave, entire or dentate; interlobes sometimes with a distinct acuminate tooth; terminal lobe usually rather small and triangular or sagittate, often divided, *acute, sometimes mucronate, at apex*; petiole unwinged below, ± pink. Scapes usually exceeding leaves, *heavily arachnoid-hairy throughout.* Exterior bracts *spreading, becoming reflexed, 11–14 × 3–4 mm*, unbordered, green, paler green on upper surface, ± *pruinose.*

Capitulum yellow, 40 mm in diameter; ligules striped grey-violet; styles exserted, discoloured; pollen present. Achenes straw-coloured; body *2.5 mm*; cone *cylindrical, 0.8–1.0 mm.*

Introduced on the verges of major roads in Great Britain, chiefly in the south. V.cc. 19, 21–23, 26, 33, 35, 37, 44, 51, 57, 60, 62, 81, 93.

Variable. Often superficially resembling **78**, but immediately recognisable by the very arachnoid-hairy scapes, which are thus rendered white when young. The exterior bracts are broader and the achene cone is long and cylindrical.

0   6cm

A medium-sized *heterophyllous* plant, with erect, oblanceolate, nearly flat leaves 80–300 mm.

Leaves *clear mid-green, smooth,* interlobes not blotched, midrib green; lateral lobes 3–5, patent to recurved, deltoid, rather short, acute at apex, with distal margin straight to sinuate, entire or filiform-dentate, the proximal margin straight or ± convex; terminal lobe variable, somewhat larger than pair of lobes below it, particularly on inner leaves, and *with a very characteristic, rhomboidal apex (or with an elongated tip and a large tooth on either side)*; petiole narrowly winged, on outer leaves pale, on inner leaves clear pink. Scapes usually exceeding leaves. Exterior bracts reflexed at first, later becoming recurved, 12–14 × 3–4.5 mm, *unbordered,* green, paler green on upper surface. Capitulum yellow, 40 mm in diameter; ligules striped grey-violet; styles exserted, *discoloured*; pollen present. Achenes straw-coloured; body 3.5 mm; cone 0.5 mm.

0 ———— 6cm

Probably introduced. Grassy places, roadsides, wasteland etc. Widespread throughout Great Britain, locally common. V.cc. 3, 14, 15, 19–23, 26, 28, 30, 34, 35, 42, 43, 46, 51, 55, 58–60, 62, 67, 70, 72, 73, 76, 81, 88, 89, 99, 112.

T. adiantifrons is a pretty plant with delicately coloured leaves. It is best recognised by its very characteristic, although variable, terminal lobe. Most British records were made under the name *T. hemicyclum* G.E. Haglund (1942).

79a T. retroflexum H. Lindb. (1909)   Map 79a

A medium-sized *heterophyllous* plant, with erect, oblanceolate, nearly flat leaves 80–300 mm.

Leaves *clear mid-green, smooth*, interlobes not blotched, midrib green; lateral lobes 3–5, patent to recurved, deltoid, rather short, acute at apex, with distal margin straight to sinuate, entire or filiform-dentate, the proximal margin straight or ± convex; terminal lobe variable, but *usually with a distinct elongated tip*; petiole narrowly winged, on outer leaves pale, on inner leaves clear pink. Scapes usually exceeding leaves. Exterior bracts mostly reflexed, 12–16 × 3–4.5 mm, *bordered*, green, paler green on upper surface. Capitulum yellow, 40 mm in diameter; ligules striped grey-violet; styles exserted, *yellow (darker when dry)*; pollen present. Achenes straw-coloured; body 3.5 mm; cone 0.5 mm.

Introduced onto road verges, but also on wasteland in London. V.cc. 17, 20, 21, 42, 43, 59, 67, 68, 81.

Very easily confused with **79** and best distinguished by having yellow stigmas when it is in fresh condition and bordered exterior bracts. In this species the large angled terminal lobes of the inner leaves usually possess elongated apices.

0   6cm

79b T. semiglobosum H. Lindb. (1907)

A medium-sized plant, with erect, oblanceolate, nearly flat leaves 80–300 mm.

Leaves *clear mid-green*, interlobes not blotched, midrib green, *obviously and densely hairy*; lateral lobes 3–5, recurved (*semi-lunate*), deltoid, *very acute at apex*, with distal margin straight to sinuate, entire or filiform-dentate, the proximal margin straight or ± convex; terminal lobe *not obviously larger than pair of lobes below it and with a distinct elongated tip*; petiole narrowly winged, on outer leaves pale, on inner leaves clear pink. Scapes usually exceeding leaves. Exterior bracts mostly recurved, *12–14 × 3–4.5 mm, bordered*, green, paler green on upper surface. Capitulum yellow, 40 mm in diameter; ligules striped grey-violet; styles exserted, discoloured; pollen present. Achenes straw-coloured; body 3.5 mm; cone 0.5 mm.

Introduced onto road verges in v.cc. 21 and 72.

Similar to **79** in colour and size, but not obviously heterophyllous and perhaps more closely related to **78** *T. angustisquameum*. Differs from both by the densely hairy green midrib to the leaf, the very acute, semi-lunate lateral lobes and the bordered bracts (broader than in **78**).

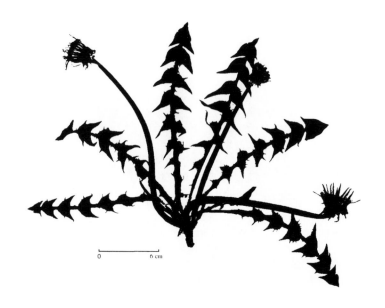

Section *Ruderalia*

80 T. aequilobum Dahlst. (1910)

Map 80

A robust *heterophyllous* plant, with erect, variably-shaped oblong to oblanceolate, highly crisped leaves 150–300 mm.

Leaves *dirty green*, interlobes *usually dark-blotched*, midrib slightly discoloured; lateral lobes *5–9, rather crowded, regular,* patent to recurved, deltoid, *rather short, with a divergent, often forward-pointing, linear process*, acute to very acute at apex, with distal margin sigmoid, concave or convex, entire or filiform-dentate, the proximal margin ± straight; interlobes dentate; terminal lobe *usually rather small and triangular or tripartite with elongated tip*; petiole *winged* or ± unwinged, very variable in length, *rose-purple*. Scapes usually exceeding leaves. Exterior bracts *twisted laterally*, spreading, becoming recurved, *10–15 × 2–4 mm, unbordered*, pale green and pruinose on upper surface, very dark on lower surface. Capitulum pale ochre-yellow, *65 mm in diameter*; ligules striped brown-purple, with *yellow* teeth; styles exserted, discoloured; pollen present. Achenes olive-brown; body 3.0 mm; cone 0.7 mm. 2n=24.

Probably introduced. Grassy places, roadsides, wasteland, gardens etc. Widespread through Great Britain and Northern Ireland; locally common. V.cc. 3, 12–16, 18, 21–23, 28, 33–39, 41–43, 46, 48, 50, 51, 55, 57–61, 67–70, 73, 74, 77, 82, 89, 93, 99, 106, H39, H40.

T. aequilobum is a deceptively variable species. In the field, the rather narrow, pale, twisted bracts are distinctive (but see also **80a** *T. latissimum*). Early-season leaves are narrowly multilobate with linear forward-pointing processes and dark interlobe blotches are also distinctive, but late-season leaves are much heavier in build.

80a   T. latissimum Palmgr. (1910a)

A robust *heterophyllous* plant, with erect, *broadly oblong to oblanceolate*, highly crisped leaves 150–300 mm.

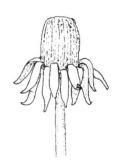

Leaves mid-green, interlobes blotched, midrib slightly discoloured; lateral lobes 4–7, rather crowded, regular, patent to recurved, deltoid or triangular, rather long, with a divergent, often forward-pointing, linear process, acute to very acute at apex, with distal margin sigmoid, concave or convex, entire or filiform-dentate, the proximal margin ± straight; interlobes highly crisped, ± dentate, often with 1 large tooth or lobule; terminal lobe usually rather small and triangular or tripartite with elongated tip; petiole unwinged, very variable in length, rose-purple. Scapes usually exceeding leaves. Exterior bracts strongly twisted laterally in the fresh state, spreading, 11–16 × 2–4 mm, unbordered, pale green and pruinose on upper surface, very dark on lower surface, often purple-tipped. Capitulum pale ochre-yellow, 65 mm in diameter; ligules striped brown-purple, with yellow teeth; styles exserted, discoloured; pollen present. Achenes olive-brown; body 3.0 mm; cone 0.7 mm.

Introduced. Widespread but scarce in Great Britain. V.cc. 1, 4, 6, 17, 19, 21–23, 27, 28, 34, 35, 39, 42, 46, 50, 51, 55, 58, 60, 67, 76, 77, 101, 106.

Similar in colour and structure to **80**, and also with large capitula and twisted bracts, but with longer, fewer lateral leaf-lobes, giving a much broader leaf outline; typically the interlobes have a single large tooth or lobule. The unwinged purple petioles and spreading, twisted bracts are diagnostic. Apart from the interlobe lobules, the leaf-shape bears a superficial resemblance to that of **85** *T. rhamphodes*.

0   6cm

80b T. latens H. Øllg. in Dudman & A.J. Richards (1994)

A medium-sized plant, with erect leaves 100–200 mm.

Leaves *light to mid-green*, interlobes *unblotched*, midrib green to slightly coloured; lateral lobes *5–6, crowded, regular*, patent to recurved, deltoid to triangular, *rather short*, acute to subacute at apex, with distal margin straight, ± convex or sigmoid, entire or dentate, the proximal margin straight, entire or sometimes with 1 tooth; interlobes plicate; terminal lobe *of outer leaves small*, triangular or tripartite with elongated tip, that *of inner leaves larger, triangular or helmet-shaped, often shallowly dissected into confluent broad lobules*, acute to subacute at apex; petiole narrowly green-winged or unwinged, *clear rose-pink*. Scapes usually exceeding leaves. Exterior bracts recurved or *straight and hanging vertically, 10–15 × 3.5 mm, bordered*, green on upper surface, darker green on lower surface. Capitulum yellow, *40 mm in diameter*; ligules striped grey-violet, with *reddish-purple* teeth; styles exserted, discoloured; pollen present. Achenes straw-coloured; body 3.0 mm; cone 0.6 mm.

Introduced. Five records from v.cc. 19, 35, 40, 50, 58.

Superficially resembles **80** closely, but the exterior bracts are not irregularly twisted, the large terminal lobes to the inner leaves are often shallowly dissected into confluent broad lobules, and the petioles are of a clearer rose-pink. Unlike those of **80, 80a** and **80c**, the tips of the inner ligules are coloured reddish-purple.

80c T. edmondsonianum H. Øllg. in Dudman   Map 80c
& A.J. Richards (1994)

A medium-sized plant, with decumbent to erect leaves 200–300 mm.

Leaves *yellowish-green*, interlobes *somewhat blotched*, midrib green to slightly coloured; lateral lobes *4–6*, regular, *patent*, triangular or deltoid, *rather short*, acute at apex, with distal margin ± *straight or sigmoid*, entire or dentate, the proximal margin *usually somewhat convex*, entire or with 1 tooth; interlobes usually moderately plicate, occasionally dentate; terminal lobe usually triangular, entire or dentate with 1 or 2 teeth, *sometimes divided into rounded lobules*; petiole *narrowly green-winged, clear rose-pink*. Scapes usually exceeding leaves. Exterior bracts *strongly reflexed, 15 × 4–5 mm, narrowly bordered*, light bluish green on upper surface, darker green on lower surface. Capitulum yellow, *50 mm in diameter*; ligules striped grey-violet, with *yellow* teeth; styles exserted, *yellow to discoloured*; pollen present. Achenes straw-coloured; body 3.0 mm; cone 0.4–0.7 mm.

Native. Recorded so far only from western England (where it seems to be widespread around Chester), Monmouthshire and Midlothian. Also known from Denmark and Germany. V.cc. 35, 36, 58, 59, 60, 83.

Related to **80** and **80b**, but with yellower leaves. Lacks the twisted bracts of **80** and shares the attractive clear rose-pink petioles with narrow green wings of **80b**, so that the petioles are reminiscent of those of **93** *T. dilatatum* (which has much shorter bracts). Distinguished from both **80** and **80b** by the shape of the lateral leaf-lobes, which are more patent and straight-sided on the distal margin and usually somewhat convex on the proximal margin, and by the strongly reflexed exterior bracts. Some of the small terminal leaf-lobes have rounded lobules. In fresh material the stigmas are yellow.

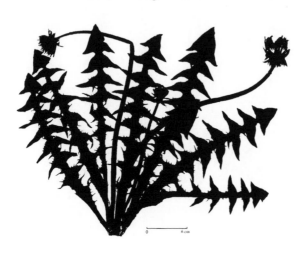

Section *Ruderalia*

Map 81

81   T. acroglossum Dahlst. (1910)

A *squat*, sometimes robust plant, with prostrate to ascending, elliptical, *flat* leaves 120–350 mm.

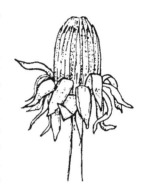

Leaves *dark greyish-green, shortly hairy above*, interlobes often blotched, midrib green to slightly coloured; lateral lobes *4–8, regular, recurved to falcate*, deltoid, sometimes narrowed to a linear process, acute to very acute at apex, with distal margin straight, ± convex or sinuate, entire or filiform-dentate, the proximal margin straight or concave; interlobes rather rounded, subentire; terminal lobe usually rather small and *very acutely triangular, or tripartite with elongated tip*; petiole entire-winged, sometimes narrowly so, *pink*. Scapes *arachnoid-hairy*, usually equalling leaves. Exterior bracts recurved, *12–14 × 4–5.5 mm*, unbordered, green, paler green on upper surface. Capitulum yellow, 50 mm in diameter; ligules striped grey-violet; styles exserted, discoloured; pollen present. Achenes straw-coloured; body 2.5 mm; cone 0.4 mm. 2n=24.

Probably introduced. Grassy places, roadsides, wasteland etc. Scattered through Great Britain; rather uncommon. V.cc. 14, 17, 21, 22, 34–36, 42, 43, 46, 50, 51, 55, 57, 58, 60, 62, 66, 67, 81, 89, 101, 112.

T. acroglossum is a squat plant of a characteristic dark greyish-green with flat leaves. The shape of the leaf, particularly of the terminal lobe, is distinctive. The exterior bracts are very broad.

81a   T. exsertum Hagend., Soest & Zevenb. (1974)   Map 81a

A *squat*, sometimes robust plant, with prostrate to ascending, oblong to oblance-olate, *rather flaccid* leaves 150–350 mm.

Leaves *light green*, interlobes often blotched, midrib green to slightly coloured, *hairy*; lateral lobes 4–8, *regular, recurved to falcate*, deltoid, sometimes narrowed to a linear process, acute to very acute at apex, with distal margin straight, ± convex or sinuate, entire or filiform-dentate, the proximal margin straight or concave; interlobes ± dentate; terminal lobe usually rather small and *very acutely triangular, or tripartite with elongated tip*; petiole entire-winged, sometimes narrowly so, *pink*. Scapes usually equalling leaves. Exterior bracts recurved, *12–14 × 4–4.5 mm*, unbordered, *callose at apex*, green, paler green on upper surface. Capitulum yellow, 40–50 mm in diameter; ligules striped grey-violet; styles exserted, at least sometimes *yellow* when fresh; pollen present. Achenes straw-coloured; body 2.5 mm; cone 0.4 mm.

Introduced. Difficult to distinguish from **81** in dried material and perhaps over-recorded; some of the following records may refer to *T. acroglossum*. V.cc. 2, 4, 11, 16–22, 28, 29, 34, 40, 42, 48, 55, 57, 60, 66, 69, 70, 72–74, 76, 82, 83, 85, 89, 99, S, H25, H38.

Very similar to **81**, but leaves light green, more flaccid and hairy only on the midrib. The inner bracts are strongly callose at the apex, and the stigmas are yellowish when fresh.

0   6cm

         Section *Ruderalia*

81b T. exsertiforme Hagend., Soest & Zevenb. (1978)

A medium-sized to large plant, with prostrate to erect, oblong to oblanceolate leaves to 100–250(–300) mm.

Leaves *light to mid-green*, interlobes often blotched, midrib green to slightly coloured; lateral lobes 5–7, deltoid, patent, acute to subacute, occasionally quite obtuse, at apex, often narrowing to a linear process, sometimes forward-pointing, with distal margin straight or sinuate, the proximal margin ± straight; terminal lobe *triangular or hastate, subacute to acute at apex*; petiole narrowly winged, that of outer leaves pallid, that of inner leaves ± reddish. Scapes usually exceeding leaves. Exterior bracts *erect to appressed (or ± spreading), 10–15 × 3–4 mm*, bordered, pale green on upper surface, darker green on lower surface. Capitulum yellow, 40–50 mm in diameter; ligules striped grey-purple; styles exserted, discoloured; pollen *absent*. Achenes straw-coloured; body 3.0 mm; cone 0.5 mm.

Introduced. V.cc. 6, 50, 51, 58.

Superficially similar to **81** in leaf-shape, but immediately recognised as the only British species of Section *Ruderalia* with a combination of an absence of pollen and erect (or ± spreading) exterior bracts. Possibly better classified within Section *Celtica*.

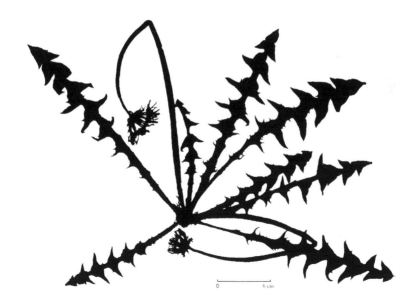

A medium-sized plant, with erect, narrowly oblance-olate, *flat* leaves 100–220 mm.

Leaves *clear dark green, hairy when young*, inter-lobes sometimes blotched, midrib usually green to slightly coloured; lateral lobes 5–7, regular, recurved, deltoid, *acute to acuminate at apex*, often abruptly narrowed from broad base, with distal margin convex or sinuate, entire (or filiform-dentate on lower lobes), the proximal margin straight or concave; terminal lobe *triangular or tripartite, uniformly very narrowly and sharply acuminate*; petiole narrowly winged, *pink to dull purple*. Scapes

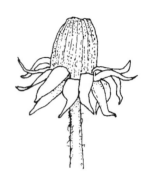

usually equalling leaves, *very arachnoid-hairy when young*. Exterior bracts mostly spreading (to recurved), *imbricate*, 14 × 4–4.5 mm, *narrowly acuminate*, unbordered, green, paler green on upper surface. Capitulum yellow, 40 mm in diameter; ligules striped grey-violet; styles exserted, discoloured; pollen present. Achenes straw-coloured; body 3.0 mm; cone 0.4 mm.

Probably introduced. Wasteland, rubbish dumps etc. Widespread throughout Great Britain, locally common, particularly in urban areas; one record from Northern Ireland. V.cc. 3, 7, 16, 17, 19–22, 25, 28, 33–36, 39, 42, 43, 49–51, 55, 57–62, 64, 66–70, 72–74, 76, 77, 82, 83, 86, 88, 96, 99, H36.

T. exacutum has a very squat capitulum with spreading, imbricate bracts which taper to an elegant point, giving a stellate appearance to the flower-head. The

flat, dark leaves have a very distinctive elongated, acuminate point to the terminal lobe, making this one of the easiest British dande-lions to identify.

82a T. valens Markl. (1938)

A medium-sized plant, with erect, oblanceolate, flat leaves 100–220 mm.

Leaves *very pale, bright green*, interlobes unblotched, midrib usually green to slightly coloured; lateral lobes 3–5, regular, patent to recurved, deltoid, *subacute to acute at apex*, with distal margin convex or sinuate, entire (or filiform-dentate on lower lobes), the proximal margin ± straight; interlobes occasionally denticulate; terminal lobe variable, *often larger than pair of lobes below it*, hastate or sometimes long and waisted, *sometimes divided*, with apex subacute to obtuse and *without a distinct elongated tip*; petiole narrowly winged or unwinged, *pink to dull purple*. Scapes usually equalling leaves, *very arachnoid-hairy when young*. Exterior bracts mostly spreading (to recurved), *strongly reflexed in bud*, 10–14 × 3.5 mm, *unbordered*, green, paler green on upper surface. Capitulum yellow, 40 mm in diameter; ligules striped grey-violet; styles exserted, discoloured; pollen present. Achenes straw-coloured; body 3.0 mm; cone 0.4 mm.

Introduced into a few sites in England, mainly in the south. V.cc. 6, 17, 20–23, 30, 59.

Related to **82**, but with pale, bright green leaves, lacking the narrowly acuminate lobe-ends of that species, and with a distinctive long, sometimes divided, subacute to obtuse terminal lobe. The exterior bracts are strongly reflexed in bud. Compare with **88b** *T. amplum*, which has clearly bordered bracts and yellowish styles.

0 ____ 6 cm

82b T. obtusifrons Markl. (1940)

A medium-sized plant, with erect, oblanceolate, flat leaves 100–220 mm.

Leaves *mid-green*, interlobes unblotched, midrib usually green to slightly coloured; lateral lobes 3–5, regular, patent to recurved, *deltoid, blunt* to subacute at apex, with distal margin convex or sinuate, entire (or filiform-dentate on lower lobes), the proximal margin straight or concave; terminal lobe regular, *tending to be larger than pair of lobes below it*, triangular, *obtuse*; petiole unwinged or narrowly winged, *red to distinctly purple*. Scapes usually equalling leaves, *very arachnoid-hairy when young*. Exterior bracts *spreading*, 14 × 4–4.5 mm, *distinctly bordered* (or unbordered), green, paler green on upper surface. Capitulum yellow, 40 mm in diameter; ligules striped grey-violet; styles exserted, discoloured; pollen present. Achenes straw-coloured; body 3.0 mm; cone 0.8 mm.

Introduced. Scattered, often in urban habitats. It has persisted at a single site in inner Newcastle upon Tyne for 14 years without spreading. V.cc. 3, 22, 50, 51, 55, 58, 67.

Similar to **94** *T. sinuatum* in colour and structure, but with broader, ± obtuse, deltoid lateral leaf-lobes, the terminal lobe small and obtuse on the outer leaves but larger than the pair of lobes below it on the inner leaves, the exterior bracts larger, and the achene cone longer (0.8 mm or more).

0 ———— 6cm

Section *Ruderalia*

82c T. leptodon Markl. (1926)

A medium-sized plant, with decumbent to erect leaves 150–300 mm.

Leaves *dark to mid-green, hairy*, interlobes not obviously blotched, midrib green to slightly coloured; lateral lobes 3–5, regular, patent to somewhat recurved, deltoid, rather short, *acute to subacute at apex*, with distal margin ± straight, entire or filiform-dentate, the proximal margin straight to concave; interlobes sometimes denticulate; terminal lobe usually larger than pair of lobes below it, sagittate or helmet-shaped and entire, or (on inner leaves) *with elongated, lingulate or acuminate apex*, sometimes divided or with 1 tooth; characteristically there are a few smaller leaves with rather narrow and recurved lateral lobes and a proportionately large terminal lobe; petiole unwinged or narrowly winged, *pink*. Scapes usually equalling leaves, *very arachnoid-hairy when young*. Exterior bracts recurved, 12–14 × 2–3.5 mm, sometimes with slight border, green suffused with purple on upper surface, darker green on lower surface. Capitulum deep yellow, 30–40 mm in diameter; ligules striped grey-violet; styles exserted, *yellowish*; pollen present. Achenes straw-coloured; body 3.5 mm; cone 0.7 mm.

0   6cm

Introduced. A few records from v.cc. 17, 34, 39 and 58.

Closely related to **82**, but with lateral leaf-lobes acute (neither acuminate nor obtuse); best distinguished by the elongated, lingulate terminal leaf-lobe on inner leaves and the yellowish stigmas.

Section *Ruderalia*   219

83   T. pannulatum Dahlst. (1910)

Map 83

A medium-sized to robust plant, with decumbent to erect, oblong to oblanceolate, crisped leaves 100–200 mm.

Leaves grey-green to mid-green, interlobes somewhat blotched, midrib *brown*; lateral lobes 5–8, *crowded, variable, patent, recurved or ± falcate*, triangular or deltoid, acute to very acute at apex, with distal margin straight, convex or sinuate, *dentate at least on lower lobes*, the proximal margin straight or concave; terminal lobe *sagittate, cordate, often divided, with falcate, obtuse to rounded lateral lobules and lingulate tip*; petiole short, winged, coloured. Scapes usually equalling leaves. Exterior bracts *recurved, 15–17 × 3.5–5 mm*, unbordered, green, paler green on upper surface. Capitulum yellow, 40 mm in diameter; ligules striped grey-violet; styles exserted, discoloured; pollen present. Achenes straw-coloured; body 3.5 mm; cone 0.4 mm. 2n=24.

Probably introduced. Grassy places, roadsides, wasteland etc. Widespread throughout Great Britain and locally common in the west; one record from Northern Ireland. V.cc. 3, 5, 6, 15, 17, 19–21, 23, 28, 33–36, 39, 40, 42–44, 50, 51, 57–60, 66, 67, 69, 70, 72, 73, 95, H36.

T. pannulatum is a very variable species, characterised by the crowded, dentate lateral leaf-lobes, the broad, pale green, recurved exterior bracts, the brown midrib, and the often rounded, falcate basal lobules to the terminal leaf-lobe, which is often divided.

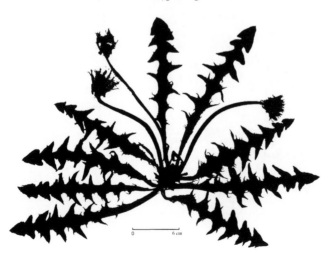

Section *Ruderalia*

84   T. lingulatum Markl. (1926)

Map 84

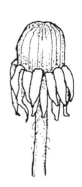

Often a large plant, *heterophyllous*, with very variable, spreading to erect, narrowly to broadly elliptical, somewhat crisped leaves 100–250 mm.

Leaves *dull green*, interlobes sometimes blotched, midrib green to slightly coloured; lateral lobes 3–6, patent to recurved, deltoid or triangular, *acute at apex, ± abruptly narrowed from a broad base*, with distal margin convex or sinuate, entire (or filiform-dentate on lower lobes), the proximal margin straight or concave; interlobes sometimes with 1 large tooth; terminal lobe *usually rather small and triangular on outer leaves, larger and triangular on inner leaves, bluntly but not very narrowly protracted*; petiole unwinged or narrowly winged, *pallid on outer, rose on inner leaves*. Scapes usually equalling leaves. Exterior bracts *strongly recurved, 11–14 × 3.5–5 mm, unbordered*, pale green, *pruinose* on upper surface, darker green on lower surface. Capitulum deep yellow, 55 mm in diameter; ligules striped violet-brown; styles exserted, discoloured; pollen present. Achenes straw-coloured; body 2.7–3.4 mm; cone 0.6 mm.

Native. Grassy places, roadsides, wasteland etc. Widespread throughout Great Britain and Ireland; one of our commonest dandelions. V.cc. 1–4, 6, 9, 11–23, 25–31, 33–37, 39, 40, 42–44, 46, 47, 50, 51, 53–63, 66–70, 72, 73, 75, 77, 78, 80–83, 96, 99, 101, 103, H19, H37, H38.

T. lingulatum is a variable plant, which is best recognised by the rather long, strongly recurved bracts and the blunt elongated process to the terminal lobe.

Section *Ruderalia*

221

84a   T. macranthoides G.E. Haglund (1943)

A medium-sized to robust plant, with decumbent to erect, narrowly oblanceolate, somewhat crisped leaves 80–220 mm.

Leaves *mid- to yellowish-green*, sometimes lobed to the base, interlobes not obviously blotched, midrib green to slightly coloured; lateral lobes 4–6, regular, patent to recurved, deltoid, *acute at apex*, with distal margin straight to convex, entire or (rarely) filiform-dentate, the proximal margin straight or concave, entire; terminal lobe *elongated, lingulate or narrowly hastate, obtuse, often divided*; petiole long, narrowly or broadly winged, *green to faintly pink*. Scapes usually exceeding leaves. Exterior bracts *recurved, 11–14 × 3.5–5 mm, ± slightly bordered, green* on upper surface, darker green on lower surface. Capitulum yellow, 50 mm in diameter; ligules striped grey-purple; styles exserted, discoloured; pollen present. Achenes straw-coloured; body 3.5 mm; cone 0.6 mm.

Introduced. V.cc. 23, 57, 60.

Related to **84**, but with paler green leaves, which have a characteristic elongated, obtusely lingulate terminal lobe.

0 ——— 6cm

Section *Ruderalia*

85 T. rhamphodes G.E. Haglund (1935a)   Map 85

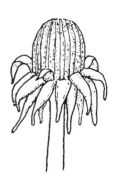

A robust plant, with erect, elliptical, slightly crisped leaves 150–300 mm.

Leaves *mid-green*, interlobes unblotched, midrib green to slightly coloured; lateral lobes 5–6, *regular, heavy*, patent to recurved, triangular or deltoid, rather short, acute to subacute at apex, ± *abruptly narrowed from a broad base*, with distal margin ± convex, entire (or filiform-dentate on lower lobes), the proximal margin straight or concave; interlobes plicate; terminal lobe variable, triangular, *sometimes divided, forming rounded basal lobules*, subacute at apex; petiole narrowly winged, *pink*. Scapes usually equalling leaves. Exterior bracts mostly recurved, 11–13 × 3–4.5 mm, *bordered, grey-green*, pruinose on upper surface, darker green on lower surface, with a pink tip. Capitulum yellow, 40 mm in diameter; ligules striped grey-violet; styles exserted, discoloured; pollen present. Achenes straw-coloured; body 2.5 mm; cone 0.5 mm.

Introduced. Grassy places, roadsides, wasteland etc. Widespread throughout Great Britain, locally common. V.cc. 8, 9, 13, 14, 17–23, 26, 30, 33–37, 39–44, 47, 50, 51, 55, 58, 60, 62, 67, 68, 70, 72, 77, 81, 89.

T. rhamphodes has rather lingulate leaf-lobes. The lobes, especially the terminal ones, are often divided, forming rounded lobules, and the general leaf-form resembles that of **80a** *T. latissimum*, but without interlobe lobules. The bracts are distinctly grey-green.

Section *Ruderalia*   223

A large, robust plant, with decumbent to erect, broadly oblanceolate, nearly flat leaves 150–300 mm.

Leaves *grey-green, shortly hairy*, interlobes unblotched, midrib often brownish; lateral lobes 3–6, *hamate, ± alternate, long to very long*, with acute apex; interlobes entire or with a large tooth; terminal lobe rather large and narrow, sagittate to hastate, usually once-divided on one side; petiole *short, broad*, winged, *green*. Inner leaves more dentate, with longer and more acute terminal lobe. Scapes usually exceeding leaves. Exterior bracts reflexed, *18 × 4.5 mm*, unbordered, green, not pruinose. Capitulum deep yellow, *50–70 mm in diameter*; ligules striped grey-violet; styles exserted, discoloured; pollen present. Achenes dark straw-brown, shortly spinulose; body 3.5 mm; cone 0.6–0.8 mm.

Introduced, mostly on road-verges. V.cc. 1, 6, 14, 17, 20–22, 33–35, 40, 42, 43, 48, 50, 51, 58, 67, 70, 73, 78, H22.

0   6cm

A distinctive, robust species with grey-green, shortly hairy leaves, only distantly related to **85**. It has short, broad, pale petioles, long, angled, ± alternate lateral leaf-lobes, a narrower helmet-shaped terminal lobe which is usually unilaterally divided, and very long exterior bracts; the capitula are massive (to 70 mm in diameter).

86 T. vastisectum Markl. ex Puol. (1933)

Map 86

A medium-sized to robust plant, with erect, oblanceolate, nearly flat leaves 150–300 mm.

Leaves mid-green, interlobes unblotched, midrib usually green to slightly coloured; lateral lobes 5–6, *regular, heavy, crowded in the centre of the leaf*, patent to recurved, deltoid to triangular, *rather short*, acute to subacute at apex, with distal margin straight, ± convex or angled, entire or dentate, the proximal margin straight, entire or *often with 1 large tooth*; terminal lobe triangular, sometimes divided, *subacute to obtuse at apex*; petiole *narrowly winged or unwinged, pink*. Scapes usually equalling leaves. Exterior bracts mostly recurved, 11–13 × 3.5 mm, *bordered, green* on upper surface, darker green on lower surface. Capitulum yellow, 40 mm in diameter; ligules striped grey-violet; styles exserted, discoloured; pollen present. Achenes straw-coloured; body 3.0 mm; cone *0.6 mm*.

Introduced. Grassy places, roadsides, wasteland etc. Scattered through Great Britain. Uncommon. V.cc. 1, 3, 11, 14, 17–23, 25, 26, 30, 32, 34, 36, 40, 42, 50, 51, 55, 58, 60, 66, 67, 69, 70, 75, 81, 99, 112.

T. vastisectum has many similarities with **85** *T. rhamphodes*. It is a rather characterless species, best characterised by the crowded central lobes, with a large tooth on some at least of the proximal margins, and pretty pink petioles.

Section *Ruderalia*

86a T. remanentilobum Soest (1975)

A medium-sized to robust *heterophyllous* plant, with erect, oblanceolate, nearly flat leaves 150–300 mm.

Leaves mid-green, interlobes unblotched, midrib usually green to slightly coloured; lateral lobes 5–6, recurved, deltoid, *narrow, ± falcate*, acute to subacute at apex, with distal margin convex, entire or (rarely) dentate, the proximal margin concave to straight, *entire*; terminal lobe sometimes larger than pair of lobes below it, particularly on inner leaves, triangular, *sometimes divided, acute, sometimes mucronate, at apex*; petiole *narrowly winged or unwinged, ± pink*. Scapes usually equalling leaves, *very arachnoid-hairy when young*. Involucre *strongly pruinose in bud*; exterior bracts mostly recurved, 11–13 × 3.5 mm, *unbordered, green* on upper surface, darker green on lower surface. Capitulum yellow, 40 mm in diameter; ligules striped grey-violet; styles exserted, discoloured; pollen present. Achenes straw-coloured; body 3.0 mm; cone *0.6–1.0 mm*.

Introduced. A few records from v.cc. 6, 23, 39, 42.

A close relative of **86**, differing mostly in leaf-shape, having 5–6, narrow, ± falcate lobes; it is heterophyllous, with a long, acute, sometimes divided terminal lobe on the inner leaves. The buds are pruinose, the exterior bracts unbordered, the achene cone longer, and the young scapes very arachnoid-hairy.

0   6cm

226

87 T. cordatum Palmgr. (1910a)

Map 87

A medium-sized plant, with spreading to erect, oblanceolate, ± flat leaves 100–200 mm.

Leaves rather pale, pure green, interlobes not blotched, midrib green; lateral lobes 3–5, *regular*, patent to slightly recurved, deltoid, rather short, *subacute to blunt at apex*, with distal margin usually straight to somewhat concave, *entire* (or occasionally slightly dentate), lower lobes sometimes filiform-dentate, the proximal margin ± straight or convex; terminal lobe *triangular, cordate*, entire or once-divided; petiole unwinged or narrowly winged, *on outer leaves pallid, on inner pink*. Scapes usually equalling leaves. Exterior bracts *spreading*, 10–12 × 3–3.5 mm, unbordered, green suffused with violet on upper surface, darker green on lower surface. Capitulum deep yellow, 45 mm in diameter; ligules striped red-purple; styles exserted, discoloured; pollen present. Achenes olive-brown; body 3.5 mm; cone 0.7 mm. 2n=24.

Native. Cliffs, sand-dunes and other natural places as well as roadsides, wasteland etc. Widespread throughout the British Isles and locally common. V.cc. 1–7, 9, 11–13, 15–17, 19–24, 26–30, 33–37, 39–44, 46–51, 54–62, 64–70, 73–77, 79–81, 83, 85, 88, 89, 93–97, 99, 101, 102, 106, 109, 112, S, H9, H13, H16, H21, H23, H38.

T. cordatum is characterised by the cordate terminal lobe and regular, ± patent, usually entire and rather blunt lateral lobes, together with spreading, dark bracts. It is an attractive plant with pretty colouring.

Section *Ruderalia*

88　T. sagittipotens Dahlst. & R. Ohlsen ex G.E. Haglund　Map 88
(1934a)

A medium-sized to large but rather slender plant, with erect, oblanceolate, *flat* leaves 200–300 mm.

Leaves *clear mid- to grey-green*, interlobes unblotched, midrib *green to slightly coloured*; lateral lobes 3–4, regular, recurved, deltoid to triangular, acute at apex, with distal margin ± straight (or slightly convex, concave or sinuate), *entire* or, occasionally, filiform-dentate or with 1 tooth, the proximal margin straight or slightly convex; terminal lobe *long, to 50 mm, sagittate to hastate-sagittate, often characteristically waisted,* usually entire, subacute to obtuse at apex, sometimes with an attenuate tip; petiole narrowly winged, *on outer leaves pallid, on inner pink.* Scapes usually exceeding leaves. Exterior bracts recurved, 11 × 2.5–4 mm, *unbordered,* pale green on upper surface, darker green on lower surface. Capitulum clear yellow, 40 mm in diameter; ligules striped violet-brown; styles exserted, *discoloured*; pollen present. Achenes straw-coloured; body 3.0 mm; cone 0.7 mm. 2n=24.

Probably native. Grassy places, roadsides, wasteland etc. Scattered through Great Britain and locally common in England and Wales; one record in eastern Ireland. V.cc. 3, 15, 17, 19–22, 26, 28, 30, 33, 34, 36, 38, 39, 42, 43, 46, 50, 51, 55–58, 60–62, 66–69, 74, 77, H21.

0　　　6cm

T. sagittipotens is usually a very distinctive and attractive species with a smooth appearance, which is characterised by its sagittate terminal lobe. Smaller, neater plants with short, regular leaf-lobes have been called *T. 'chamelum'* Sahlin ined. Such plants are known from v.cc. 17, 21, 30, 66 and 67. It is not certain how distinct they are from **88** or from *T. vanum* H. Øllg.

　　　　　　　　　　　　　　　　Section *Ruderalia*

A robust plant, with erect, broadly oblanceolate leaves to 300 mm.

Leaves *clear, often pale green*, unblotched, midrib *clear reddish-purple*; lateral lobes 3–4(–5), patent, rather wide, subdeltoid, entire, acute or obtuse, with distal margin concave or sigmoid, the proximal margin convex; interlobes entire or minutely and regularly denticulate; terminal lobe *often rather long, entire or once-dissected, helmet-shaped, with apex obtuse, mucronate*; petiole winged to one third of length of leaf, *clear reddish-purple, contrasting with green wings.* Scapes usually exceeding leaves, purple at the base, arachnoid-hairy above. Exterior bracts 8–11 × 2.4–3.5 mm, recurved, pale green, sometimes suffused purplish, *scarcely bordered.* Capitulum yellow, 40 mm in diameter; styles exserted, *yellowish or faintly discoloured*; pollen present. Achenes *bright golden brown*, shortly spinulose above, otherwise smooth; body 2.7–2.9 mm; cone poorly demarcated, 0.4 mm.

Apparently native and endemic. Grows on banks and walls in shaded humid areas in a limited part of Hexham, Northumberland, but has also been recorded from a few other widely disjunct localities. V.cc. 4, 22, 25, 42, 44, 67.

0   6cm

A distinctive species with clear, rather pale green leaves and a well demarcated red petiole with parallel-sided green wings, which is not closely related to **88** or any other British species, but is closely related to, and possibly identical with, a little-known Swedish species, *T. longifrons* G.E. Haglund. The usually entire terminal leaf-lobe is helmet-shaped and rounded at the apex with a mucronate tip; the styles are yellowish and the achenes are of a distinctive bright golden brown.

Section *Ruderalia*

88b T. amplum Markl. (1940)

A medium-sized to robust plant, with prostrate to ascending, broadly oblong, slightly crisped leaves (150–)250–300 mm.

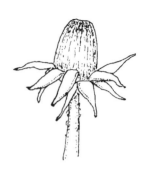

Leaves *very light green*, interlobes not obviously blotched, midrib *not coloured*; lateral lobes 4–6, regular, patent to recurved, deltoid, rather short and broad, acute at apex, with distal margin straight, concave or convex, ± *dentate or denticulate*, the proximal margin ± straight; interlobes *crisped*; terminal lobe often larger than pair of lobes below it, *helmet-shaped, sagittate, hastate or triangular, often once-divided, often dentate*; petiole winged or unwinged, *pink to purple*. Scapes usually equalling leaves, *thickly arachnoid-hairy when young*. Exterior bracts spreading to recurved, 11–14 × 3.5–4.5 mm, *clearly bordered*, green suffused with violet on upper surface, darker green on lower surface. Capitulum yellow, 40 mm in diameter; ligules striped grey-violet; styles exserted, *yellowish*; pollen present. Achenes straw-coloured; body 3.5 mm; cone 0.7 mm.

0 ————— 6cm

Introduced. V.cc. 14, 34, 51, 58, 66.

Similar to **88** in colouring and in the ± sagittate terminal lobe to the leaves, but with both terminal and lateral leaf-lobes more obviously dentate and divided; the interlobes are crisped, the styles yellowish, the young scapes very arachnoid-hairy, and the outer bracts obviously bordered. See also **82a** *T. valens*.

89 T. ekmanii Dahlst. (1911a) Map 89

A medium-sized to robust *strongly heterophyllous* plant, with spreading to erect, oblanceolate to obovate, crisped leaves 150–300 mm.

Leaves *pale lettuce-green*, interlobes not blotched, midrib *green to ± coloured*; lateral lobes of early (outer) leaves 3–6, narrow, ± patent, lingulate, scarcely dentate, with distal margin ± sigmoid, the proximal margin ± straight; terminal lobe ± entire, shortly triangular; later leaves (during main flowering) *gross, very variable*, with few, large, broad, highly dentate lateral lobes and a large, dentate, irregularly dissected terminal lobe; petiole short, *narrowly to broadly winged, pale pink on inner leaves*. Scapes usually exceeding leaves. Exterior bracts spreading to recurved, 9–13 × 2–4 mm, unbordered or with a distinct border, pale green on upper surface, green suffused with violet on lower surface. Capitulum *deep yellow*, 55 mm in diameter; ligules striped violet-brown; styles exserted, discoloured; pollen present. Achenes straw-coloured; body 3.0 mm; cone 0.4–0.7 mm.

Native? Grassy places, roadsides, wasteland etc. Widespread throughout the British Isles; common and locally abundant, often as a weed. V.cc. 3–6, 11–26, 28–31, 33–37, 39–44, 46, 49–51, 55, 57–62, 66–70, 73–76, 78, 80–83, 85, 86, 88, 89, 94–97, 99, 101, 104, 106, 109, 112, S, H17, H21, H28, H38, H39.

T. ekmanii is characterised by being strongly heterophyllous, with leaves of a characteristic, pale lettuce-green. Until the heterophylly is appreciated, it can be difficult to identify (see pages 10–11). Mid-season plants often resemble abnormal, grass-sward plants of some other species which would not normally be considered for identification. It is one of the commonest and most widespread British and Irish dandelions.

89a T. ochrochlorum G.E. Haglund ex Rail. (1942)

A medium-sized to robust plant, *not strongly heterophyllous*, with spreading to erect, oblanceolate to obovate, crisped leaves 150–300 mm.

Leaves *very pale, dull green*, interlobes not blotched, midrib *a characteristic honey colour* in centre of upper surface of leaf; lateral lobes 3–6, ± patent, lingulate, sometimes dentate, with distal margin ± sigmoid, the proximal margin ± straight, often with a ± conspicuous tooth; interlobes plicate; terminal lobe entire, shortly triangular; later leaves *gross, very variable*, with few, large, broad, highly dentate lateral lobes and a large, dentate, irregularly dissected terminal lobe; petiole short, *very broadly winged, pale pink on all leaves*. Scapes usually exceeding leaves, *thickly arachnoid-hairy when young*. Exterior bracts spreading to strongly recurved, 9–13 × 2–4 mm, unbordered or with a distinct border, pale green on upper surface, green suffused with violet on lower surface. Capitulum *deep yellow*, 55 mm in diameter; ligules striped violet-brown; styles exserted, discoloured; pollen present. Achenes straw-coloured; body 3.0 mm; cone 0.4–0.7 mm.

Probably introduced, but possibly under-recorded in favour of **89**. Woodland banks, shaded road-verges etc. V.cc. 6, 18, 21, 34–36, 42, 43, 50, 57, 58, 61, 81, 93.

A close relative of **89**, but more gross, with very broadly winged petioles, which are faintly pink on all leaves, and leaves of a duller, very pale colour, differing from the bright lettuce-green of **89**, with the midrib golden brown above in the centre of the leaf. The terminal and upper lateral lobes on the outer leaves are often somewhat angled so that they appear slightly kinked. The exterior bracts are spreading to strongly recurved and the young scapes are thickly arachnoid-hairy.

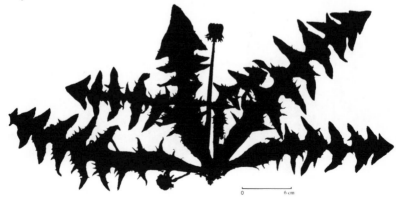

0   6 cm

Section *Ruderalia*

89b   T. aurosulum H. Lindb. (1909)

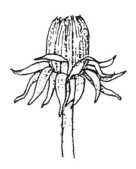

A medium-sized to robust, *strongly heterophyllous* plant, with spreading to erect, oblanceolate to obovate, crisped leaves 150–300 mm.

Leaves *mid-green*, interlobes sometimes blotched, midrib *green to coloured*; lateral lobes of early (outer) leaves 3–6, narrow, ± patent, lingulate, often dentate, often divided, usually narrowing into linear processes with ± blunt, swollen apices, with distal margin ± sigmoid, *convexly expanded at base*, the proximal margin ± straight; terminal lobe ± entire, *not larger than pair of lobes below it*, triangular, sometimes divided, *often with short, narrowly lingulate tip*; later leaves (during main flowering) *gross, very variable*, with few, large, broad, highly dentate lateral lobes and a large, dentate, irregularly dissected terminal lobe; petiole short, *narrowly to broadly winged, pale pink on inner leaves*. Scapes usually exceeding leaves. Exterior bracts spreading to recurved, 9–13 × 2–4 mm, unbordered or with a distinct border, pale green on upper surface, green suffused with violet on lower surface. Capitulum *deep yellow*, 55 mm in diameter; ligules striped violet-brown; styles exserted, discoloured; pollen present. Achenes straw-coloured; body 3.0 mm; cone *very short*.

Probably introduced. Widespread but rather uncommon on shady road-verges etc. V.cc. 5, 12, 14–24, 28, 29, 33–35, 37, 39–42, 46, 48, 50, 51, 56–62, 66, 67, 69, 70, 72, 74, 76, 77, 90, 96–98, 101, 109, S, H16, H39.

Another gross, heterophyllous species, but with mid-green leaves. Best known by the early, outer leaves, whose upper lateral lobes have convexly expanded bases and long patent linear processes with blunt, swollen tips; on these outer leaves the short triangular terminal lobe often has a short but narrowly lingulate tip.

Section *Ruderalia*

89c T. lunare M.P. Christ. in Raunk. (1934)

A medium-sized to robust plant, with spreading to erect, oblanceolate to obovate, crisped leaves 150–300 mm.

Leaves *mid to dark green,* interlobes not blotched, midrib *green to somewhat coloured;* lateral lobes of early (outer) leaves 3–6, *consistently heavy, falcate, semilunar;* terminal lobe ± entire, shortly triangular; later leaves (during main flowering) *gross, very variable,* with few, large, broad, highly dentate lateral lobes and a large, dentate, irregularly dissected terminal lobe; petiole short, *narrowly to broadly winged, green.* Scapes usually exceeding leaves. Exterior bracts recurved, *12–16 mm (or more)* × *3–5 mm (or more), parallel-sided,* unbordered, pale green on upper surface, green suffused with violet on lower surface. Capitulum *deep yellow,* 55 mm in diameter; ligules striped violet-brown; styles exserted,

discoloured; pollen present. Achenes straw-coloured; body 3.0 mm; cone 0.4–0.7 mm.

Introduced. A few records from v.cc. 34, 39, 42, 44, 60.

Not closely related to **89, 89a** or **89b**, although superficially similar to their early-season forms, but with the leaves mid to dark green, with long, heavy, scythe-like, semi-lunar lateral lobes, the petioles quite green, the buds long and pale green, and the exterior bracts long and parallel-sided.

6cm

Section *Ruderalia*

89d T. coartatum G.E. Haglund (1942)

A medium-sized to large plant, with erect, ± oblong, somewhat crisped leaves 100–250 mm.

Leaves *mid-green*, interlobes not obviously blotched, midrib green to slightly coloured; lateral lobes 4–6, regular, patent to slightly recurved, deltoid, *rather short with broad base*, acute to subacute at apex, with distal margin *convex and often high-shouldered*, the proximal margin ± straight; interlobes sometimes dentate, *sometimes with 1 large tooth*; terminal lobe not usually large, *triangular, often equilaterally so*, entire or sometimes divided, with acute apex; petiole *winged, pink*. Scapes usually exceeding leaves, *distinctly arachnoid-hairy throughout*. Exterior bracts *irregularly arranged or twisted*, spreading to recurved, *with strongly recurved margins, 15 mm (or more) × 3.5–4.5 mm*, unbordered, green, not obviously pruinose, paler green on upper surface. Capitulum *pale yellow*, 50 mm in diameter; ligules striped grey-violet; styles exserted, ± discoloured; pollen present. Achenes straw-coloured; body 3.0 mm; cone 0.5 mm.

Introduced. V.cc. 3, 34, 36, 50.

Superficially similar to **89c** *T. lunare*, but with pink petioles. The lateral leaf-lobes are shorter and less acute than in that species and have a high convex 'shoulder' to the distal margin; the exterior bracts are longer and somewhat twisted and have recurved margins, the scapes are persistently arachnoid-hairy, and the styles are less discoloured. See also **72** *T. intumescens*.

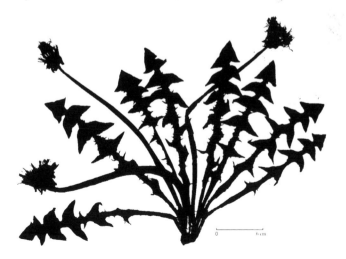

90 T. aberrans Hagend., Soest & Zevenb. (1974)

A medium-sized to large plant, with erect, oblong to oblanceolate-spathulate, somewhat crisped leaves 100–250 mm.

Leaves dull mid-green, often drying yellowish green, interlobes not obviously blotched, midrib green to slightly coloured; lateral lobes 3–4, *regular*, patent to slightly recurved, deltoid, rather short with broad base, acute to subacute at apex, with distal margin ± *sinuate, usually dentate* (sometimes entire or filiform-dentate), the proximal margin ± straight; terminal lobe *usually large, triangular, cordate or helmet-shaped*, entire or dentate, *mucronate*, sometimes divided; petiole unwinged, at least below, *pink*. Scapes usually exceeding leaves. Exterior bracts *recurved*, 11–14 × 3.5–4.5 mm, *unbordered*, green, pruinose, paler green on upper surface. Capitulum deep yellow, 50 mm in diameter; ligules striped grey-violet; styles exserted, discoloured; pollen present or sometimes absent.

Achenes straw-coloured; body 3.0 mm; cone 0.5 mm. 2n=24.

Probably introduced. Grassy places, roadsides, wasteland etc. Uncommon. V.cc. 3, 33, 34, 44, 62, 67, 68, 70, 73.

T. aberrans is characterised by its large, mucronate terminal lobe and regularly lobed leaves, with pink petioles. British material was formerly identified with *T. caudatulum* Dahlst. (1910).

0   6cm

236

There is a related plant (**90a**), illustrated below, which differs from **90** by having dark, rather dirty-coloured leaves with plicate interlobes bearing dark acuminate teeth, rounded terminal lobes which are divided and bear large recurved teeth, and dark brown achenes, the body of which is only 2.5 mm long. This is related to the Danish species *T. severum* M.P. Christ., but seems to be distinct. It is currently known by its workname *T. 'non-severum'*.

Possibly endemic. Grassy places in v.cc. 3, 30, 33–35, 37, 42, 52, 60.

90b T. pseudoretroflexum M.P. Christ. (1971)

A medium-sized to large plant, with erect, oblong to oblanceolate-spathulate, somewhat crisped leaves 100–300 mm.

Leaves mid-green, interlobes not obviously blotched, midrib green to slightly coloured; lateral lobes 3–5, regular, patent to slightly recurved, deltoid, acute to very acute at apex, with distal margin *convex, usually entire* (sometimes filiform-dentate), the proximal margin ± straight; terminal lobe not larger than pair of lobes below it except on inner leaves, *triangular with a well-differentiated and elongated tip*; petiole unwinged, at least towards base, *pink*. Scapes usually exceeding leaves. Exterior bracts *strongly reflexed or hanging vertically*, 11–14 × 3.5–4.5 mm, *bordered*, green, paler green on upper surface. Capitulum deep yellow, 50 mm in diameter; ligules striped grey-violet; styles exserted, discoloured; pollen present. Achenes straw-coloured; body 3.0 mm; cone 0.4–0.7 mm.

Introduced. V.cc. 9, 42, 50, 59, 60, but plants informally known as *T. 'pseudo-cordatum'* from South Northumberland (v.c. 67) may also belong here.

Resembles **90**, but readily identified by the shape of the terminal leaf-lobe, which has a narrow elongated apex, and by the strongly reflexed or vertically hanging exterior bracts. The distal margin of the lateral leaf-lobes is convex and usually entire.

0   6cm

238

A medium-sized plant, with erect, oblong-spathulate, ± *flat* leaves 50–200 mm.

Leaves dull, mid- to olive-green, interlobes not blotched, midrib green to slightly coloured; lateral lobes *3–5*, regular, recurved, deltoid, short, acute to subacute at apex, with distal margin ± *convex*, usually filiform-dentate (sometimes entire), the proximal margin straight to sinuate; terminal lobe usually rather small on early (outer), but larger on inner leaves, ± *rounded*, ± entire, *cordate at base*, sometimes minutely mucronate at apex; petiole narrowly winged to unwinged at base, deep pink. Scapes usually exceeding leaves. Exterior bracts *recurved, 9–12 × 2–3 mm*, unbordered, *often becoming suffused with purple on upper surface*, very dark green on lower surface. Capitulum yellow, *30–40 mm in diameter, strongly convex*; ligules striped *grey-violet*; styles exserted, *discoloured to blackish*; pollen present. Achenes straw-coloured; body 2.8 mm; cone 0.6 mm. 2n=24.

Native. Grassy places, especially fertile, damp pastures. Widespread through most of Great Britain and locally common; scattered in Ireland. V.cc. 1–3, 5, 6, 9, 11, 12, 15–26, 28, 30–37, 39, 41–47, 50, 51, 55, 57–60, 62, 66, 68–70, 73, 74, 76, 77, 81, 88, 100, 112, S, H12, H21.

T. oblongatum is a characteristic species best known by its small, rounded flowering heads with rather small, narrow, recurved bracts, and by its neat, regularly lobed, flat leaves, somewhat recalling those of Section *Hamata*, with an obtuse to rounded terminal lobe, cordate at the base.

91a   T. cophocentrum Dahlst. (1929)

Map 91a

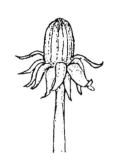

A medium-sized to robust plant, with erect, oblanceolate-spathulate, *flat* leaves 150–300 mm. Leaves dull, dark green, interlobes not blotched, midrib green to slightly coloured; lateral lobes *2–4(–5)*, regular, *broad*, patent to recurved, deltoid or triangular, acute to subacute at apex, with distal margin ± straight to convex, ± dentate, the proximal margin ± straight; terminal lobe *large, about one quarter length of leaf*, helmet-shaped, broad, *rounded*, entire or dentate below, obtuse to subacute at apex; petiole narrrowly winged to unwinged at base, dull purple. Scapes usually equalling leaves. Exterior bracts spreading to recurved, 9 × 2 mm, unbordered, often becoming suffused with purple on upper surface, very dark green on lower surface. Capitulum yellow, *45 mm in diameter*; ligules striped *brown-purple*; styles exserted, *discoloured*; pollen present. Achenes straw-coloured; body 3.5 mm; cone 0.6 mm.

Endemic. Widespread and scattered but locally common in grassy places, wood margins and scrub, especially in the south. V.cc. 1–3, 6, 8, 12–16, 18–26, 28, 30, 32–34, 37, 42, 44, 46, 48, 50, 51, 55, 57, 60, 66, 67, 70, 82, 83, 93, 101, 104, S, H16, H23.

Closely related to **91**, of which it is essentially a robust version with a large, rounded, often entire terminal leaf-lobe, especially on inner leaves, 2–4(–5) broad lateral lobes, and ligules striped brown-purple. The styles are only lightly discoloured. The rather small heads and small, narrow bracts are distinctive.

Section *Ruderalia*

92 T. pachymerum G.E. Haglund (1946)   Map 92

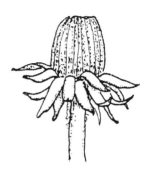

A medium-sized *squat* plant, with usually decumbent, broadly oblong, slightly crisped leaves 150–250 mm.

Leaves *dark to bluish green, smudged with dirty markings centrally*, interlobes dark-blotched, midrib *dirty red*; lateral lobes 4–6, *crowded, sometimes overlapping*, regular, patent to recurved, deltoid, *rather short and broad*, acute at apex, with distal margin *convex, ± dentate or denticulate*, the proximal margin straight to *convex*; interlobes narrow or, especially between upper lobes of leaf, *reduced to a single cut, often obviously plicate*; terminal lobe usually rather *small*, triangular or cordate, *often once-divided, often dentate*; petiole *narrowly to broadly winged, pink to purple*. Scapes usually equalling leaves. Exterior bracts spreading to recurved, 11–14 × 3.5–4.5 mm, unbordered, green suffused with violet on upper surface, darker green on lower surface. Capitulum yellow, 40–50 mm in diameter; ligules striped grey-violet; styles exserted, discoloured; pollen present. Achenes straw-coloured; body 3.5 mm; cone 0.7 mm. 2n=24.

Probably introduced. Grassy places, roadsides, wasteland etc. Scattered throughout Great Britain, locally common; also in eastern Ireland. V.cc. 3, 12, 15, 17–19, 21–23, 25, 26, 28, 30, 33, 34, 42, 43, 50, 51, 55, 57, 58, 60, 61, 66, 67, 70, 72, 73, 77, 82, H21.

T. pachymerum is characterised by the usually decumbent leaves of a dark, dirty colour with very crowded, sometimes overlapping, lateral lobes, which are

short, broad and usually toothed, and by the dull red midribs. Superficially very similar to **72** *T. intumescens*, which however has green petioles and midribs; diagnostically, the latter has red tips to the inner ligules.

Section *Ruderalia*   241

93   T. dilatatum H. Lindb. (1907) Map 93

A medium-sized to large plant, with decumbent to erect, narrowly oblong to elliptical, slightly crisped leaves 150–250 mm.

Leaves dull, mid-green, with margins, especially of inter-lobes, sometimes blackish, midrib green to slightly coloured; lateral lobes 3–5, *patent to recurved*, deltoid to triangular, acute to very acute at apex, with distal margin straight, convex or sinuate, often dentate, sometimes with large teeth, the proximal margin straight or concave; inter-lobes *regularly plicate*, and interlobes or lobes *often with 1 long, broad-based, filiform tooth*; terminal lobe on early (outer) leaves rather small and triangular or, *on inner leaves, large and helmet-shaped*, when it is often divided; petiole *about one quarter length of leaf, red, contrasting sharply with narrow parallel-sided green wings*. Scapes 50–200 mm, *shorter than leaves*. Exterior bracts *spreading, 11–13 × 3–5 mm, unbordered*, conspicuously *brownish-purple on upper surface*, darker green on lower surface. Capitulum *deep yellow, 35–45 mm in diameter*; styles exserted, discoloured; pollen present. Achenes straw-coloured; body 3.5 mm; cone 0.5 mm. 2n=24.

Native. Grassy places, perhaps particularly in rich grasslands, roadsides, waste-land etc. Scattered through Great Britain, mainly in the west, and locally com-mon, but only recently correctly diagnosed in Britain and consequently under-recorded. V.cc. 3, 6, 23, 34, 35, 39, 42, 44, 51, 57, 58, 60, 61, 69, 70, 72, 77.

Easily recognised by the red petioles contrasting sharply with the parallel-sided green wings; amongst British *Ruderalia*, only **93a** *T. dia-stematicum* and **80c** *T. ed-mondsonianum* also unmis-takably have this character. *T. dilatatum* is similar to various *Celtica* species (e.g. **34** *T. duplidentifrons*) and possibly better classi-fied there.

Section *Ruderalia*

93a T. diastematicum Markl. (1940)

A medium-sized to large plant, with decumbent to erect, narrowly oblong to elliptical, slightly crisped leaves 150–250 mm.

Leaves dull, mid-green, with margins, especially of inter-lobes, sometimes blackish, midrib pallid at base and darkening towards apex, *with small striations*; lateral lobes 3–5, *patent to recurved*, deltoid to triangular, acute to very acute at apex, with distal margin straight, convex or sinuate, *abruptly narrowing to form a characteristic high 'shoulder'*, usually entire, sometimes with large teeth, the proximal margin straight or concave; interlobes *regularly plicate, often with 1 long, broad-based, filiform tooth*; terminal lobe *normally not larger than pair of lobes below it*; petiole *on outer leaves ± pallid, on inner leaves reddish, narrowly green-winged.* Scapes 50–200 mm, *shorter than leaves.* Exterior bracts spreading, *11–13 × 3–5 mm, unbordered, white or green or faintly coloured on upper surface,* not obviously pruinose, darker green on lower surface.

Capitulum *deep yellow, 35–45 mm in diameter*; styles exserted, discoloured; pollen present. Achenes straw-coloured; body 3.5 mm; cone 0.5 mm.

Introduced. V.cc. 32, 42, 51, 58.

Closely related to **93**, but with rather more uniform leaves. The lateral leaf-lobes have characteristic 'humps' on the distal margin. Inner leaves lack large terminal lobes. Outer leaves tend to have pallid petioles, but those on inner leaves are as in **93**.

0   6cm

93b T. tanyphyllum Dahlst. (1932)

A medium-sized to *tall* plant, with ascending to erect, narrowly oblanceolate to oblong, slightly crisped leaves 80–300 mm.

Leaves mid to darkish green, glabrous, interlobes sometimes slightly blotched, midrib green to slightly coloured, *with small striations*; lateral lobes 4–6, *patent, narrow, ± parallel-sided or slightly recurved*, triangular or deltoid, rather short, acute to subacute at apex, with distal margin straight to convex, entire, dentate or filiform-dentate, the proximal margin straight or concave; interlobes often dentate; terminal lobe ± hastate, *larger than pair of lobes below it*; petiole *long, narrowly winged, on outer leaves sometimes pallid, on middle and inner leaves reddish*. Scapes *usually equalling leaves.* Exterior bracts *recurved, 15 × 4 mm, bordered, pale green on upper surface,* darker green on lower surface.

Capitulum *pale yellow, 40 mm in diameter*; ligules striped grey-violet; styles exserted, discoloured; pollen present. Achenes straw-coloured; body 3.5–4.0 mm; cone 0.6–0.7 mm.

Introduced. A rare plant of road-verges etc. V.cc. 1, 3, 6, 22, 24, 25, 28, 30, 39, 42, 57, 60, 70, 75, 79, 112.

The long, narrowly winged petioles are reddish on inner leaves, but pallid on outer leaves. The lateral leaf-lobes are patent, narrow and ± parallel-sided, and the exterior bracts are large and bordered.

Section *Ruderalia*

A medium-sized *squat* plant, with spreading to erect, broadly oblong, *crisped* leaves 120–200 mm.

Leaves *bright green, shiny,* interlobes *not blotched,* midrib pink; lateral lobes 3–5, *irregular, sinuate on both margins, ± obovate or with short, narrower processes pointing in various directions, frequently divided, sometimes with 1 large tooth on proximal margin, subacute to obtuse at apex*; interlobes regularly plicate, dentate; terminal lobe *usually rather small and divided, obtuse* (to subacute) *at apex*; petiole *unwinged, purple to red.* Scapes usually exceeding leaves. Exterior bracts *spreading to recurved, 9–11 × 2–4 mm, ± bordered,* green, somewhat pruinose on upper surface, darker green on lower surface. Capitulum yellow, 40–50 mm in diameter; ligules striped grey-violet; styles exserted, discoloured; pollen present. Achenes olive-brown; body 2.5 mm; cone 0.4 mm. 2n=24.

Possibly native. Grassy places, roadsides etc. Scattered, mainly in Wales and the west of England. V.cc. 3, 4, 14, 22, 23, 33–35, 40, 42, 44, 50, 51, 58, 60, 69, 103, H21.

T. sinuatum is characterised by bright green, shiny, crisped leaves with highly sinuate, omnidirectional lobes and striking purple to red petioles. See also **82b** *T. obtusifrons.*

0   6 cm

94a   T. laciniosifrons Wiinst. in Raunk. (1934)

A medium-sized *squat* plant, with spreading to erect, broadly oblong, *crisped* leaves 120–200 mm.

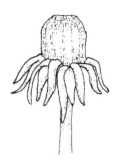

Leaves *mid-green, matt, shortly pubescent*, interlobes *frequently blotched*, midrib pink; lateral lobes 3–5, *irregular, sinuate on both margins, ± obovate or with short, narrower processes pointing in various directions, frequently divided, sometimes with 1 large tooth on proximal margin, subacute to acute at apex*; interlobes regularly plicate, dentate; terminal lobe *usually rather small and divided, obtuse* (to subacute) *at apex*; petiole *winged, purple*. Scapes usually exceeding leaves, *arachnoid-hairy throughout*. Exterior bracts *recurved or hanging vertically, 10–15 mm (or more) × 3.5 mm, bordered*, green, somewhat pruinose on upper surface, darker green on lower surface. Capitulum yellow, 40–50 mm in diameter; ligules striped grey-violet; styles exserted, discoloured; pollen present. Achenes olive-brown, sometimes spinulose; body 2.5 mm; cone 0.4 mm.

Probably native. Grassy places and roadsides. Local and scattered through Great Britain and Ireland. V.cc. 1, 3, 6, 15, 16, 19, 21–26, 28, 33, 34, 39, 42, 46, 51, 55, 57, 58, 61, 66, 69, 72, 73, 85, H25, H38–H40.

Similar to **94** in general appearance, but with *matt*, shortly pubescent leaves with *winged* petioles and more acute lateral lobes. The exterior bracts are longer, bordered and more recurved. The young scapes are thickly arachnoid-hairy.

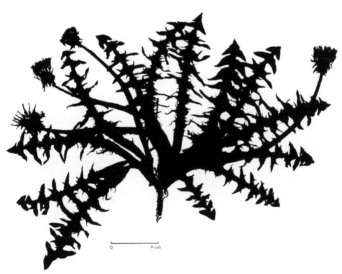

95 T. dahlstedtii H. Lindb. (1907)

Map 95

A medium-sized plant, with ascending to erect, narrowly oblanceolate-spathulate, slightly crisped leaves 80–250 mm. Leaves *mid to darkish green, somewhat hairy*, interlobes sometimes slightly blotched, midrib green to slightly pink; lateral lobes 4–6, patent or slightly recurved, triangular or deltoid, rather short, decurrent and usually dentate at base, acute to subacute at apex, with distal margin straight or convex, entire, dentate or filiform-dentate, the proximal margin straight or concave, sometimes with a single tooth; interlobes often dentate; terminal lobe *usually larger than pair of lateral lobes below it, usually dentate or divided*; petiole *unwinged*, narrow, *vivid crimson to purple*. Scapes usually equalling leaves. Exterior bracts *recurved, 11–15 × 1.5–3 mm*, unbordered, green, paler green on upper surface. Capitulum pale yellow, 40 mm in diameter; ligules striped grey-violet, inner ones with *yellow* tips; styles exserted, discoloured; pollen present. Achenes straw-coloured; body 3.5–4.0 mm; cone 0.6–0.7 mm. 2n=24, 27.

Native. Grassy places, roadsides, wasteland etc. Widespread throughout the British Isles; locally common, particularly near the coast. V.cc. 1–5, 11, 12, 15, 17, 19–23, 25–29, 33–36, 38–40, 42, 44–46, 48–51, 55, 57–62, 66–70, 72–78, 80–86, 89–99, 103–106, 112, S, H9, H11, H13, H18, H23, H38, H39.

T. dahlstedtii is characterised by the narrow, vivid crimson to purple petioles, the narrow, curved bracts, and the usually large, often divided, terminal lobe to the leaf.

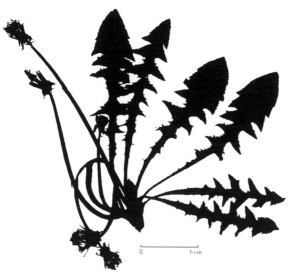

95a   T. obliquilobum Dahlst. (1910)   Map 95a

A medium-sized plant, with decumbent to erect, narrowly oblong to elliptical, slightly crisped leaves 80–250 mm.

Leaves *dull, olive-green, glabrous*, interlobes unblotched when fresh (but can appear blotched in the herbarium), midrib green to slightly coloured; outer and middle leaves lobate, inner leaves less obviously so; lateral lobes 4–8, deltoid, rather short, decurrent and usually dentate at base, acute to subacute at apex, with distal margin straight or convex, entire, dentate or filiform-dentate, the proximal margin straight or concave, sometimes with a single tooth; interlobes often dentate; terminal lobe *usually larger than pair of lateral lobes below it*, sometimes markedly so, *usually dentate or divided*; petiole *narrowly winged*, narrow, *dull pink on inner leaves*. Scapes usually equalling leaves. Exterior bracts *spreading to recurved, 15 mm (or more) × 3.5 mm (or more)*, unbordered, green, paler green on upper surface, *with margins strongly recurved*. Capitulum pale yellow, 40 mm in diameter; ligules striped grey-violet, inner ones with *reddish-orange* tips; styles exserted, discoloured; pollen present. Achenes straw-coloured; body 3.5–4.0 mm; cone 0.6–0.7 mm.

0 ———— 6cm

Introduced. Scarce and scattered on road-verges etc. V.cc. 9, 14, 15, 17–19, 21–24, 26–28, 33, 42, 43, 50, 51, 53, 55, 57–59, 62, 68, 72, 77, 82, 85, 95.

Similar to **95**, and differing by the narrowly winged, dull pink inner petioles and by the longer (15 mm or more), spreading to recurved exterior bracts, the margins of which are recurved. The lateral leaf-lobes are neat and ± acute. Unlike those of **95**, the inner ligule tips are reddish-orange.

Section *Ruderalia*

95b T. pachylobum Dahlst. (1910)

A medium-sized plant, with ascending to erect, narrowly oblanceolate to elliptical, slightly crisped leaves 80–250 mm.

Leaves *mid to darkish green, glabrous,* interlobes sometimes slightly blotched, midrib green to slightly coloured; lateral lobes 4–6, patent or slightly recurved, triangular or deltoid, *short,* decurrent and usually dentate at base, most of them acute to subacute but *some obviously rounded at apex,* with distal margin straight or convex, entire, dentate or filiform-dentate, the proximal margin straight or concave, sometimes with a single tooth; interlobes often dentate; terminal lobe *usually no larger than pair of lateral lobes below it, sometimes divided*; petiole *winged,* narrow, *vivid crimson to purple.* Scapes usually equalling leaves. Exterior bracts *spreading, 11–15 × 1.5–3 mm,* unbordered, green, paler green on upper surface. Capitulum pale yellow, 40 mm in diameter; ligules striped grey-violet, inner ones with *yellow* tips; styles exserted, discoloured; pollen present. Achenes straw-coloured; body 3.5–4.0 mm; cone 0.6–0.7 mm.

Introduced and rare. V.cc. 42, 66, 70.

Very similar to **95**, but leaves glabrous and with some lateral lobes very obviously rounded. The vividly coloured petiole is narrowly winged and the exterior bracts are spreading.

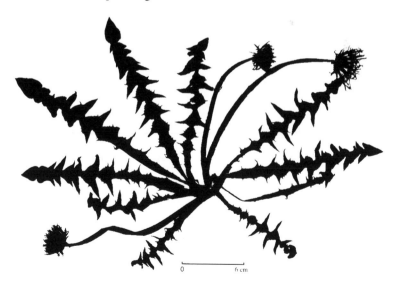

0   6 cm

95c T. latisectum H. Lindb. (1907)

A medium-sized plant, with erect, oblong-spathulate to elliptical-spathulate, ± *flat* leaves 50–200 mm.

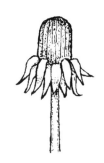

Leaves *bluish green*, interlobes not blotched, midrib green to slightly coloured; lateral lobes 4–6, *rather crowded*, regular, recurved, deltoid, short, acute to subacute (to obtuse) at apex, with distal margin ± convex, dentate to filiform-dentate (rarely entire), the proximal margin straight to sinuate; terminal lobe *somewhat elongated, ± divided but usually untoothed*, usually rather small on early (outer), larger on inner leaves, cordate at base, ± rounded, but sometimes minutely mucronate at apex; petiole *narrowly winged to unwinged at base, dullish pink*. Scapes usually exceeding leaves. Exterior bracts *spreading to recurved, 9–12 × 3.5 mm*, unbordered, *often becoming suffused with purple on upper surface*, very dark green on lower surface. Capitulum yellow, 30–40 mm in diameter, *strongly convex*; ligules striped grey-violet, inner ones with tips *suffused blackish*; styles exserted, discoloured; pollen present. Achenes straw-coloured; body 2.8 mm; cone 0.6 mm.

Native. Grassy places, especially fertile pastures. Widespread but very local in England and Wales, with a few records from Scotland and Ireland. V.cc. 12, 21, 23, 24, 28, 30, 34–36, 42, 47, 50, 55, 60, 61, 66–68, 70, 72, 86, 112, H39.

Resembles **95** in colour and structure, but with oblong- to elliptical-spathulate leaves with rather crowded lobes and a rounded, usually untoothed terminal

lobe, cordate at the base. The exterior bracts are less recurved and broader (about 3.5 mm in width) and the petiole dullish pink. Diagnostically within this small group, the apices of the inner ligules are suffused blackish.

Section *Ruderalia*

A tall plant, with decumbent to erect, narrowly oblong-spathulate, somewhat crisped leaves 80–300 mm.

Leaves *dull, dark green, somewhat hairy*, interlobes *dark-blotched*, midrib green to slightly coloured; lateral lobes 5–7, *regular, cut ± to midrib*, patent to recurved, deltoid, rather short, acute or tapering and very acute at apex, with distal margin *straight to convex or angled with 'heavy-shouldered' effect*, dentate to filiform-dentate (upper ones often entire), the proximal margin ± straight, entire or subulate-dentate; interlobes sometimes dentate; terminal lobe of outer leaves small, triangular, that of inner leaves *tending to be larger than pair of lobes below it*, sometimes divided, entire or dentate, subacute to acute at apex; petiole *long*, narrowly winged, *pallid on outer leaves, pink on inner leaves*. Scapes usually equalling leaves, *sometimes distinctly arachnoid-hairy*. Exterior bracts *spreading, separated to form a stellate involucre*, 12–15 × 3–4 mm, unbordered, pale green on upper surface, darker green on lower surface. Capitulum yellow, 40–50 mm in diameter; ligules striped grey-violet; styles exserted, discoloured; pollen present. Achenes straw-coloured; body 3.0 mm; cone 0.7 mm.

Probably introduced. Grassy places, roadsides, wasteland etc. Scattered through Great Britain; not recorded from Ireland. V.cc. 4, 17–19, 21–23, 26, 28, 34, 35, 40, 42, 43, 50, 51, 55, 57, 58, 60–62, 66–70, 72, 73, 75, 81, 85, 89.

Continued overleaf

0   6cm

T. huelphersianum is characterised by its stellate involucre with separated, spreading exterior bracts, and by its angled lateral lobes, cut ± to the midrib. It is not always an easy species to identify, but the long, differently coloured petioles can be a good guide.

96a   T. fagerstroemii Såltin (1971)   Map 96a

A medium-sized to tall plant, with decumbent to erect, narrowly oblong, somewhat crisped leaves 80–300 mm.

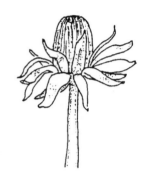

Leaves *light to mid green, glabrous*, interlobes *unblotched to narrowly dark-bordered*, midrib green to slightly coloured; lateral lobes 5–7, regular, patent to recurved, *frequently divided*, deltoid, rather short, subacute at apex, with distal margin straight to convex or sinuate, dentate to denticulate, the proximal margin ± straight, entire or subulate-dentate; interlobes sometimes dentate; terminal lobe of outer leaves small, triangular, that of inner leaves tending to be larger than pairs of lateral lobes, *frequently divided, sometimes more than once*, entire or dentate, subacute to obtuse at apex, *frequently with elongated to lingulate tip, often with obtuse lateral lobules, producing a characteristic 'waisted' effect*; petiole long, narrowly winged, *pink*. Scapes usually equalling leaves, ± *glabrous*. Exterior bracts recurved, 12–15 × 3–4 mm, slightly bordered, pale green, darker green on lower surface. Capitulum yellow, 40–45 mm in diameter; ligules striped grey-violet; styles exserted, discoloured; pollen present. Achenes straw-coloured; body 3.0 mm; cone 0.7 mm.

0   6cm

Introduced. Grassy places and road verges, with a few scattered records through Great Britain. V.cc. 3, 9, 16, 21, 22, 34–36, 42, 44, 51, 57, 58, 60, 62, 70, 72, 77, 82.

Differs from **96** by having paler, glabrous leaves, which are usually unblotched, the inner ones characteristically with both the terminal and the upper lateral lobes strongly divided, so as to appear 'double', and with the terminal lobe ± rounded and with a contracted 'waist'. The scapes are ± glabrous, and the exterior bracts are recurved.

It is generally considered today that *T. sublacerifolium* Hagend., Soest & Zevenb. (1978) is synonymous with *T. fagerstroemii*. In recent years, some British records have been made under the former name.

96b T. hepaticum Rail. (1957)

Similar in general aspect to **96**, but with smoother leaves with a bluish cast and unblotched interlobes and with very regular lobes which are almost invariably entire. All petioles are rose-purple. The capitulum is bigger, about 65 mm in diameter, and a pale ochre-yellow with brown-purple ligule stripes. In fresh material the styles are yellow.

Probably introduced. Breconshire. V.c. 42 only.

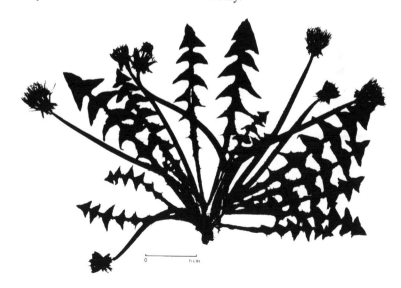

97 T. subundulatum Dahlst. (1923)

Map 97

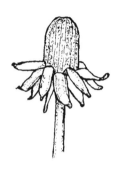

A medium-sized to robust, squat plant, with decumbent to erect, elliptical, crisped leaves 100–250 mm.

Leaves *bright green*, interlobes sometimes *with darkish blotches*, midrib green to slightly coloured; lateral lobes 4–7, *irregular, patent or forward-pointing*, triangular, narrow, rather short, with acute apex, *dentate, often on both margins*, with distal margin straight or concave, the proximal margin straight or convex; terminal lobe *short, wide, divided, often dentate, obtuse to subacute at apex*; petiole short, broad, *narrowly winged at base, bright rose-pink.* Scapes usually equalling or exceeding leaves. Exterior bracts mostly spreading to erect, *12–15 × 4–6 mm, unbordered, dark green.* Capitulum deep yellow, 45 mm in diameter; ligules striped grey-violet; styles exserted, discoloured; pollen present. Achenes straw-coloured; body 3.5 mm; cone 0.8 mm.

Native. Herb-rich water-meadows, lush roadsides etc. Scattered through Great Britain, with one Irish record; locally common. A characteristic component of the flora of the Thames 'meads'. V.cc. 12, 14–17, 19–24, 28, 30, 31, 33, 34, 36, 37, 42, 44, 50, 51, 55, 56, 58, 61, 63, 66–69, 72, 83, 112, H21.

T. subundulatum is characterised by the complex leaf-lobation, usually with at least some lateral lobes pointing forward, and the dark, spreading to erect, heavy, broad bracts. The leaf colours, bright green on the blade, often with interlobe blotches, and bright pink on the petiole, are attractive.

0   6cm

Section *Ruderalia*

A medium-sized to robust plant, with decumbent to erect, narrowly elliptical leaves 100–300 mm.

Leaves *very light green*, interlobes *not obviously blotched*, midrib green to slightly coloured; lateral lobes 4–6, *regular, patent or forward-pointing*, triangular, *narrowing rapidly to an extended patent or forward-pointing process* with acute apex, *dentate mainly on distal margin*, with distal margin straight or concave, the proximal margin straight or convex; terminal lobe *short*, hastate, sometimes divided but *not often dentate*, with apex *gradually elongated, lingulate to a sometimes very thin, acute or subacute tip*; petiole short, broad, unwinged, *bright rose-pink* at base. Scapes usually equalling or exceeding leaves. Exterior bracts mostly *spreading to erect, 12–15 × 4–6 mm, bordered, dark green*. Capitulum deep yellow, 45 mm in diameter; ligules striped grey-violet; styles exserted, discoloured; pollen present. Achenes straw-coloured; body 3.5 mm; cone 0.8 mm.

Introduced. Scattered, mostly on waste ground in cities, as in Dublin, where it is abundant. V.cc. 3, 5, 9, 14, 16–18, 21–23, 29, 30, 35, 42, 43, 50, 66, 67, H21.

Although extremely variable, a most distinctive and readily recognised species. The combination of very pale green leaves and brilliant rose-pink petioles is

seen in no other British species, while the leaf-shape, with an often very finely acuminate apex to the terminal lobe and narrow, usually forward-pointing processes to the lateral lobes, is instantly diagnostic.

A medium-sized, *rather delicate* plant, with erect, oblong to oblanceolate, *flat* leaves 150–300 mm.

Leaves *dark green, somewhat hairy*, interlobes not blotched, midrib *pinkish-red to tip*, with usually at least some small striations; lateral lobes 6–12, *rapidly narrowing from a broad base to become long, narrow, ± linear, forward-pointing or patent or recurved, often deeply divided into parallel linear lobules*, acute to very acute at apex, with distal margin of basal part usually convex, usually with narrow to filiform teeth; terminal lobe usually ± tripartite with a narrow acute apex, but sometimes broader, triangular or helmet-shaped, divided and/or with long teeth; petiole *poorly differentiated, very short, reddish-purple*. Scapes usually equalling leaves. Exterior bracts *recurved, 10–12 × 2.5–3.5 mm, narrowly bordered*, green, paler green on upper surface, sometimes suffused reddish. Capitulum pale yellow, 50 mm in diameter; ligules striped grey-violet; styles exserted, discoloured; pollen present. Achenes straw-coloured; body 4.0 mm; cone 0.6 mm.

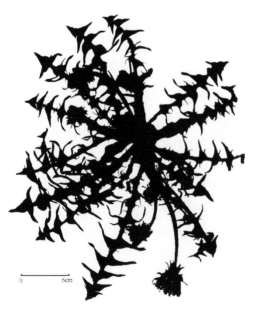

0   6cm

Probably introduced. Grassy places, roadsides, wasteland etc. Scattered throughout Great Britain, with one Irish record; uncommon, though locally abundant. V.cc. 6, 7, 11, 12, 15, 16, 20–23, 25, 27–29, 33–35, 42, 43, 50, 57, 58, 60, 67, 69, 70, 73, 82, 93, 95, 103, 106, 112, H39.

T. pectinatiforme, though variable, is, in its typical form, a very distinctive species characterised by the flat leaves with a pinkish-red midrib and bearing many long narrow linear processes. The bracts are small and recurved.

98a T. caloschistum Dahlst. (1911a)

A medium-sized, *rather delicate* plant, with erect, oblong to oblanceolate, *flat* leaves 150–300 mm.

Leaves *mid-green, somewhat hairy*, interlobes not blotched, sometimes dentate, midrib greenish to faintly coloured; lateral lobes 6–10, *rapidly narrowing from a broad base to become long, narrow, ± linear, forward-pointing or patent or recurved, sometimes divided into parallel linear lobules*, acute to subacute or subobtuse at apex, with distal margin of basal part usually convex, usually with narrow to filiform teeth; interlobes *sometimes dentate*; terminal lobe usually ± tripartite with a narrow acute apex, but sometimes broader, triangular or helmet-shaped, divided and/or with long teeth, on inner leaves often larger than pair of lobes below it and helmet-shaped; petiole *unwinged, at least below, deep reddish-purple*. Scapes usually equalling leaves. Exterior bracts *reflexed, 10–12 × 2–3 mm, unbordered*, green, paler green on upper surface, sometimes suffused reddish. Capitulum pale yellow, 50 mm in diameter; ligules striped grey-violet; styles exserted, discoloured; pollen present. Achenes straw-coloured; body 4.0 mm; cone 0.6 mm.

Introduced. A few records from v.cc. 51, 58, 86, 88.

Similar to **98**, but generally less extreme in leaf-form, often with greeenish midribs to the mid-green leaves, with deep reddish-purple petioles, and with the apices of the lateral lobes often subobtuse. It is more heterophyllous, with inner leaves often having a large helmet-shaped terminal lobe, and the small unbordered exterior bracts are reflexed.

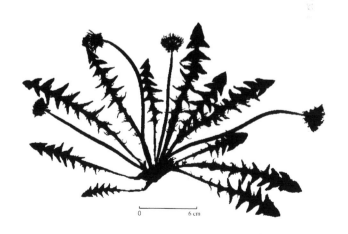

0   6 cm

A *robust* plant, with decumbent to erect, broadly elliptical, *strongly crisped* leaves 150–300 mm.

Leaves *dull green*, somewhat hairy, interlobes sometimes blotched, midrib ± coloured; lateral lobes 5–7, ± patent, *rapidly narrowing from a broad base to form long, narrow, linear, often divided processes*, acute to obtuse and *swollen at apex*, with distal margin ± concave, *grossly dentate*, the proximal margin straight or concave, entire or sometimes with 1 large tooth; interlobes denticulate; terminal lobe *tripartite*, helmet-shaped or sagittate, *but always with an elongated, lingulate or acuminate tip*, acute or very acute at apex; petiole *short, very broadly winged, shining violet-purple*. Scapes usually equalling leaves. Exterior bracts recurved, 12–15 × 2–3 mm, unbordered, green on upper surface, darker green on lower surface. Capitulum yellow, *40 mm in diameter*; outer ligules striped grey-violet; inner ligules with reddish tips; styles exserted, *dark to blackish*; pollen present. Achenes straw-coloured; body *3–3.5 mm, with relatively large, recurved spines apically*; cone *1.0 mm*, spinous at base.

Introduced. Grassy places, roadsides, wasteland etc. Scattered through Great Britain; uncommon. V.cc. 3, 4, 11, 14, 17, 19–21, 25, 26, 28, 30, 33–36, 42, 43, 51, 60, 61, 67, 70, 72, 93.

T. trilobatum is a large, untidy, ugly plant with complex leaves, which is readily identified by its short, broadly winged, shining purple petioles and narrow lingulate or acuminate terminal leaf-lobes. The achenes with large spines and a long cone are diagnostic.

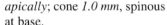

0   6cm

99a   T. planum Raunk. (1906), emend. H. Øllg. (1972)

A *squat*, sometimes robust, ± heterophyllous plant, with prostrate to ascending, elliptical, *plicate* leaves 120–350 mm.

Leaves *very light green*, interlobes often blotched, midrib green to slightly coloured; lateral lobes 4–8, *crowded, regular, recurved to falcate, short*, deltoid, sometimes narrowed to a linear process, *acute to very acute at apex*, with distal margin straight, ± convex or sinuate, *entire or filiform-dentate*, the proximal margin straight or concave; interlobes ± dentate, *plicate*; terminal lobe *of outer leaves tripartite, with or without elongated tip, of inner leaves* sometimes larger than pair of lateral lobes below it, *helmet-shaped or triangular with long, acute tip*; petiole ± *broadly winged, pink or, on outer leaves, pallid*. Scapes *glabrous*, usually equalling leaves. Exterior bracts recurved, *somewhat twisted*, 12–14 × 3.5–5 mm, unbordered, green, paler green on upper surface. Capitulum yellow, *50 mm in diameter*; ligules striped grey-violet; styles exserted, *discoloured*; pollen present. Achenes straw-coloured; body *2.5 mm*; cone *0.4 mm*.

Introduced on the verges of major roads, uncommon. V.cc. 19, 25, 28, 35, 42, 43, 60, 61, 62, 67, 73, 89.

A distinctive species sharing the elongated terminal lobes and broad-winged petioles of **99**, but with pale green leaves with short, crowded, regular lateral lobes and noticeably plicate interlobes. It is heterophyllous, the inner leaves having longer terminal lobes. The scapes are glabrous and the exterior bracts rather twisted.

A medium-sized heterophyllous plant, *often becoming robust* later, with spreading to erect, elliptical to oblanceolate, ± *flat* leaves 80–200(–300) mm.

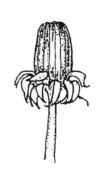

Leaves *mid-green*, interlobes *usually dark-blotched at first*, midrib green to slightly coloured; lateral lobes 5–6, regular, usually opposite, patent to slightly recurved, deltoid, rather short, acute to subacute at apex, with distal margin straight or convex, *strongly dentate (with teeth often black-tipped)*, the proximal margin ± straight, usually entire; interlobes *usually dentate*; later leaves much larger and less regularly lobed, often losing the interlobe blotches and teeth; terminal lobe on early (outer) leaves usually rather small and triangular, with apex subacute to obtuse but sometimes with an elongated tip, sometimes divided but *usually entire*, on later (inner) leaves often much larger, dentate and divided; petiole narrowly winged or unwinged, *light to deep pink*. Scapes usually equalling leaves. Exterior bracts *irregularly untidy, claw-shaped,* spreading to recurved, *11 × 2–3 mm, unbordered*, green suffused with purple, *becoming purple*, on upper surface, darker on lower surface. Capitulum yellow, 40–50 mm in diameter; ligules striped *purple*; styles exserted, *discoloured*; pollen present. Achenes straw-coloured; body 3.2 mm; cone 0.7 mm. 2n=21, 22, 23, 24, 48.

Native or possibly introduced. Grassy places, roadsides, wasteland etc. Widespread throughout the British Isles; one of our commonest dandelions. V.cc. 1, 3, 5–6, 8, 9, 11, 12, 14, 15–30, 32–39, 41, 42, 44–46, 49–51, 53–62, 66–101, 103–106, 108, 109, 111, 112, H5, H11, H12, H20, H21, H28, H33, H36, H38–H40.

T. polyodon is best distinguished from the other strongly dentate species with coloured petioles and dark interlobes by the untidy, wispy, claw-shaped, purplish exterior bracts. It is very distinctive and easily identified early in the year, but later forms are more problematical. Compare with **101** and **103b** (which are less heterophyllous).

100a   T. multicolorans Hagend., Soest & Zevenb. (1972)

Map 100a

A medium-sized heterophyllous plant, *often becoming robust* later, with spreading to erect, elliptical to oblanceolate, *crisped* leaves 80–200(–300) mm.

Leaves *dark green, rough*, interlobes *obviously blotched*, midrib coloured; lateral lobes 5–6, regular, *tending to be alternate*, patent to slightly recurved, deltoid, rather short, acute to subacute at apex, with distal margin straight, convex or concave, *usually dentate (with teeth often black-tipped)*, the proximal margin ± straight, usually entire; interlobes *dentate*; terminal lobe on early (outer) leaves usually rather small, long-triangular, cordate, with apex subacute to obtuse but sometimes with an elongated tip, *often divided, often dentate or denticulate*, on later (inner) leaves often much larger, dentate and divided; petiole narrowly winged or unwinged, *dark purple*. Scapes usually equalling leaves. Exterior bracts spreading, *11 × 3.5 mm, bordered, green* on upper surface, darker green on lower surface. Capitulum mid to dark yellow, 40–50 mm in diameter; ligules striped *purple*; styles exserted, *yellowish*; pollen present. Achenes straw-coloured, spinulose; body 3.2 mm; cone 0.7 mm.

Introduced. A few records, mainly from the south of England. V.cc. 3, 6, 9, 19, 22, 23, 33–35, 37, 60.

Superficially similar to **100**, but differing subtly in leaf-shape (see silhouette), particularly by tending to have more distant, more obtuse, somewhat alternate leaf-lobes, and especially by the green exterior bracts, which are spreading and wider, and by the yellowish styles.

100b   T. nitidum Hagend., Soest & Zevenb. (1976)

A medium-sized plant, with spreading to erect, elliptical to oblanceolate leaves 80–200 mm.

Leaves *mid to dark, rather shiny green, sometimes heavily black-blotched*, inter-lobes *with a black margin*, midrib *reddish*; lateral lobes 5–6, regular, patent to slightly recurved, deltoid, rather short, subacute to obtuse at apex, with distal margin straight or convex, *strongly dentate (with teeth often black-tipped)*, the proximal margin straight to convex, usually entire; interlobes *dentate*; terminal lobe on early (outer) leaves usually rather small and triangular, with apex sub-acute to obtuse but sometimes with an elongated tip, sometimes divided, but *usually entire*, on later (inner) leaves often much larger, dentate and divided; petiole narrowly or broadly winged, *dark purple*. Scapes usually equalling leaves. Exterior bracts spreading to recurved, *11 × 3.5 mm, faintly bordered*, dark green suffused with purple, *becoming purple*, on upper surface, even darker on lower surface. Capitulum yellow, 40–50 mm in diameter; ligules striped *grey-violet*; styles exserted, *somewhat discoloured*; pollen present. Achenes straw-coloured; body 3.2 mm; cone 0.7 mm.

Introduced. Scattered in England and Wales. V.cc. 6, 19, 33, 34, 44, 50, 51, 58, 70.

Similar to **100** and **100a**, but the leaves are mid to dark green, shiny, with a red-dish midrib, sometimes heavily black-blotched, and with regular leaf-lobes, often blunt, often with convex proximal margins; the styles are less discoloured than in **100** and the exterior bracts are dark green, suffused purple, and 3.5 mm wide.

Section *Ruderalia*

101   T. incisum H. Øllg. (1972)

Map 101

A medium-sized to tall, *rather delicate* plant, with spreading to erect, elliptical, *crisped* leaves 80–200(–300) mm.

Leaves *dark green*, interlobes *strongly blotched*, midrib green to slightly coloured; lateral lobes 5–8, *distant*, patent to slightly recurved, triangular to deltoid, *long, rapidly narrowing from broader base, acute to subacute at apex, strongly dentate on both margins*; interlobes also *strongly dentate*; terminal lobe *tripartite*, with an elongated, lingulate tip, often divided, often with long teeth; petiole *unwinged* (or narrowly winged), *pink*. Scapes usually equalling leaves. Exterior bracts spreading to recurved, *10–12 × 2.5–4.5 mm*, unbordered, green, becoming suffused with purple later, on upper surface, darker on lower surface. Capitulum yellow, 45–50 mm in diameter; outer ligules striped purple, inner ligules *with blackish apices*; styles exserted, discoloured; pollen present. Achenes straw-coloured; body 3.8 mm; cone 0.7 mm.

Introduced. Grassy places, roadsides, wasteland etc. Scattered throughout Great Britain; uncommon, except in the London area, where it is locally abundant. V.cc. 17, 20–23, 34, 50, 57, 58, 63, 67–70, 72, 80, 89, 93, 94, 112.

T. incisum is characterised by the dark green, black-blotched leaves with long, narrow, highly dissected ('incised') lateral lobes with teeth on both margins. It differs from **100** *T. polyodon* by the lingulate terminal lobe and the broader exterior bracts.

Section *Ruderalia*

263

102 T. xanthostigma H. Lindb. (1910)   Map 102

A medium-sized, *robust, squat, heterophyllous* plant, with erect, *oblanceolate*, ± crisped leaves 100–250 mm.

Leaves *mid to dark green*, interlobes usually *very obviously dark-blotched*, midrib green to slightly coloured; lateral lobes *3–5*, regular, patent to recurved, deltoid or triangular, rather short, acute to subacute at apex, with distal margin straight or slightly angled (convexly or concavely), entire or, lower on leaf, fili-form-dentate, the proximal margin ± straight; interlobes *often with 1 triangular tooth*; terminal lobe *on early (outer) leaves rather small triangular, sagittate or cordate, on later (inner) leaves large, wide, often hastate, entire or once-divided*, obtuse to subacute at apex; petiole a quarter to a third length of leaf, *narrowly winged, purple*. Scapes usually exceeding leaves. Exterior bracts spreading to recurved 10–13 × 3–4 mm, *bordered*, pale green on upper surface, darker green on lower surface. Capitulum yellow, *40–50 mm in diameter*; ligules striped grey-purple; styles exserted, *yellowish-orange in both fresh and dried condition*; pollen present. Achenes *straw-coloured*; body 3.0 mm; cone 0.5 mm. 2n=24.

Possibly introduced. Grassy places, roadsides, wasteland etc. Widespread throughout Great Britain and locally common; scattered in Ireland. V.cc. 1–4, 12, 15–23, 26, 28–30, 34–36, 41–44, 46, 50, 55, 57, 59–62, 67, 69, 70, 74, 76–80, 85, 98, 99, 104, 108, 112, S, H14, H21, H38, H39.

T. xanthostigma is a generally common species, distinguished by the heavy interlobe blotching and by the yellow-ish-orange styles, which are unusual in Section *Ruderalia*. The heterophylly is often clear and diag-nostic.

A plant superficially similar to **102**, but non-heterophyllous, with dark green leaves with whitish petioles and with distinctive exterior bracts, the outer of which are much narrower (1.5 mm) than the inner (4 mm), has been called *T. 'anceps'* H. Øllg. ined. and has been recorded from v.cc. 3, 20, 34, 35, 39, 40, 44, 50, 51, 58–60, 69 and 70. Only recently recognised and possibly under-recorded in favour of **102**.

102a T. longisquameum H. Lindb. (1907)   Map 102a

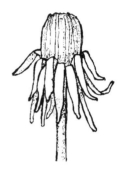

A medium-sized plant, with erect, *oblong* leaves 70–200(–250) mm.

Leaves *mid to dark green*, interlobes usually *very obviously dark-blotched*, midrib green to slightly coloured; lateral lobes *3–5*, regular, slightly to strongly recurved, deltoid, rather short, acute to subacute at apex, with distal margin straight or slightly angled (convexly or concavely), entire or, lower on leaf, filiform-dentate, the proximal margin ± straight; interlobes ± *dentate*; terminal lobe *narrowly triangular, often divided, subacute to acute at apex, sometimes with elongated lingulate tip*; petiole a quarter to a third length of leaf, *unwinged or almost so, purple.* Scapes usually exceeding leaves. Exterior bracts spreading to recurved, 10 mm × 3–4 mm (or more), *unbordered or bordered*, pale green on upper surface, darker green on lower surface, sometimes suffused with purple. Capitulum yellow, *45 mm in diameter*; ligules striped grey-purple; styles exserted, *yellowish*; pollen present. Achenes *olive-brown*; body 3.0 mm; cone 0.5 mm.

Native. Grassy places, often in rather 'natural' habitats; locally common, especially near the sea. V.cc. 3, 5, 12, 15–23, 25, 26, 28, 29, 33, 34, 39, 41, 42, 57, 60, 66–68, 70, 73, 77, 81, 83, 85, 86, 89, 96, 99, 112, H38, H40.

Very similar to **102**, from which it is best distinguished by the leaf-shape, being scarcely heterophyllous, with narrower leaves with a long (but narrower), ± acute, often strongly once- to thrice-divided terminal lobe; the petioles are ± unwinged and the achenes olive-brown.

102b T. scotiniforme Dahlst. ex G.E. Haglund (1936)

A medium-sized plant, with erect, *oblanceolate-spathulate* leaves 80–150 mm.

Leaves *dark or bluish-green*, interlobes *heavily blotched black*, midrib green to slightly coloured; lateral lobes *3–5*, regular, patent to slightly recurved, deltoid, rather short, acute to subacute at apex, with distal margin *usually convex, dentate or filiform-dentate*, the proximal margin straight or concave, entire; interlobes *denticulate*; terminal lobe *triangular or ± shortly lingulate at apex, often shallowly once-divided and rounded*; petiole *narrowly winged, pink*. Scapes usually equalling leaves, *thickly arachnoid-hairy when young*. Exterior bracts ± recurved, 10–15 × 4–5 mm, *unbordered*, pale green on upper surface, green on lower surface. Capitulum yellow, *35 mm in diameter*; ligules striped grey-violet; styles exserted, *yellow*; pollen present. Achenes *straw-coloured*; body 3.5 mm; cone 0.4 mm.

Introduced? Grassy places, mainly in the south of England; scarce. V.cc. 15, 17–20, 22, 23, 34, 42, 60, 69, 70, 112.

Shares in common with **102** and **102a** leaves with strong blackish blotches and ± yellow styles. In common with **102d**, the leaves have regular deltoid lateral lobes, but these are dentate or filiform-dentate on their usually convex distal margins and have a pink petiole. The young scapes are thickly arachnoid-hairy.

0   6cm

102c T. maculatum Jord. (1852)

A medium-sized, *robust, squat* plant, with erect, *elliptical* leaves 100–250(–300) mm.

Leaves *very light green* (though darkening in the herbarium), interlobes usually *very obviously dark-blotched*, midrib green to slightly coloured, *becoming darker towards apex*; lateral lobes 5–7, patent to recurved or sometimes forward-pointing, deltoid or triangular, sometimes divided, to become double, acute at apex or *sometimes narrowing abruptly to form a subobtuse lingulate process*, with distal margin convex, entire or dentate to denticulate, the proximal margin ± straight; terminal lobe *triangular, tripartite or hastate, sometimes divided*, subacute to acute at apex or *sometimes with a subobtuse lingulate tip*; petiole *narrowly winged, that of outer leaves whitish, that of inner leaves somewhat reddish*. Scapes usually exceeding leaves. Exterior bracts spreading to recurved, 10–15 × 3–5 mm, *unbordered*, pale green on upper surface, darker green on lower surface. Capitulum yellow, *50–65 mm in diameter*; ligules striped grey-purple; styles exserted, *discoloured*; pollen present. Achenes *straw-coloured*; body 4.0 mm; cone 0.4–0.7 mm.

Introduced. Recorded only from West Gloucestershire (v.c. 34).

Another species with strongly black-blotched leaves, not dissimilar to **102a** and **102b** in leaf-shape, but with more lobes and with pale yellowish-green leaves, the outer (only) with whitish petioles, and with discoloured styles; on some leaves the lateral and terminal lobes form narrow, subobtuse lingulate processes. See also **103a** *T. subxanthostigma*.

0   6cm

Section *Ruderalia*   267

102d T. sublongisquameum M.P. Christ. (1971)

A medium-sized, *robust, squat* plant, with erect, *elliptical* leaves 100–250 mm.
Leaves *mid to dark green*, interlobes *blotched*, midrib *from a pallid petiole
increasingly dark towards leaf apex, with a pattern of small striations on upper
surface*; lateral lobes *3–5*, regular, patent to recurved, usually deltoid, rather
short, very acute to mucronate at apex, with distal margin straight or slightly
angled (convexly or concavely), entire, or, lower on leaf, filiform-dentate, the
proximal margin ± straight; terminal lobe *triangular to hastate, with apex acute
to mucronate*; petiole a quarter to a third length of leaf, *narrowly winged,
whitish*. Scapes usually exceeding leaves. Exterior bracts spreading to recurved,
15 × 3.5–4.5 mm, unbordered, pale green on upper surface, darker green on
lower surface. Capitulum yellow, *40–50 mm in diameter*; ligules striped grey-
purple; styles exserted, *discoloured*; pollen present. Achenes *straw-coloured or
greyish-brown*; body 3.0 mm; cone 0.4–0.7 mm.

Introduced. Road verges in England and Scotland. V.cc. 17, 20, 23, 35, 60, 99.

The dark leaf-blotches and regular, usually deltoid leaf-lobes give this species a
resemblance to the four preceding species, but all petioles are whitish (graduat-
ing to darker midribs) and the styles are discoloured. *T. sublongisquameum* has
rather narrow leaves, but this species has few distinctive characters, though the
exterior bracts are rather large.

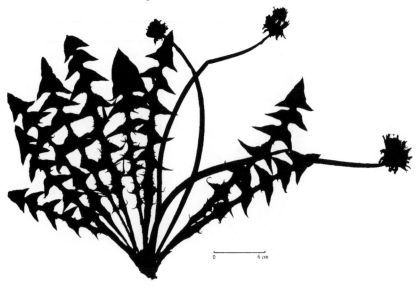

0   6 cm

Section *Ruderalia*

103 T. fasciatum Dahlst. (1906) Map 103

A medium-sized to robust plant, with spreading to erect, oblong to oblanceolate leaves 100–250 mm.

Leaves dark green, interlobes usually *very obviously blotched (tar-coloured)*, midrib *green*; lateral lobes *3–5, regular, forward-pointing, patent or recurved, deltoid or triangular*, acute at apex, with distal margin straight or slightly angled (convexly or concavely) or sigmoid, *entire or, on lower lobes, filiform-dentate*, the proximal margin ± straight; interlobes *often with 1 or 2 filiform teeth*; terminal lobe *helmet-shaped to subsagittate, often slightly narrowed near the middle, obtuse at apex, sometimes with mucronate tip*; petiole narrowly winged, *pale rose to dull reddish-purple*. Scapes usually exceeding leaves. Exterior bracts spreading to recurved, *crowded, ± imbricate, broad, 12–15 × 3.5–4.5 mm, unbordered, pale green, later somewhat suffused with purple, on upper surface*, darker green on lower surface. Capitulum yellow, 50 mm in diameter; ligules striped grey-purple; styles exserted, *discoloured*; pollen present. Achenes straw-coloured; body 3.0 mm; cone *0.5 mm*. 2n=24.

Possibly native. Grassy places, almost invariably on roadsides etc. Widespread in England and Wales and locally abundant; scattered through the rest of the British Isles. V.cc. 3, 4, 6–9, 12, 15–23, 26–30, 32–36, 39, 40, 42, 43, 46, 47, 50, 51, 55, 57–62, 66, 67, 69–73, 76–78, 81–83, 89, 93, 96, 98, 106, 109, 112, S, H21, H38.

T. fasciatum has heavily blotched interlobes and capitula with characteristically crowded, wide, imbricate, pale green exterior bracts. The variously directed lateral leaf-lobes and the shape of the terminal lobe are also characteristic. It is a common species; most species that it is likely to be confused with have yellow styles and (except **102** *T. xanthostigma*) are much less common.

103a T. subxanthostigma M.P. Christ. ex H. Øllg. (1978)

A medium-sized plant, with erect, elliptical leaves 150–200 mm.

Leaves dark green, interlobes *tar-coloured*, midrib *pink to purple*; lateral lobes *5–6*, regular, *recurved, patent or forward-pointing*, broad, ± *triangular*, acute at apex, with distal margin ± straight, *entire*, the proximal margin straight; interlobes *crisped, entire or rarely filiform-dentate*; terminal lobe *rather small, triangular or cordate-sagittate, acute at apex*; petiole narrowly winged, *darkish pink to purple*. Scapes usually exceeding leaves. Exterior bracts spreading to recurved, *13 × 4 mm, unbordered, violet-coloured on upper surface*, dark green on lower surface. Capitulum deep yellow, 45–50 mm in diameter; ligules striped grey-violet; styles exserted, *discoloured*; pollen present. Achenes straw-coloured, shortly spinulose; body 3.6 mm; cone *0.8 mm*.

Introduced. A few records from v.cc. 22, 23, 42, 60.

Closely related to **103**, and only readily differentiated when well developed, when the more numerous (5–6) ± triangular lateral leaf-lobes, small, acute, ± triangular terminal lobes and dark purple petioles are evident. Diagnostically, the achene cone is longer (0.8 mm). Compare also with **102c** *T. maculatum*, which has whitish outer petioles.

0 ⎯⎯⎯⎯ 6cm

Section *Ruderalia*

103b T. acutifidum M.P. Christ. (1936)

A medium-sized to robust plant, with decumbent to erect, ± oblong, *somewhat crisped* leaves 100–250 mm.

Leaves dull, dark green, interlobes *blotched*, midrib *green to slightly coloured*; lateral lobes *4–6*, regular, *patent to recurved, deltoid*, acute to very acute at apex, with distal margin straight to convex, *dentate, sometimes with 1 or more large teeth, or filiform-dentate*, the proximal margin straight or concave, entire; interlobes *often dentate, sometimes with 1 large tooth*; terminal lobe *broadly triangular or helmet-shaped*, sometimes divided, *subacute to obtuse at apex*; petiole narrowly winged or unwinged, *green to faintly pink*. Scapes usually exceeding leaves. Exterior bracts recurved, *11–14 × 2.5–3.5 mm, ± slightly bordered, becoming purple on upper surface*, darker green on lower surface. Capitulum yellow, 40–50 mm in diameter; ligules striped grey-purple; styles exserted, *discoloured*; pollen present. Achenes straw-coloured; body 3.5 mm; cone *0.6 mm*.

Introduced. Known only from Wales, the West Midlands and northern England. V.cc. 35, 39, 40, 50, 51, 58, 60, 66.

Superficially very similar to **100** *T. polyodon*, but non-heterophyllous and with slightly broader exterior bracts which are not claw-shaped.

0   6 cm

104   T. melanthoides Dahlst. ex M.P. Christ. & Wiinst.   **Map 104**
in Raunk. (1934)

A medium-sized plant, with spreading to erect, *narrowly oblanceolate* leaves 50–180(–250) mm, ± flat, but crisped at interlobes.

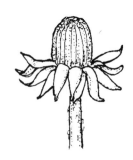

Leaves *pale to mid bluish-green, hairy, with small punctate spots*, interlobes usually blotched, midrib green to slightly coloured; lateral lobes 3–5, regular, slightly recurved, deltoid, rather short, acute at apex, with distal margin ± straight or sigmoid, *dentate*, the proximal margin straight or concave; interlobes crisped, dentate; terminal lobe *somewhat longer than pair of lateral lobes below, ± helmet-shaped, sagittate or tripartite*, cordate at base, sometimes once-divided on one side, acute or very acute at apex; petiole narrowly winged, pink to purple. Scapes usually exceeding leaves. Exterior bracts spreading to recurved, 12 × 2–4 mm, unbordered or with an obvious border, *green on upper surface*, darker green on lower surface. Capitulum deep yellow, 45 mm in diameter; ligules striped *dark purple-brown*; styles exserted, discoloured; pollen present. Achenes *brown*; body 3.0 mm; cone 0.4–0.7 mm.

Native. Water meadows and old pastures. Scattered sites in Great Britain; uncommon. V.cc. 22, 23, 34, 35, 40, 42, 50, 51, 58, 60, 66, 67, 89.

The hairy, bluish, sparsely spotted leaves are rare amongst British and Irish members of *Ruderalia*, and this species could be classified in Section *Naevosa* or in Section *Borea* Sahlin ex A. J. Richards (1985). However, the exterior bracts and general facies are those of a member of *Ruderalia*. The coloration and the leaf-shape are, together, distinctive.

0   6 cm

105   T. lucidum Dahlst. (1910)

A medium-sized to robust plant, with spreading to erect, *narrowly obovate-spathulate, crisped* leaves 80–220 mm.

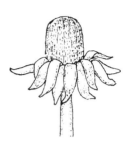

Leaves *pale shining green*, interlobes often blotched, dentate or denticulate, midrib greenish-pink; lateral lobes *2–3*, regular, patent to recurved, deltoid, rather short, acute at apex, with distal margin ± straight, dentate, the proximal margin straight to convex, entire; interlobes *dentate or denticulate*; terminal lobe *long, up to one quarter length of leaf, to 80 mm, ± helmet-shaped, sometimes waisted*, sometimes divided, sometimes ± dentate, obtuse to subacute at apex; petiole *unwinged, shining purple*. Scapes usually exceeding leaves. Exterior bracts *spreading to erect, 10–15 × 3.5–4.0 mm*, bordered, dark green, *pruinose*. Capitulum yellow, 40 mm in diameter; ligules striped grey-violet; styles exserted, discoloured; pollen present. Achenes straw-coloured; body 3.0 mm; cone 0.5 mm. 2n=24.

Probably introduced. Grassy places, roadsides, wasteland etc. A few widely scattered sites in England; uncommon. V.cc. 19, 21, 23, 31, 33, 34, 44, 67, 70.

T. lucidum is characterised by the large spreading to erect bracts, bright purple petioles, shining pale green leaves and large helmet-shaped terminal lobe. The bracts and general coloration are highly suggestive of *Celtica* species, but *T. lucidum*, particularly when well-grown late in the season, is much more gross, untidy and 'three-dimensional' than members of that section.

Section *Ruderalia*

105a T. sundbergii Dahlst. (1912)

A robust plant, with erect, *oblong to oblanceolate-spathulate, highly crisped, fleshy* leaves 150–300 mm.

Leaves *pale, slightly glaucous green, glabrous,* interlobes sometimes blotched, midrib green to slightly coloured; lateral lobes *2–3,* regular, *heavy,* patent to recurved, deltoid, rather short, acute to subacute at apex, ± abruptly narrowed from a broad base, with distal margin ± convex, entire (or filiform-dentate on lower lobes), the proximal margin straight or concave; interlobes *sometimes dentate, plicate;* terminal lobe *hastate,* rarely divided, subacute at apex; petiole *narrowly winged, pink.* Scapes usually equalling leaves. Exterior bracts *spreading to recurved, 14–16* × *4–6 mm,* slightly bordered, grey-green, *pruinose* on upper surface, darker green on lower surface, *with pink tips.* Capitulum yellow, 40–45 mm in diameter; ligules striped grey-violet; styles exserted, discoloured; pollen present. Achenes straw-coloured; body 2.5 mm; cone 0.5 mm.

Introduced. Scattered records in v.cc. 17, 30, 42, 67.

When fresh, easily distinguished by the highly crisped, fleshy, pale, glabrous, slightly glaucous leaves. The exterior bracts are large, spreading to recurved, grey-green, pruinose, with pink tips, and slightly bordered. British material placed here resembles the type, but differs in having discoloured, not yellow, styles and may not be conspecific.

0 ⊢——— 6cm

Section *Ruderalia*

DISTRIBUTION MAPS

The maps were produced by the DMAP program written by Dr Alan Morton. The species chosen for mapping are those for which either there are enough records for the distribution to be clearly perceptible or the few records are geographically significant; in the latter case a larger-scale map of part of the British Isles is often used. Records are mapped by 10-km squares and all those available by the end of 1996 are included. Allowance should always be made for the obvious influence of the small number of active taraxacologists; for example, note the relative frequency of records in South Wales, Cheshire, Cumberland and Northumberland.

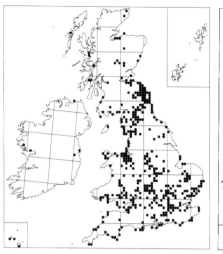

1 T. lacistophyllum

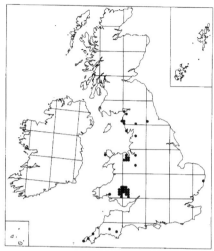

1a T. inopinatum

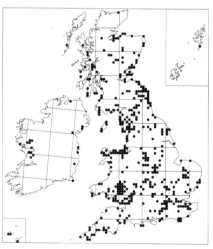

2 T. brachyglossum

2a T. scanicum

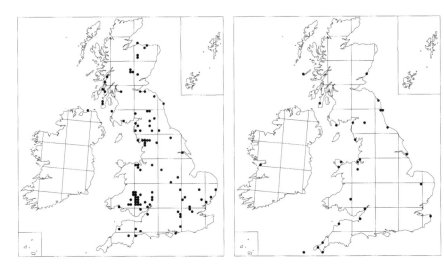

3 T. argutum

4 T. arenastrum

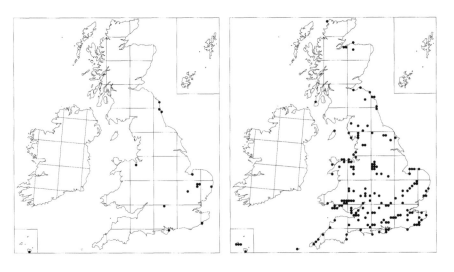

4a T. commixtum

5 T. rubicundum

Section *Erythrosperma*

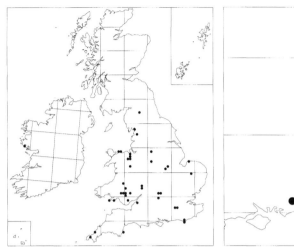

5a T. parnassicum

5b T. cenabense

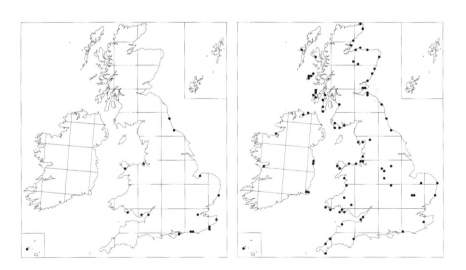

6 T. dunense

7 T. haworthianum

279

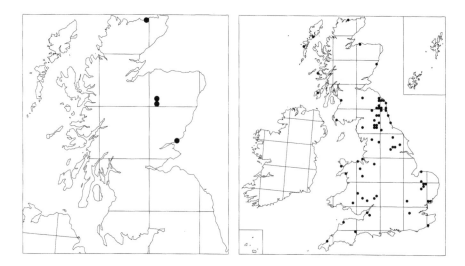

7a T. gotlandicum   **8 T. proximum**

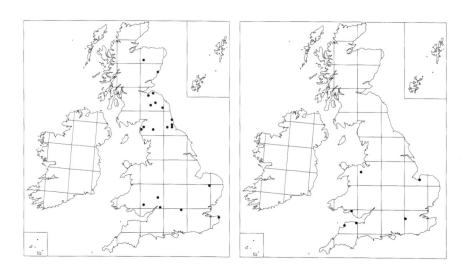

8a T. proximiforme   **8c T. disseminatum**

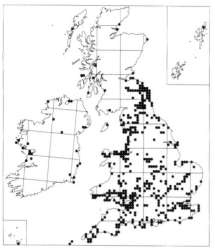

9 T. oxoniense

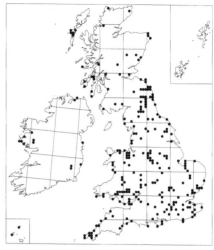

10 T. fulviforme

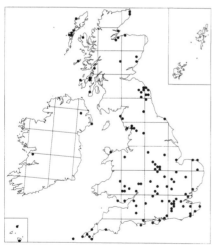

11 T. fulvum

11a T. scoticum

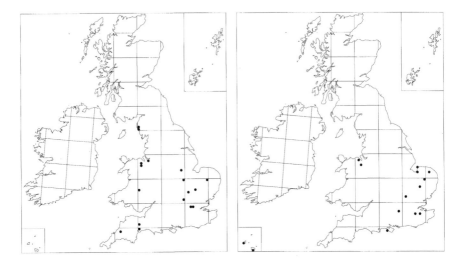

11b T. falcatum   **11c T. retzii**

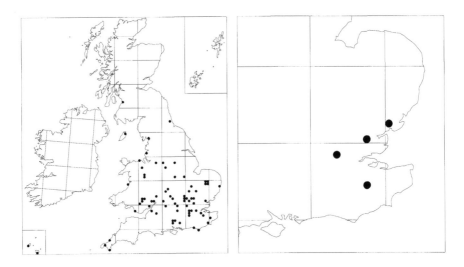

12 T. glauciniforme   **12a T. wallonicum**

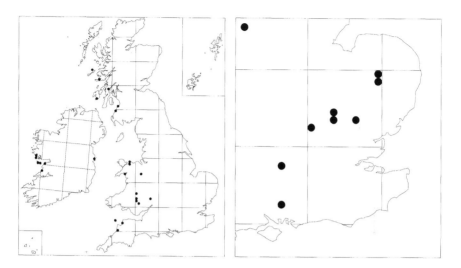

13 T. degelii

13a T. acutum

14 T. tortilobum

Section *Obliqua*

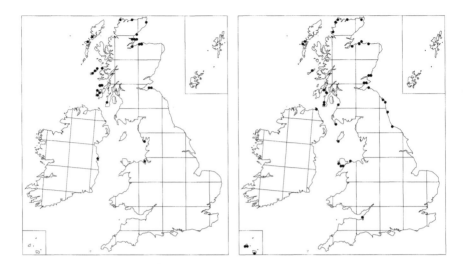

15 T. obliquum   **15a T. platyglossum**

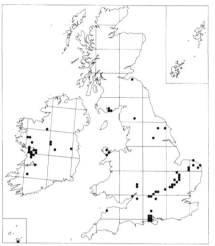

16 T. palustre

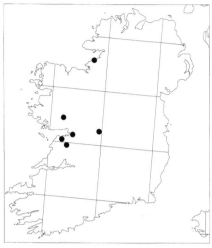

16a T. webbii

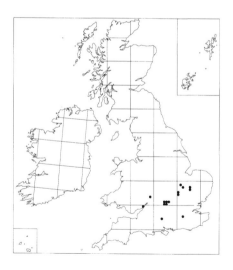

17 T. anglicum

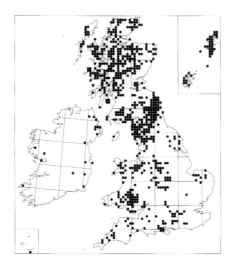

18 T. faeroense

18a T. geirhildae

18b T. serpenticola

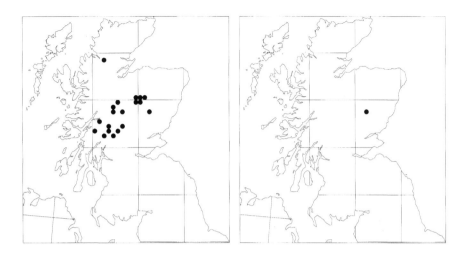

19 T. ceratolobum

19a T. clovense

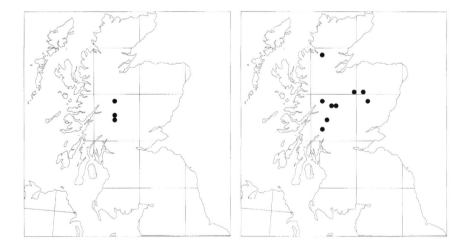

19b T. xiphoideum

20 T. craspedotum

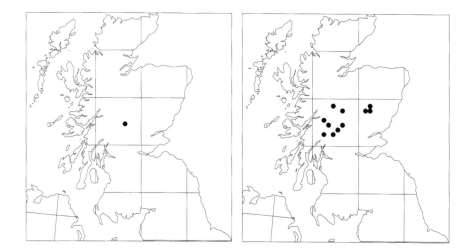

21 T. cymbifolium   **22 T. pycnostictum**

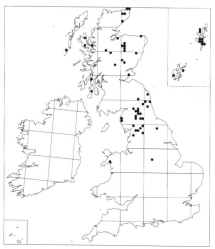

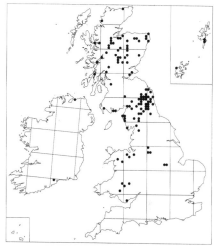

23 T. naevosum

23a T. naevosiforme

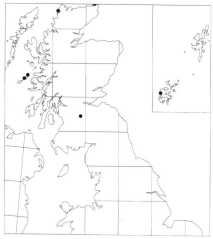

23b T. rubellum

24 T. euryphyllum

Section *Naevosa*

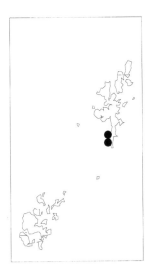 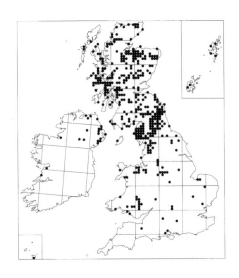

24a T. hirsutissimum   **25 T. maculosum**

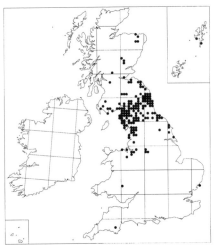 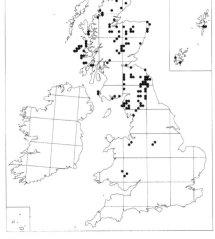

26 T. pseudolarssonii   **27 T. subnaevosum**

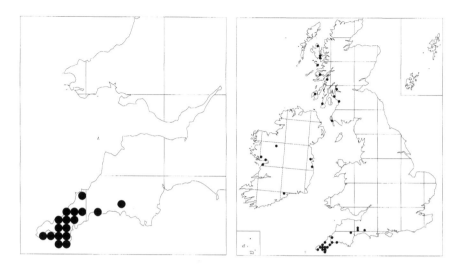

27a T. cornubiense

28 T. drucei

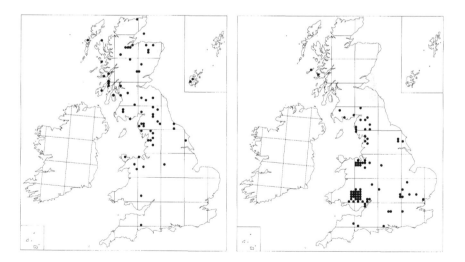

29 T. stictophyllum

29a T. richardsianum

Section *Celtica*

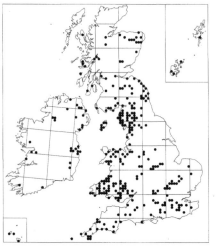

30 T. gelertii

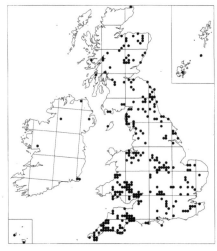

31 T. bracteatum

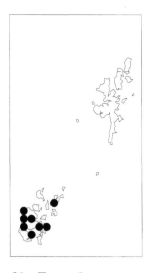

31a T. orcadense

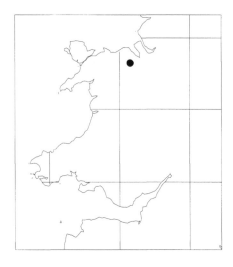

31b T. nietoi

292

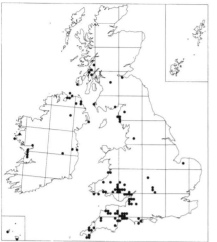

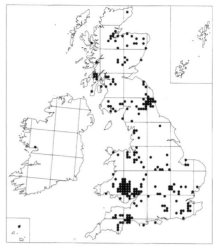

32 T. britannicum

33 T. subbracteatum

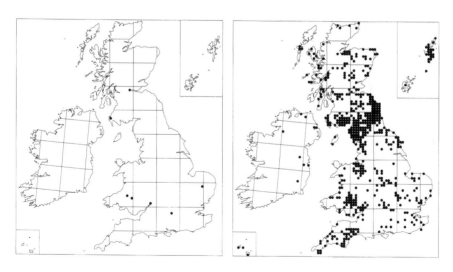

33a T. oellgaardii

34 T. duplidentifrons

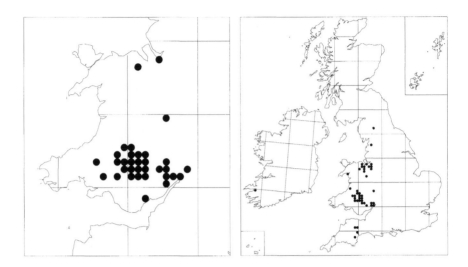

34a T. porteri　　　　　　　　　**35 T. celticum**

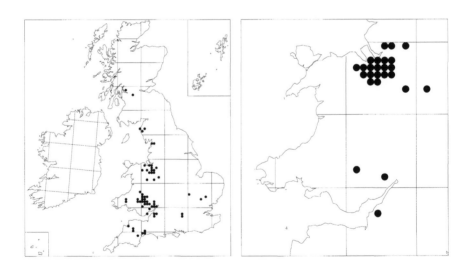

36 T. hesperium　　　　　　　　　**36a T. 'cestrense'**

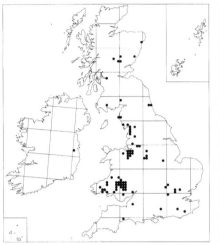

37 T. excellens

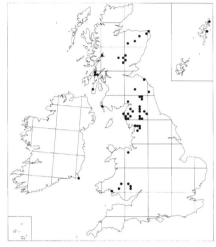

38 T. inane

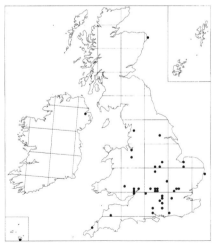

39 T. fulgidum

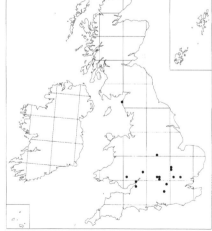

39a T. tamesense

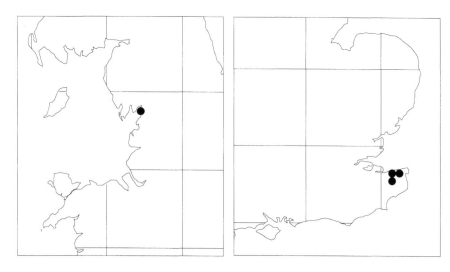

39b T. texelense

39c T. hygrophilum

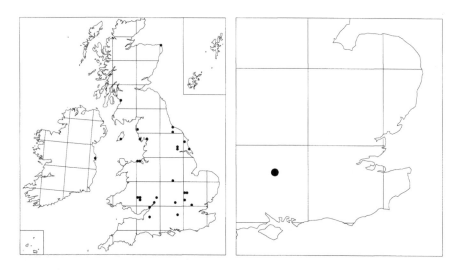

40 T. haematicum

40a T. akteum

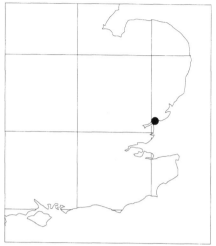

40b T. beeftinkii

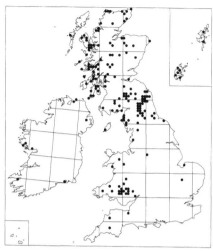

41 T. landmarkii

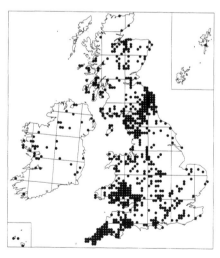

42 T. nordstedtii

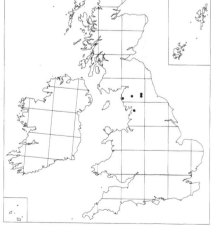

42a T. pseudonordstedtii

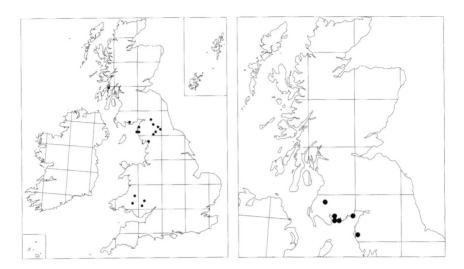

42b T. berthae

42c T. olgae

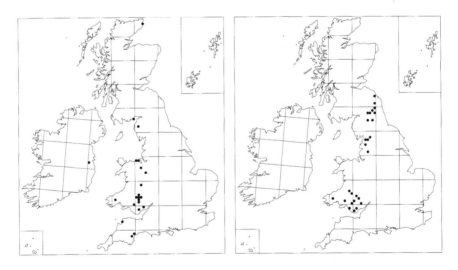

42d T. cambricum

42e T. lancastriense

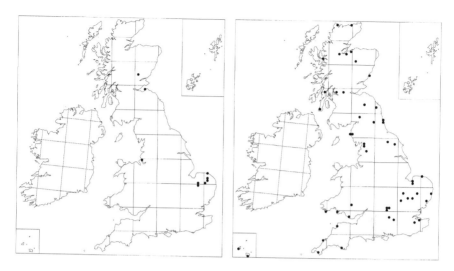

42f T. palustrisquameum

43 T. ostenfeldii

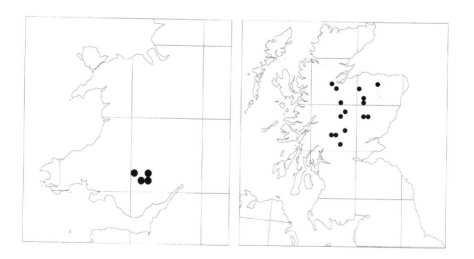

43a T. breconense

44 T. caledonicum

Section *Celtica*

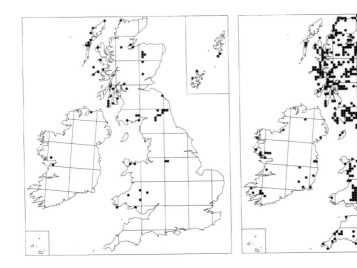

45 T. fulvicarpum

46 T. unguilobum

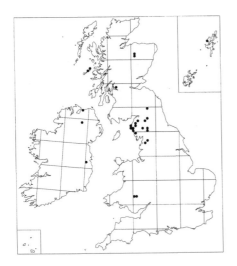

46a T. luteum

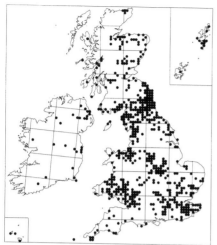

47 T. hamatum

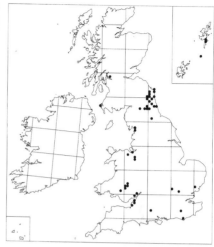

47a T. hamatulum

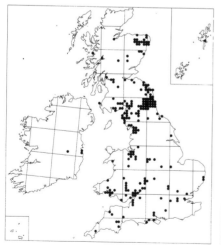

48 T. subhamatum

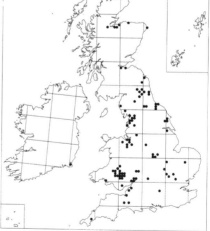

48a T. marklundii

Section *Hamata*

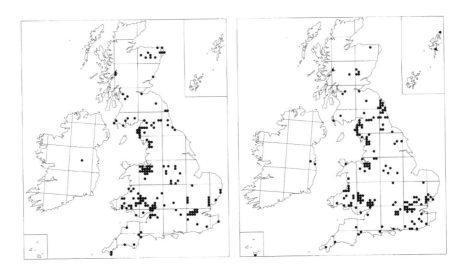

49 T. hamiferum

49a T. quadrans

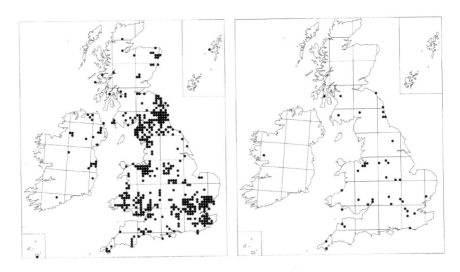

50 T. pseudohamatum

50a T. fusciflorum

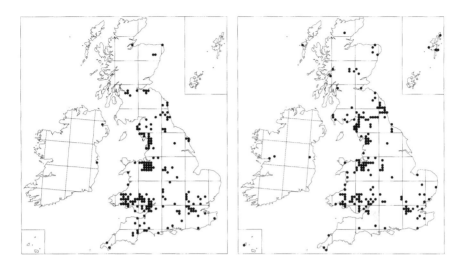

51 T. boekmanii

52 T. atactum

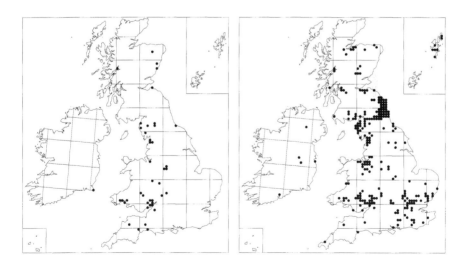

52a T. sahlinianum

53 T. hamatiforme

Section *Hamata*

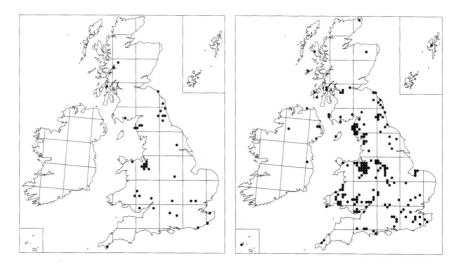

54 T. kernianum   **55 T. lamprophyllum**

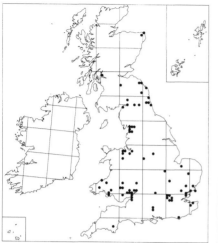

56 T. laeticolor

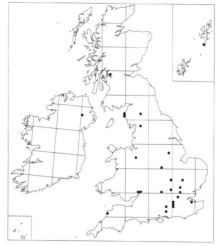

56a T. macrolobum

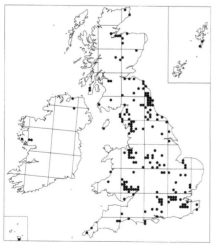

57 T. pannucium

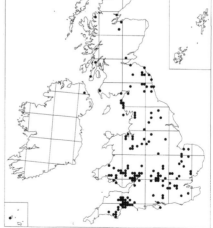

57a T. subexpallidum

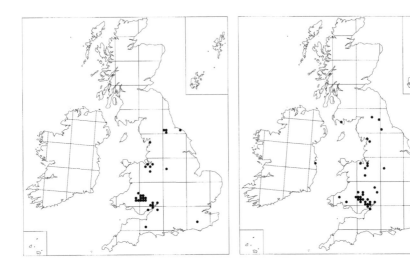

58 T. corynodes   **59 T. undulatum**

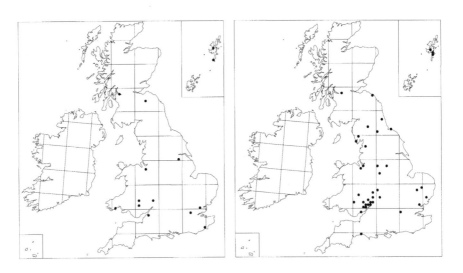

59a T. tenebricans   **59b T. dilaceratum**

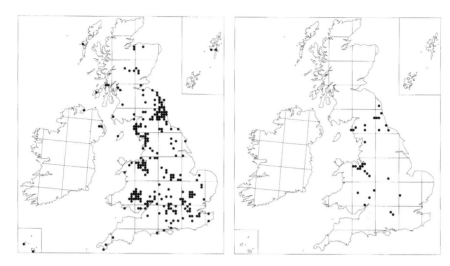

60 T. alatum

60a T. horridifrons

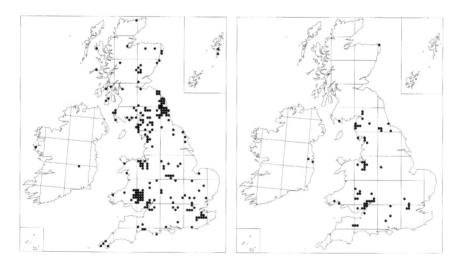

61 T. insigne

62 T. pannulatiforme

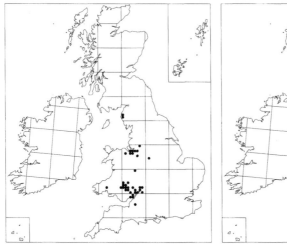

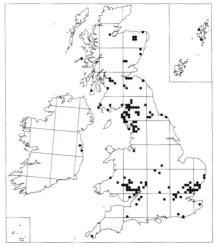

62a T. nigridentatum

63 T. laticordatum

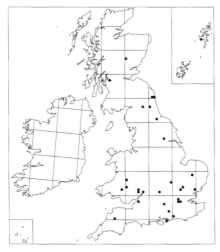

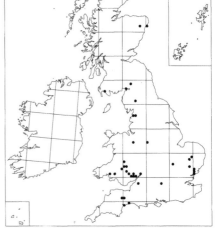

63a T. pallescens

63c T. necessarium

Section *Ruderalia*

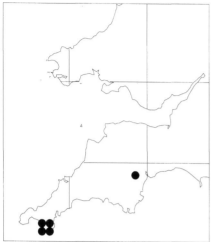

63d T. margettsii

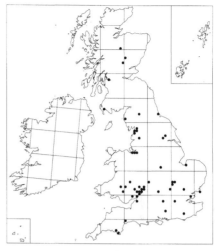

64 T. sublaeticolor

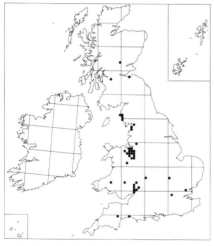

64a T. lepidum

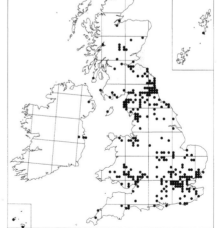

65 T. expallidiforme

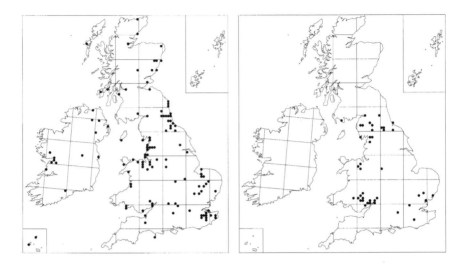

65a T. subcyanolepis   **65b T. pallidipes**

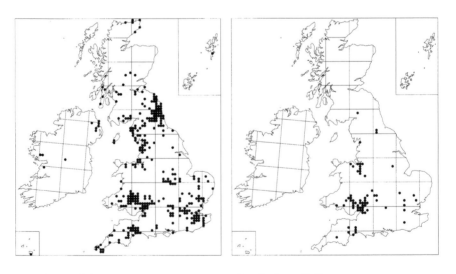

66 T. croceiflorum   **66a T. lacerifolium**

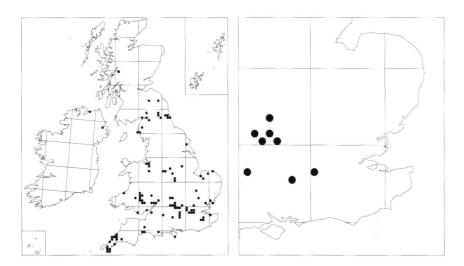

67 T. stenacrum   **67a T. cherwellense**

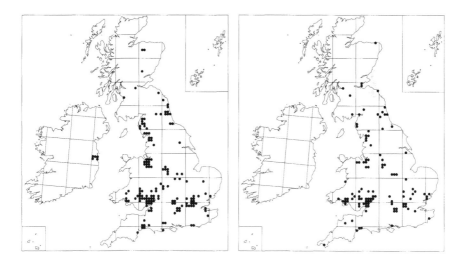

69 T. undulatiflorum   **70 T. piceatum**

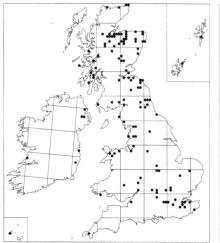

70a T. cyanolepis

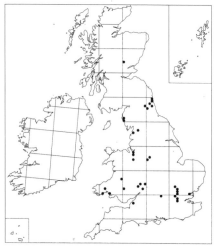

71 T. tumentilobum

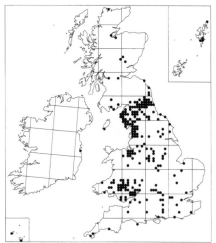

73 T. ancistrolobum

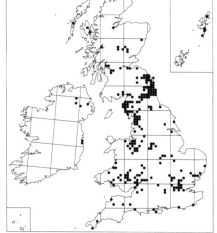

74 T. sellandii

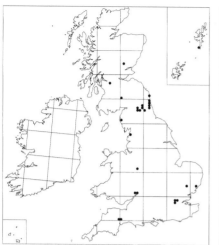

75 T. altissimum

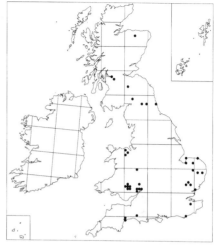

76 T. aequisectum

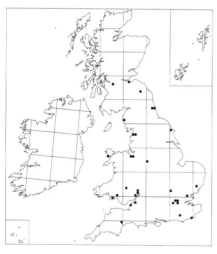

77 T. interveniens

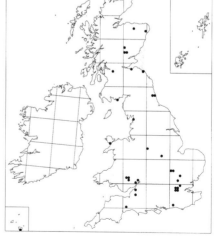

78 T. angustisquameum

Section *Ruderalia*

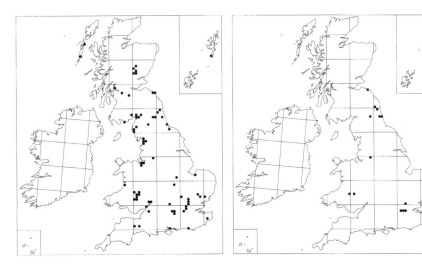

79 T. adiantifrons

79a T. retroflexum

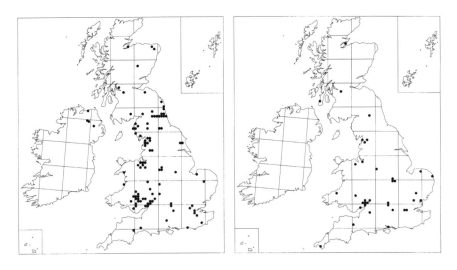

80 T. aequilobum

80a T. latissimum

Section *Ruderalia*

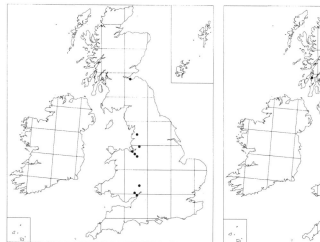
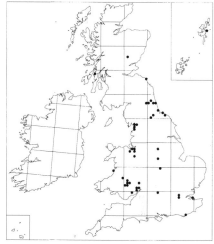

80c T. edmondsonianum

81 T. acroglossum

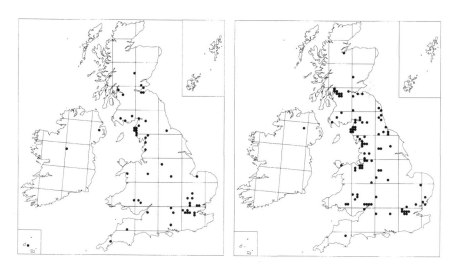

81a T. exsertum

82 T. exacutum

315

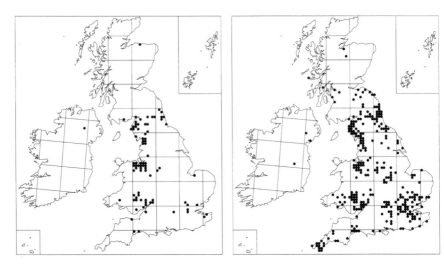

83 T. pannulatum   **84 T. lingulatum**

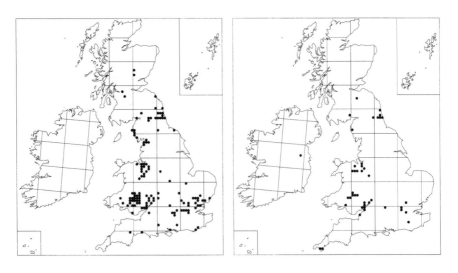

85 T. rhamphodes   **85a T. procerisquameum**

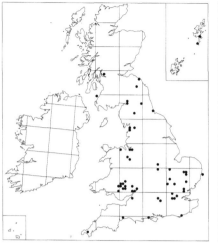

86 T. vastisectum

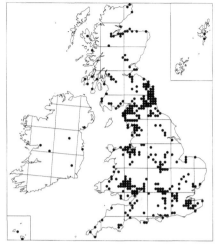

87 T. cordatum

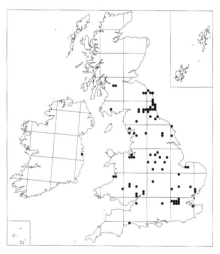

88 T. sagittipotens

88a T. hexhamense

Section *Ruderalia*

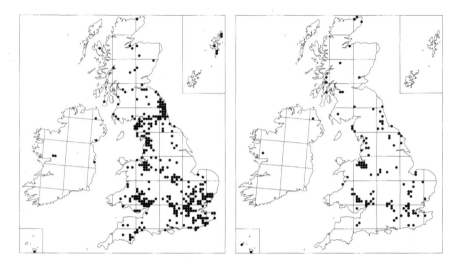

89 T. ekmanii

89b T. aurosulum

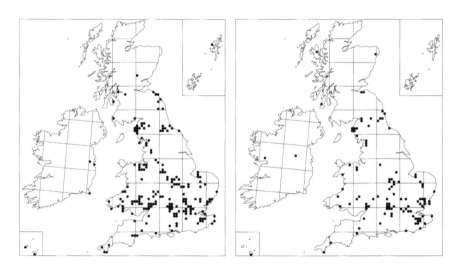

91 T. oblongatum

91a T. cophocentrum

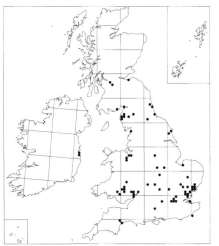

92 T. pachymerum

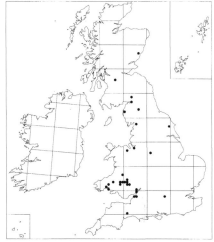

93 T. dilatatum

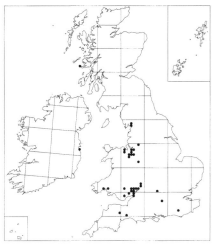

94 T. sinuatum

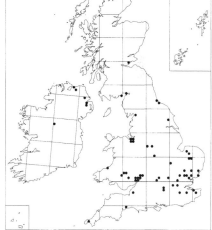

94a T. laciniosifrons

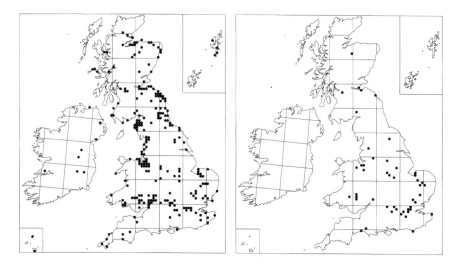

95 T. dahlstedtii

95a T. obliquilobum

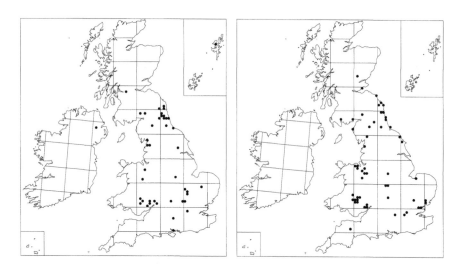

95c T. latisectum

96 T. huelphersianum

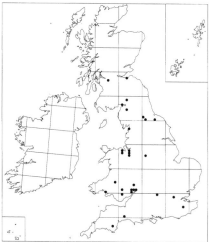

96a T. fagerstroemii

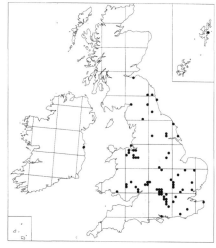

97 T. subundulatum

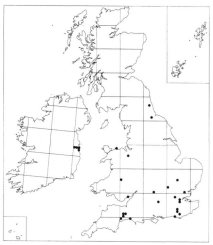

97a T. pulchrifolium

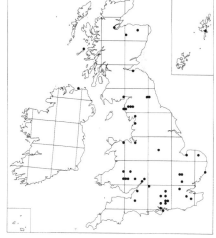

98 T. pectinatiforme

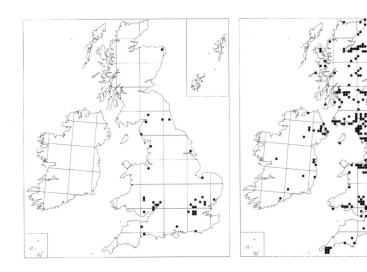

99 T. trilobatum   **100 T. polyodon**

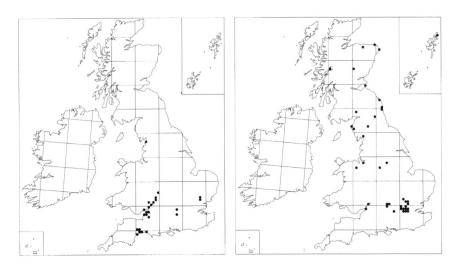

100a T. multicolorans   **101 T. incisum**

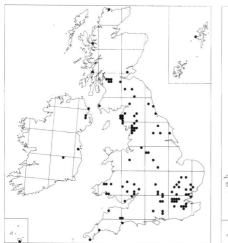

102 T. xanthostigma

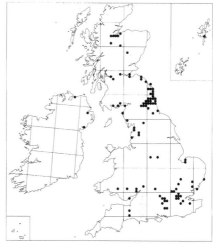

102a T. longisquameum

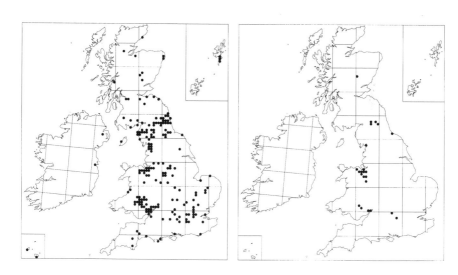

103 T. fasciatum

104 T. melanthoides

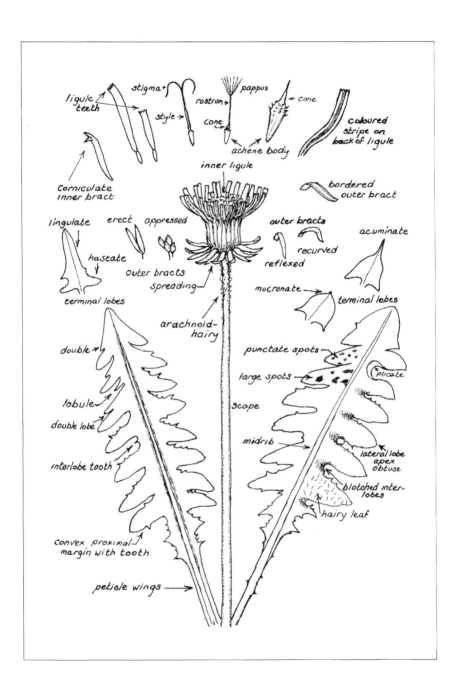

GLOSSARY

Achene: the fruit or cypsela. Measurements are given for the achene body and for the cone (q.v.).

Achene colour: This refers to the colour of the achene body; the cone is normally ± the same colour, while the rostrum is always ± silvery.

Acuminate: gradually tapering to a point with concave sides (see Figure 2).

Acute: sharply pointed with more or less straight sides (see Figure 2).

Arachnoid-hairy: hairy, with the indumentum having the appearance of a spider's web.

Arcuate: curved so as to form a quarter of a circle or more.

Attenuate: gradually tapering.

Bifurcate: dividing into two branches.

Border (of exterior bracts of the involucre): Most frequently, the edge of the exterior bract has a pale or scarious border. This is often very narrow and is best examined with a lens.

Callose: thickened.

Capitulum: the flower-head.

Cone: the apical appendage to the achene body, connecting it to the rostrum (q.v.).

Connate: fused, though distinct in origin.

Corniculate (of the exterior and interior bracts of the involucre of species in Sections *Erythrosperma* and *Obliqua*): having a small appendage on the lower (outer) surface near the apex. On the interior bracts this is most easily seen in bud.

Crisped (of leaves): arranged in three dimensions, especially owing to the plicate nature of interlobes and interlobe teeth.

Deltoid (of leaf-lobes): with the proximal margin shorter than the distal margin (see Figure 1; cf *triangular*).

deltoid   triangular

Figure 1: Shapes of leaf-lobes

Distal: away from the point of attachment (cf *proximal*).

Elongated: drawn out as a distinct process (q.v.) at the apex (including *acuminate* and *lingulate*).

Exterior bracts (or outer phyllaries): the smaller external row of bracts surrounding the involucre, which may be described as appressed (to the involucre, i.e. to the interior bracts), erect, spreading, arcuate, recurved, hanging vertically or reflexed. These bracts vary in their posture, and these adjectives describe the average bract posture in a mature involucre bud. See also *border.*

Falcate: sickle-shaped.

Filiform: very narrow and frequently flexuose (literally, wire-shaped).

Hamate (of lateral leaf-lobes or basal lobules of terminal leaf-lobes): hooked, with the distal margin convex and the proximal margin concave.

Hastate: shaped like a spear-head, with the two equal basal lobes turned outwards (cf *sagittate*).

Heterophyllous: with the inner leaves at flowering time differing conspicuously from the outer leaves, often by having a much larger terminal lobe.

Imbricate: closely overlapping, like tiles on a roof.

Interior bracts (or inner phyllaries): the bracts of the involucre within the exterior bracts (q.v.).

Interlobes: the narrower parts of the leaf-blade lying between the lobes.

Involucre: the exterior and interior bracts of the capitulum together, best viewed in late bud.

Involute: rolled inwards.

Laciniate: highly and irregularly divided and cut (as opposed to *lobate*).

Ligule stripe: The back (outer face) of a ligule of a marginal (outer) floret usually has a single-coloured (grey, purple, red, etc.) longitudinal stripe.

Ligule teeth: The apex of a central (inner, tubular) ligule has teeth, which may be either yellow or coloured red, black, etc.

Lingulate: narrowly tongue-shaped (see Figure 2).

Lobate: gently divided, with more or less rounded projections (cf *laciniate*).

Lobule: a small lobe positioned on a lobe or at an interlobe.

Mucronate: abruptly terminating in a small point (see Figure 2).

Obtuse: blunt, terminating at an angle greater than 90° (see Figure 2).

Patent: spreading more or less at right-angles.

Petiole colour: This is judged on the underside of the petiole. Petioles which are said to be "green" or "pallid" are very frequently white in the fresh-condition. In species with petioles coloured pink or purple on the underside, the very base is often white; ignore this. Also, species which typically have coloured petioles may be 'blanched' in shaded or etiolated plants.

326

Petiole wings: Proximally, below the lobes, the midrib becomes the petiole. The petiole is said to be winged (or alate) if the lamina continues to the ground. It is said to be unwinged (or exalate) if the basal portion is lacking a lamina.

Plicate: folded into a third dimension.

Pollen present: The emerging style and stigma branches brush past the anther tube, thus carrying pollen to the exterior. The presence of pollen on fresh or dried material is usually determined by examining the style and stigma branches with a lens. After rain, it may prove necessary to pull out the anther tubes and examine these with a lens.

Process: a clearly differentiated narrow projection on a leaf-lobe.

Proximal: towards the point of attachment (cf *distal*).

Pruinose: covered with a 'bloom' which rubs off.

Punctate (of spots): like small dots.

Regular (of lateral leaf-lobes): ± equal in size and arranged at ± regular intervals.

Rostrum: the beak of the fruit, connecting the cone of the achene to the pappus; very narrow and usually silver in colour.

Rugose: wrinkled.

Sagittate: shaped like an arrow-head, with the two equal basal lobes directed downwards (cf *hastate*).

Scape length: This is described relative to the leaves at the time of first flowering.

Sigmoid: shaped like an 'S'.

Sinuate: having a wavy margin.

Spathulate (of leaves): shaped like a spoon or paddle, with the petiole forming the 'shaft'.

Spinulose: bearing small spine-like projections.

Style colour: This refers also to the colour of the stigma branches. In some species the style and stigma branches are usually yellow in both a fresh and a dried condition, but poor drying or disease can discolour them in the press. It may be wise to examine several heads. Fresh stigmas which are dark in colour usually dry black in the press.

Triangular (of leaf-lobes): forming two sides of an isosceles triangle, so that the apex is patent to the centre of the base (see Figure 1; cf *deltoid*).

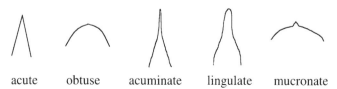

acute   obtuse   acuminate   lingulate   mucronate

Figure 2: Shapes of leaf-lobe apices

REFERENCES

BORGVALL, T. 1960. The *Taraxacum* Flora of Boluslän. *Acta Horti gotoburgensis*, **23**: 1–40.

BRENNER, M. 1907. Några *Taraxacum officinale*-former. *Meddelanden af Societas pro Fauna et Flora fennica*, **34**: 22–26.

BRUMMIT, R.K. & POWELL, C.E. 1992. *Authors of Plant Names*. Kew: Royal Botanic Gardens.

CHRISTIANSEN, M.P. 1936. Nye *Taraxacum*-arter af Gruppen *Vulgaria*. *Dansk botanisk Arkiv*, **9 (2)**: 1–32, tab. 1–23.

CHRISTIANSEN, M.P. 1942. The *Taraxacum*-flora of Iceland. In: J. Gröntved, O. Paulsen & T. Sørensen (eds), *The Botany of Iceland*, **3 (3)**, pp. 229–343, plates I–XXXXIV.

CHRISTIANSEN, M.P. 1971. Nye *Taraxacum*-arter i Danmark. *Botanisk Tidsskrift*, **66**: 76–97.

DAHLSTEDT, H. 1905. Om skandinaviska *Taraxacum*-former. *Botaniska Notiser*, **1905**: 145–172.

DAHLSTEDT, H. 1906. Einige wildwachsende *Taraxaca* aus dem Botanischen Garten zu Upsala. In: R. Sernander, N. Svedelius & C.O. Norén (eds), *Botaniska Studier tillägnade F.R. Kjellman*, pp. 164–183. Uppsala.

DAHLSTEDT, H. 1907. *Taraxacum*. In: E. Warming *et al.* (eds), *Botany of the Færöes*, **3**. Copenhagen & Christiania. (Page 840).

DAHLSTEDT, H. 1909. Nya skandinaviska *Taraxacum*-arter, jämte öfversikt af grupperna *Erythrospermm* och *Obliqua*. *Botaniska Notiser*, **1909**: 167–179.

DAHLSTEDT, H. 1910. Östsvenska *Taraxaca*. *Arkiv för Botanik (Stockholm)*, **9 (10)**: 1–74.

DAHLSTEDT, H. 1911a. Nya östsvenska *Taraxaca*. *Arkiv för Botanik (Stockholm)*, **10 (6)**: 1–36.

DAHLSTEDT, H. 1911b. Västsvenska *Taraxaca*. *Arkiv för Botanik (Stockholm)*, **10 (11)**: 1–74.

DAHLSTEDT, H. 1912. Nordsvenska *Taraxaca*. *Arkiv för Botanik (Stockholm)*, **12 (2)**: 1–122.

DAHLSTEDT, H. 1913. *Taraxaca scandinavica exsiccata*, **3**. Stockholm. (Page 14).

DAHLSTEDT, H. 1920. *Taraxacum anglicum* Dahlst., n. sp. In: G.C. Druce (ed.), Plant notes, etc., for 1919. *Report of the botanical Exchange Club of the British Isles*, **5**: 547–585.

DAHLSTEDT, H. 1921. De svenska arterna av släktet *Taraxacum*. I. *Erythrosperma*. II. *Obliqua*. *Acta Florae Sueciae*, **1**: 1–160.

DAHLSTEDT, H. 1923. Some new English species of *Taraxacum*. *Report of the botanical Exchange Club of the British Isles*, **6**: 773–780.

DAHLSTEDT, H. 1925a. *Taraxaca* från västra Norge. *Bergens Museums Årbok*, **1923–24 (6)**: 1–36.

DAHLSTEDT, H. 1925b. Om Ölands *Taraxacum*-flora. *Arkiv för Botanik (Stockholm)*, **19 (18)**: 1–19.

DAHLSTEDT, H. 1926. *Taraxacum orcadense*, Dahlstedt, n. sp. In: H.H. Johnston, Additions to the Flora of Orkney. [9]. *Transactions and Proceedings of the botanical Society of Edinburgh*, **29**: 297–307.

DAHLSTEDT, H. 1927a. *Taraxacum fulvicarpum*, Dahlstedt, n. sp. In: H.H. Johnston, Additions to the Flora of Orkney. [10]. *Transactions and Proceedings of the botanical Society of Edinburgh*, **29**: 408–428.

DAHLSTEDT, H. 1927b. *T. britannicum* Dahlst., nova sp. In: G.C. Druce (ed.), Plant notes, etc., for 1926. *Report of the botanical Exchange Club of the British Isles*, **8**: 18–37.

DAHLSTEDT, H. 1929a. *Taraxacum argutum* Dahlst., nova sp. *T. glauciniforme* Dahlst., nova sp. *T. duplidentifrons* Dahlst., nova sp. In: G.C. Druce (ed.), Plant notes, etc., for 1928. *Report of the botanical Exchange Club of the British Isles*, **8**: 608–641.

DAHLSTEDT, H. 1929b. Über einige orientalische *Taraxacum* - Arten. *Acta Horti bergiani*, **9**: 1-36, 2pp. of plates.

DAHLSTEDT, H. 1930a. *T. oblongatum* Dahlst., nova sp. In: G.C. Druce (ed.), Plant notes, etc., for 1929. *Report of the botanical Exchange Club of the British Isles*, **9**: 18–44.

DAHLSTEDT, H. 1930b. De svenska arterna av släktet *Taraxacum*. VIII. – *Spectabilia*. *Kungliga svenska Vetenskapsakademiens Handlingar*, **ser. 3, 9 (2)**: 1–99, 5 plates, 6 maps.

DAHLSTEDT, H. 1932. *T. pannulatiforme* Dahlst., n. sp. *T. pseudohamatum* Dahlst., n. sp. *T. tanyphyllum* Dahlst., n. sp. In: G.C. Druce (ed.), Plant notes, etc., for 1931. *Report of the botanical Exchange Club of the British Isles*, **9**: 552–574.

DAHLSTEDT, H. 1935. Nya skandinaviska *Taraxaca*. *Botaniska Notiser*, **1935**: 295–316. [G.E. Haglund evidently wrote much of this paper, but he headed it "H. Dahlstedt †" and attributed the new species described in it to Dahlstedt. As it seems that these are based on Dahlstedt's notes rather than being full descriptions written by him before his death, the species should perhaps be attributed to "Dahlst. ex G.E. Haglund".]

DANDY, J.E. 1969. *Watsonian Vice-Counties of Great Britain*. London: Ray Society.

DUDMAN, A.A. & RICHARDS, A.J. 1994. Seven new species of *Taraxacum* Wigg. (Asteraceae), native to the British Isles. *Watsonia*, **20**: 119–132.

FLORSTRÖM, B.L. 1914. Studier öfver *Taraxacum*-Floran i Satakunta. *Acta Societatis pro Fauna et Flora fennica,* **39 (4):** 1–125.

HAGENDIJK, A., SOEST, J.L. VAN & ZEVENBERGEN, H.A. 1972. Neue Taraxacumarten der Niederlande. *Acta botanica neerlandica,* 21: 491–511.

HAGENDIJK, A., SOEST, J.L. VAN & ZEVENBERGEN, H.A. 1973. Neue Taraxacumarten der Niederlande II. *Acta botanica neerlandica,* 22: 616–636.

HAGENDIJK, A., SOEST, J.L. VAN & ZEVENBERGEN, H.A. 1974. Neue Taraxacumarten der Niederlande. III. *Acta botanica neerlandica,* 23: 439–459.

HAGENDIJK, A., SOEST, J.L. VAN & ZEVENBERGEN, H.A. 1976. Neue Taraxacumarten der Niederlande. IV. *Acta botanica neerlandica,* 25: 81–105.

HAGENDIJK, A., SOEST, J.L. VAN & ZEVENBERGEN, H.A. 1978. Neue Taraxacumarten der Niederlande V. *Acta botanica neerlandica,* 27: 307–331.

HAGLUND, G.E. 1934a. Några nya eller i Sverige nyfunna *Taraxacum*-arter. *Botaniska Notiser,* **1934:** 1–42.

HAGLUND, G.E. 1934b. Om Bornholms *Taraxacum*-flora. *Botaniska Notiser,* **1934:** 369–402.

HAGLUND, G.E. 1935a. *Taraxaca* från södra och mellersta Sverige samt Danmark. *Botaniska Notiser,* **1935:** 96–130.

HAGLUND, G.E. 1935b. Some *Taraxacum*-species from Ireland and Wales cultivated in the Botanic Garden of Lund. *Botaniska Notiser,* **1935:** 429–438.

HAGLUND, G.E. 1936. Några *Taraxaca* huvudsakligen från västra Sverige. *Acta Horti gotoburgensis,* **11:** 19–41.

HAGLUND, G.E. 1937. On some *Taraxacum* species of the Group *Vulgaria* Dahlst. *Botaniska Notiser,* **1937:** 56–62.

HAGLUND, G.E. 1938. Bidrag till kännedomen om Skandinaviens *Taraxacum*-flora. II. *Botaniska Notiser,* **1938:** 499–508.

HAGLUND, G.E. 1942. *Taraxacum.* In: B. Holmgren, *Blekinges Flora,* pp. 322–346. Karlshamn.

HAGLUND, G.E. 1943. Några nya *Taraxaca* från Skåne och Danmark. *Botaniska Notiser,* **1943:** 232–242.

HAGLUND, G.E. 1946. Zur *Taraxacum*-flora der Insel Öland. *Botaniska Notiser,* **1946:** 335–363.

HAGLUND, G.E. 1947. Über die *Taraxacum*-flora der Insel Rügen. *Svensk botanisk Tidskrift,* **41 (1):** 81–103.

HAGLUND, G.E. & LILLIEROTH, C.G. 1941. Beiträge zur *Taraxacum*-Flora der Inselgruppe Lofoten. *Nytt Magasin for Naturvidenskapene (Oslo),* **82:** 83–99.

HAGLUND, G.E. & MORANDER, R. 1937. Till Hjälmarlandskapens *Taraxacum*-flora. *Svensk botanisk Tidskrift*, **31**: 339–353.

HAWORTH, C.C. 1990. Six native species of *Taraxacum* new to the British Isles. *Watsonia*, **18**: 131–138.

HAWORTH, C.C. & RICHARDS, A.J. 1990. The lectotypification and revision of Dahlstedt's species of *Taraxacum* Weber based on British or Irish plants. *Watsonia*, **18**: 125–130.

HJELT, H. 1924–1926. Conspectus Florae fennicae, VII. *Acta Societatis pro Fauna et Flora fennica*, **54**: 1–397.

HUGHES, J. & RICHARDS, A.J. 1988. The genetic structure of populations of sexual and asexual *Taraxacum* (dandelions). *Heredity*, **60**: 161–171.

HUGHES, J. & RICHARDS, A.J. 1989. Isozymes, and the status of *Taraxacum* (Asteraceae) agamospecies. *Botanical Journal of the Linnean Society*, **99**: 365–376.

JORDAN, A. 1852. *Pugillus Plantarum novarum praesertim gallicarum*. Paris. (Page 117).

KING, L.M. & SCHAAL, B.A. 1990. Genotype variation within asexual lineages of *Taraxacum officinale*. *Proceedings of the National Academy of Sciences of the U.S.A.*, **87**: 998–1002.

KIRSCHNER, J. & ŠTĚPÁNEK, J. 1987. Again on the sections in *Taraxacum* (Cichoriaceae) (Studies in *Taraxacum* 6). *Taxon*, **36**: 608–617.

KIRSCHNER, J. & ŠTĚPÁNEK, J. 1997. A nomenclatural checklist of supraspecific names in *Taraxacum*. *Taxon*, **46**: 87–98.

LAMBINON, J. & SOEST, J.L. VAN 1962. Deux *Taraxaca* nouveaux de Belgique. *Lejeunia*, **n.s.**, **8**: 1–2.

LANGE, T.A. 1938. Jämtlands kärlväxtflora. *Acta botanica fennica*, **21**: 1–204.

LINDBERG, H. 1907. *Taraxacum*-former från södra och mellerstra Finland. *Acta Societatis pro Fauna et Flora fennica*, **29 (9)**: 1–48.

LINDBERG, H. 1909. Nytt bidrag till kännedomen af *Taraxacum*-formerna i södra och mellersta Finland. *Meddelanden af Societas pro Fauna et Flora fennica*, **35**: 13–31.

LINDBERG, H. 1910. Finska *Taraxacum*-former. *Meddelanden af Societas pro Fauna et Flora fennica*, **36**: 5–6.

LINDBERG, H. & MARKLUND, G. 1911. *Acta Societatis pro Fauna et Flora fennica*, **34 (7)**: 5.

LINDMAN, C.A.M. 1926. *Svensk Fanerogamflora*. Ed. 2. Stockholm. (*Taraxacum* on pp. 559–589 by H. Dahlstedt).

MARKLUND, G. 1925. Nya *Taraxaca*. *Acta Societatis pro Fauna et Flora fennica*, **55 (5)**: 1–25, with plates.

MARKLUND, G. 1938. Die *Taraxacum*-Flora Estlands. *Acta botanica fennica*, **23**: 1–150.

MARKLUND, G. 1940. Die *Taraxacum*-Flora Nylands. *Acta botanica fennica*, **26**: 1–187.

MOGIE, M. & RICHARDS, A.J. 1983. Satellited chromosomes, systematics and phylogeny in *Taraxacum* (Asteraceae). *Plant Systematics and Evolution*, **141**: 219–229.

ØLLGAARD, H. 1972. Om nogle danske mælkebøtte. *Botanisk Tidsskrift*, **67**: 139–145.

ØLLGAARD, H. 1978. New species of *Taraxacum* from Denmark. *Botaniska Notiser*, **131** (**4**): 497–521.

ØLLGAARD, H. 1983. Hamata, a new section of *Taraxacum* (Asteraceae). *Plant Systematics and Evolution*, **141**: 199–217.

ØLLGAARD, H. 1986. *Taraxacum discretum* sp. nov. (Compositae). *Nordic Journal of Botany*, **6**: 21–24.

ØLLGAARD, H. & WITTZELL H. 1995. Validation of the name *Taraxacum haematicum* G. Hagl. (Asteraceae). *Annales botanici fennici*, **32**: 229–232. [See also Haglund & Morander (1937).]

PALMER, R.C. & SCOTT, W. 1995. A forgotten Shetland Dandelion. *Watsonia*, **20**: 279–281.

PALMGREN, A. 1910a. Bidrag till kännedomen om Ålands vegetation och flora. I. *Taraxaca. Acta Societatis pro Fauna et Flora fennica*, **34** (**1**): 1–53.

PALMGREN, A. 1910b. Bidrag till kännedomen om Ålands vegetation och flora. II. *Taraxacum*-former. *Acta Societatis pro Fauna et Flora fennica*, **34** (**4**): 1–16.

PUOLANNE, M. 1933. Helsingin ja sen lähiseudun kasvisto. 1. *Taraxacum*-lajit. *Memoranda Societatis pro Fauna et Flora fennica*, **8**: 136–181.

RAILONSALA, A. 1942. *Annales botanici Societatis zoologicae botannicae fennicae Vanamo*, **16** (**5**): 11.

RAILONSALA, A. 1957. *Taraxaca* nova I. *Archivum Societatis zoologicae botanicae fennicae Vanamo*, **11**: 148–171.

RAILONSALA, A. 1967. *Taraxaca* nova VI. *Annales botanici fennici*, **4**: 102–115.

RAUNKIAER, C. 1903. Kimdannelse uden befrügtning hos mælkebøtte. *Botanisk Tidsskrift*, **25** (**2**): 139.

RAUNKIAER, C. 1906. *Dansk Ekskursions-Flora*, ed. 2. Copenhagen & Christiania. ('*Taraxacum*, Mælkbøtte' on pp. 254–258).

RAUNKIAER, C. 1922. *Dansk Ekskursions-Flora*, ed. 4. Copenhagen & Christiania. ('*Taraxacum*, Mælkbøtte, Fandens Mælkbøtte, Løvetand' on pp. 303–307).

RAUNKIAER, C. 1934. *Dansk Ekskursions-Flora*, ed. 5. Copenhagen. ('*Taraxacum*, Mælkbøtte, Løvetand' on pp. 302–318 by M.P. Christiansen & K. Wiinstedt).

RICHARDS, A.J. 1970. Eutriploid facultative agamospermy in *Taraxacum*. *New Phytologist*, **69**: 761–774.

RICHARDS, A.J. 1972. The *Taraxacum* Flora of the British Isles. *Watsonia*, **9** (supplement): 1–141.

RICHARDS, A.J. 1973. The origin of *Taraxacum* agamospecies. *Botanical Journal of the Linnean Society*, **66**: 189–211.

RICHARDS, A.J. 1981. New species of *Taraxacum* from the British Isles. *Watsonia*, **13**: 185–193.

RICHARDS, A.J. 1985. Sectional nomenclature in *Taraxacum* (Asteraceae). *Taxon*, **34**: 633–644.

RICHARDS, A.J. 1986. *Plant Breeding Systems*. Allen & Unwin, London & New York.

RICHARDS, A.J. 1989. A comparison of within-plant karyological heterogeneity between agamospermous and sexual *Taraxacum* (Compositae) as assessed by the nucleolar organiser chromosome. *Plant Systematics and Evolution*, **163**: 177–185.

RICHARDS, A.J. 1992. The *Taraxacum* flora of the Sierra de Guadarrama and its surroundings (Spain). *Anales del Instituto botánico A.J. Cavanilles* [*Jardín botánico de Madrid*], **50**: 201–208.

RICHARDS, A.J. & HAWORTH, C.C. 1984. Further new species of *Taraxacum* from the British Isles. *Watsonia*, **15**: 85–94, plates 1–3.

SAHLIN, C.I. 1983. *Taraxacum cenabense* Sahlin, a new Anglo-French species. *Watsonia*, **14**: 281–282.

SAHLIN, C.I. & SOEST, J.L. VAN 1970. *Taraxacum atactum*, spec. nov. *Acta botanica neerlandica*, **19**: 197–200.

SÅLTIN, H. 1971. Sieben neue nordische *Taraxaca*. *Memoranda Societatis pro Fauna et Flora fennica*, **47**: 38–59, plates 1–9.

SOEST, J.L. VAN 1956. New *Taraxaca* from the Netherlands. *Acta botanica neerlandica*, **5**: 94–101.

SOEST, J.L. VAN 1961. Quelques nouvelles espèces de *Taraxacum*, natives d'Europe. *Acta botanica neerlandica*, **10**: 280–306.

SOEST, J.L. VAN 1975. Quelques espèces nouvelles de *Taraxacum*, de France. *Acta botanica neerlandica*, **24**: 139–154.

SOEST, J.L. VAN, HAGENDIJK, A. & ZEVENBERGEN, H.A. 1968. *Taraxacum kernianum*, spec. nov. *Gorteria*, **4**: 123–126.

STACE, C.A. 1991. *New Flora of the British Isles*. Cambridge: Cambridge University Press.

SYMONS, J. 1798. *Synopsis Plantarum Insulis britannicis indigenarum*. London. (Page 172).

WENDELBO, P. 1959. *Taraxacum gotlandicum*, a pre-boreal relic in the Norwegian flora? *Nytt Magasin for Botanikk (Oslo)*, **7**: 161–167.

OTHER NAMES

Wrong identifications are indicated by †. Numbers preceded by F refer to 'The *Taraxacum* Flora of the British Isles' by A.J. Richards (1972).

acidodontum Dahlst. [under F51] = *naevosiforme* Dahlst.

acrifolium Dahlst. [F40] nom. dub.

adamii Claire [F64]: † for *gelertii* Raunk.

adsimile Dahlst. [F104] = *longisquameum* H. Lindb.

aequatum Dahlst. [under F79] = *lingulatum* Markl.

alienum Dahlst., nom. confusum

amphiodon Dahlst. ex G.E. Haglund [under F85] = *subundulatum* Dahlst. [F85]

ardisodon Dahlst. [under F125] = *polyodon* Dahlst. [F125]

ardlense A.J. Richards: see Richards & Haworth (1984) = *inane* A.J. Richards [F73]

atrovirens Dahlst. [under F115, but not this] = *hamiferum* Dahlst.

austriacum Soest: material needs re-examination.

austrinum G.E. Haglund [F43]: † variously reinterpreted as:
  palustrisquameum A.J. Richards: see Richards (1981).
  sarniense A.J. Richards: see Richards & Haworth (1984).
  webbii A.J. Richards: see Richards (1981).

biforme Dahlst. [F96]: † for ?

'*bifurcatum*' Hagend., Oosterveld & Zevenb. ined.: used for plants determined as *commixtum* G.E. Haglund from Britain and the Netherlands

brachylepis Markl.: all material so named needs re-examining.

'*bracteatiforme*': a discontinued workname for *oellgaardii* C.C. Haw.

'*British atactum*': a discontinued workname for *sahlinianum* Dudman & A.J. Richards

calophyllum Dahlst. [F41] = *stictophyllum* Dahlst.

cambriense A.J. Richards [F65]: holotype is *nordstedtii* Dahlst.

canoviride Puol. [F128]: † material needs re-examining.

canulum G.E. Haglund: for the present, all material has been referred to *falcatum* Brenner.

caudatulum Dahlst.: † British material is *aberrans* Hagend., Soest & Zevenb.

chloroleucophyllum Dahlst. = *unguilobum* Dahlst.

christiansenii G.E. Haglund [F112]: † material is mainly spp. of Section *Hamata*.

cimbricum Wiinst. = *faeroense* (Dahlst.) Dahlst.

connexum Dahlst. [under F104] = *ekmanii* Dahlst.

copidophyllum Dahlst.: † all material needs re-examining.

crispifolium H. Lindb. [F127]: † mainly for *subbracteatum* A.J. Richards

Crocea (Section): see under *officinale.*

croceum Dahlst. [F52]: † for *ceratolobum* Dahlst.

duplidens H. Lindb. [F107] = *ostenfeldii* Raunk.

edmondsonii A.J. Richards: see Richards & Haworth (1984) = *pseudolarssonii* A.J. Richards

erythrospermum Andrz.: this taxon has now been typified, using a specimen which was sexual, so that it is now used as a 'coverall' name for sexual members of Section *Erythrosperma* from central Europe.

eximium Dahlst. [F38] lectotype nom. dub.: all British material is *faeroense* (Dahlst.) Dahlst.

'*explanatum*' H. Øllg.: workname for *subbracteatum* A.J. Richards

glaucinum Dahlst.: dubiously British

grossum Soest: † for '*non-sundbergii*'

hamatifrons Dahlst. [under F115] = *naevosiforme* Dahlst.

helvicarpum Dahlst. [under F17] = *oxoniense* Dahlst.

hemicyclum G.E. Haglund = *adiantifrons* Ekman ex Dahlst.

hemipolyodon Dahlst. = *subundulatum* Dahlst.

hibernicum G.E. Haglund [under F64] = *britannicum* Dahlst.

hispanicum H. Lindb. [F10]: all material needs re-examining.

hypochaeris Dahlst. [F57]: † British material is *xiphoideum* G.E. Haglund.

inarmatum M.P. Christ.: there is a single record of this species, which appears to be correct, from v.c. 50 (Denbigh); it is a Danish *Ruderalia* species somewhat related to *T. aequilobum* Dahlst.

intermedium Raunk.: † material needs re-examining.

johnstonii Dahlst. [under F46] = *unguilobum* Dahlst.

lacerabile Dahlst. [F82] = *macrolobum* Dahlst.

lacerilobum Dahlst. [under F82] nom. dub.

lacinulatum Markl.: † for *lacerifolium* G.E. Haglund in part

laetiforme Dahlst.: † for *haworthianum* Dudman & A.J. Richards

laetifrons Dahlst. [F51] = *stictophyllum* Dahlst.

laetum (Dahlst.) Raunk. [F12]: † for *haworthianum* Dudman & A.J. Richards

laevigatum (Willd.) DC has been used in a sense more or less synonymous with Section *Erythrosperma*. It is based on *Leontodon laevigatus* Willd., the type of which has been destroyed, so that it is unlikely that we shall be able to equate any 'modern' species with it.

lainzii Soest [F49]: material is *drucei* Dahlst.

latispina Dahlst. [under F101] = *longisquameum* H. Lindb.

leptaleum M.P. Christ.: † material needs re-examining.

linguatum Dahlst. ex M.P. Christ. & Wiinst. in Raunk. = *subexpallidum* Dahlst.

linguicuspis H. Lindb.: † material needs re-examining.

maculigerum H. Lindb. [F34]: † for *maculosum* A.J. Richards: see Richards (1981); post-1980 records = *drucei* Dahlst.

magnihamatum = *excellens* Dahlst.

'*mericyclum*' is a recent workname, but = *subexpallidum* Dahlst.

mirum H. Øllg.: † material needs re-examining.

mucronatum H. Lindb. [F101]: † for ?

naeviferum Dahlst. [under F91] = *polyodon* Dahlst.

'*non-maculigerum*': a previous workname for *drucei* Dahlst.

'*non-sundbergii*' is now placed in *sundbergii* Dahlst.

obscuratum Dahlst. [F123] nom. dub.

officinale Weber is a binomial which is often equated with the whole genus. It is the type species for the genus, being based on *Leontodon taraxacum* L., which has now been typified from a specimen collected by Linnaeus in *Flora Lapponica*. This specimen belongs to the later taxon *T. campylodes* G.E. Haglund, which is classified in the arctic section previously known as *Crocea*, which now becomes Section *Taraxacum*. Thus, *T. officinale* now refers to a species localised to Swedish Lapland and is not correctly used in the British and Irish Floras (Richards 1985, p. 634).

oppositum H. Øllg. has been renamed *edmondsonianum* H. Øllg.

ordinatum Hagend., Soest & Zevenb.: † mainly for *insigne* M.P. Christ. & Wiinst.

ornatum G.E. Haglund: † material is now referred to *geirhildae* (Beeby) R. Palmer & Walter Scott.

parvuliceps H. Lindb.: † mainly for *ostenfeldii* Raunk.

percrispum M.P. Christ. = *densilobum* Dahlst.

perhamatum Dahlst. [under F118] = *oblongatum* Dahlst.

perlacinatum Dahlst. [under F131] = *orcadense* Dahlst.

plicatum Dahlst. [under F46] = *naevosiforme* Dahlst.

pollichii Soest: † probably for *palustre* (Lyons) Symons

polyhamatum H. Øllg.: this *Hamata* species from northern Europe is distinguished by many (6–8) lateral lobes to the leaves. Earlier records from northern Britain are now considered unsafe.

porrectidens Dahlst. [F95] nom. dub.

praeradians Dahlst.: † material is *acroglossum* Dahlst.

praeradiantifrons Dahlst. nom. dub.: type material untraced

praestans H. Lindb. [F44]: † covers many species.

privum Dahlst. [F130]: † for a variety of species

procerum G.E. Haglund [F74]: † mainly for *procerisquameum* H. Øllg.

pseudolacistophyllum Soest: † all material needs re-examining.

'*pseudolamprophyllum*' is a previous workname for *hesperium* C.C. Haw.

raunkiaerii Wiinst. = *duplidentifrons* Dahlst.

reclinatum M.P. Christ. [F39]: † a handful of records renamed

recurvilobum Dahlst. [under F95] nom. confusum

recurvum Dahlst.: † material needs re-examining.

reflexilobum H. Lindb. [F126]: † for a variety of species

semiprivum Dahlst. [under F78] = *alatum* H. Lindb.

serratilobum Dahlst. [under F51] = *unguilobum* Dahlst.

shetlandicum Dahlst. [under F51] nom. dub.

silesiacum Dahlst. ex G.E. Haglund = *parnassicum* Dahlst.

similatum Dahlst. [under F129] may be *subundulatum* Dahlst. but needs revision.

simile Raunk. [F21]: † material is mainly *fulviforme* Dahlst.

spectabile Dahlst. [F37]: all British material is referred to *faeroense* (Dahlst.) Dahlst.

spilophyllum Dahlst. [F90]: † mainly referable to *exacutum* Markl.

subditivum Hagend., Soest & Zevenb. = *spiculatum* M.P. Christ.

sublacerifolium Hagend., Soest & Zevenb. = *fagerstroemii* Såltin

sublaciniosum Dahlst. & H. Lindb. [F71] nom. dub.

sublaetum = *haworthianum* Dudman & A.J. Richards

sublatissimum Dahlst. [under F120] = *fasciatum* Dahlst.

sublutescens Dahlst. nom. dub.

submucronatum Dahlst. [under F95] nom. dub.

subpallescens Dahlst. [under F79] = *lingulatum* Markl.

subpraticola G.E. Haglund: all British material is referable to *lepidum* M.P. Christ.

subsagittipotens Dahlst. [F104 in part?] is still under consideration.

subsimile Dahlst. [F47] = *naevosum* Dahlst.

tanylepioides Dahlst. = *orcadense* Dahlst.

tarachodum Hagend., Soest & Zevenb. = *pannulatum* Dahlst.

trigonum M.P. Christ. & Wiinst.: † for a variety of species

uncosum G.E. Haglund: † mainly for *laticordatum* Markl.

unguilobiforme Dahlst. = *unguilobum* Dahlst.

vachellii Dahlst. nom. confusum

valdedentatum Dahlst. [F89] nom. dub.

vulgare Schrank: this binomial is best regarded as being synonymous with *officinale* Weber.

INDEX OF SPECIES (WITH SPECIES NUMBERS)

Names in single inverted commas are informal 'worknames' which have not been validly published. Names in italics are synonyms. The numbers are species numbers, *not* page numbers.

diastematicum 93a
dilaceratum 59b
dilatatum 93
disseminatum 8c
'distendens' see 57
drucei 28
dunense 6
duplidentifrons 34
edmondsonianum 80c
ekmanii 89
euryphyllum 24
exacutum 82
excellens 37
expallidiforme 65
exsertiforme 81b
exsertum 81a
faeroense 18
fagerstroemii 96a
falcatum 11b
fasciatum 103
fulgidum 39
fulvicarpum 45
fulviforme 10
fulvum 11
fusciflorum 50a
geirhildae 18a
gelertii 30
glauciniforme 12
gotlandicum 7a
haematicum 40
hamatiforme 53
hamatulum 47a
hamatum 47
hamiferum 49
haworthianum 7
hemicyclum see 79
hepaticum 96b
hesperium 36
hexhamense 88a
hirsutissimum 24a

horridifrons 60a
huelphersianum 96
hygrophilum 39c
inane 38
incisum 101
inopinatum 1a
insigne 61
interveniens 77
intumescens 72
kernianum 54
lacerifolium 66a
laciniosifrons 94a
laciniosum 61a
lacistophyllum 1
laeticolor 56
lamprophyllum 55
lancastriense 42e
lancidens 53b
landmarkii 41
latens 80b
laticordatum 63
latisectum 95c
latissimum 80a
lepidum 64a
leptodon 82c
leucopodum 68
linguatum see 57a
lingulatum 84
longifrons see 88a
longisquameum 102a
lucidum 105
lunare 89c
luteum 46a
macranthoides 84a
macrolobum 56a
maculatum 102c
maculosum 25
margettsii 63d
marklundii 48a
melanthoides 104

mimulum 78a
multicolorans 100a
naevosiforme 23a
naevosum 23
necessarium 63c
nietoi 31b
nigridentatum 62a
nitidum 100b
'non-severum' 90a
nordstedtii 42
obliquilobum 95a
obliquum 15
oblongatum 91
obtusifrons 82b
obtusilobum 68a
ochrochlorum 89a
oellgaardii 33a
olgae 42c
'opertum' see 66
orcadense 31a
ostenfeldii 43
oxoniense 9
pachylobum 95b
pachymerum 92
pallescens 63a
pallidipes 65b
palustre 16
palustrisquameum 42f
pannucium 57
pannulatiforme 62
pannulatum 83
parnassicum 5a
pectinatiforme 98
piceatum 70
placidum 13b
planum 99a
platyglossum 15a
polyodon 100
porrigens 67b
porteri 34a

prionum 50b
procerisquameum 85a
proximiforme 8a
proximum 8
pruinatum 52b
'pseudo-cordatum' see 90b
pseudohamatum 50
pseudolacistophyllum see 13c
pseudolarssonii 26
pseudonordtstedtii 42a
pseudoproximum 8b
pseudoretroflexum 90b
pulchrifolium 97a
pycnostictum 22
quadrans 49a
remanentilobum 86a
retroflexum 79a
retzii 11c
rhamphodes 85
richardsianum 29a
rubellum 23b
rubicundum 5
sagittipotens 88
sahlinianum 52a
sarniense 16b
scanicum 2a
scoticum 11a
scotiniforme 102b
sellandii 74
semiglobosum 79b
serpenticola 18b
severum see 90a
sinuatum 94
speciosum 69b
spiculatum 53a
stenacrum 67
stereodes 78b
stictophyllum 29
subbracteatum 33
subcyanolepis 65a

The Botanical Society of the British Isles

The BSBI is for everyone who is interested in the flora of Britain and Ireland. It traces its origins back to 1836, when it was founded as the Botanical Society of London. From its earliest days it has welcomed both professional and amateur members, and it remains the biggest and most active organisation devoted to the study of botany in the British Isles.

Information on the status and distribution of British and Irish flowering plants, ferns and charophytes is gathered through a network of vice-county recorders; this is the basis for plant atlases, county Floras and publications on rare and scarce species and is vital for botanical conservation. The BSBI was a major partner in the production of *New Atlas of the British and Irish Flora* and a related CD-ROM published by Oxford University Press in September 2002. This title is now out of print but much of the data has been incorporated in the online Atlas of the British and Irish Flora, a project developed jointly by the BSBI and the Biological Records Centre.

The atlas can be viewed at <http://www.brc.ac.uk/plantatlas/>

The BSBI organises plant distribution surveys, publishes handbooks on difficult groups of plants and has national referees available to members to name problematic specimens. Conferences and field meetings are held throughout Britain and Ireland and sometimes abroad. The society also publishes a scientific journal, *New Journal of Botany* (formerly *Watsonia*) and conference reports. Members are kept informed by a newsletter three times a year.

An education programme supported by the BSBI aims to bring high-quality botanical training within the reach of all, from A Level students to professional development and postgraduate courses.

Details of membership and other information about the BSBI maybe obtained from The Hon. General Secretary, Botanical Society of the British Isles, c/o Department of Botany, The Natural History Museum, Cromwell Road, London SW7 5BD.

The society's web site is <http://www.bsbi.org.uk/index.html>.

The following books are available from the official agents for BSBI publications, Summerfield Books, Unit L, Skirsgill Business Park, Penrith, Cumbria, CA11 0FA (Telephone 01768 210793; Email <info@summerfieldbooks.com>. Full details are available on this website: <http://www.summerfieldbooks.com/bsbi-publications.asp>.

BSBI handbooks

Each handbook deals in depth with one or more difficult groups of British and Irish plants.

No. 1 **Sedges of the British Isles** – A. C. Jermy, D. A. Simpson, M. J. Y. Foley & M. S. Porter. Third edition, 2007, incorporating full accounts of 35 species of Cyperaceae and 47 hybrids in addition to the 76 species and subspecies of *Carex*. 566 pp., with descriptions, line drawings and distribution maps. A5 paperback. [Previous editions 1968 and 1982.]

No. 2 **Umbellifers of the British Isles** – T. G. Tutin. 1980, reprinted 2006. 200 pp., with descriptions of 73 species facing line drawings by Ann Farrer. Small paperback.

No. 3 **Docks and knotweeds of the British Isles** – J. E. Lousley & D. H. Kent. 1981. Out of print.

No. 4 **Willows and poplars of Great Britain and Ireland** – R. D. Meikle. 1984, reprinted 2006. 200 pp., with descriptions of 65 species, subspecies, varieties and hybrids of *Salix* and *Populus*, illustrated with line drawings by Victoria Gordon. Small paperback.

No. 5 **Charophytes of Great Britain and Ireland** – Jenny A. Moore. 1986, reprinted 2005 with a new preface and corrections by C. D. Preston. 144 pp., with descriptions of 39 species and varieties of Characeae (stoneworts), line drawings by Margaret Tebbs and 17 distribution maps. Small paperback.

No. 6 *Crucifers of Great Britain and Ireland* – T. C. G. Rich. 1991, reprinted 2006. 344 pp., with descriptions of 148 taxa of Brassicaceae (Cruciferae), 129 of them with line drawings by various artists, and 60 distribution maps. Small paperback.

No. 7 *Roses of Great Britain and Ireland* - G. G. Graham & A. L. Primavesi. 1993, reprinted with corrections 2005. 208 pp., with descriptions, facing line drawings by Margaret Gold, of 13 native and nine introduced taxa of *Rosa,* briefer descriptions of 76 hybrids, and 33 maps. A5 paperback.

No. 8 *Pondweeds of Great Britain and Ireland* – C. D. Preston. 1995, reprinted 2003. 352 pp., with descriptions and line drawings of all 50 species and hybrids of *Potamogeton, Groenlandia* and *Ruppia,* most with distribution maps; detailed introductory material and bibliography. A5 paperback.

No. 9 *Dandelions of Great Britain and Ireland* - A. A. Dudman & A. J. Richards. 1997, reprinted with minor alterations 2000. 344 pp., with descriptions of 235 species of *Taraxacum,* most of them illustrated by silhouettes of herbarium specimens; drawings of bud involucres of 139 species by Olga Stewart and 178 distribution maps. A5 paperback.

No. 10 *Sea beans and nickar nuts* – E. Charles Nelson. 2000, reprinted 2003. 156 pp., with descriptions of nearly 60 exotic seeds and fruits found stranded on beaches in north-western Europe (many illustrated by Wendy Walsh) and of the mature plants (some with drawings by Alma Hathway), accounts of their history and folklore, growing instructions, etc. A5 paperback.

No. 11 *Water-starworts* (**Callitriche**) *of Europe* – R. V. Lansdown. 2008. 184 pp., with descriptions, line drawings by F. 1. Rumsey and the author, and maps showing distribution in the British Isles and in Europe for all 16 *Callitriche* species and one hybrid reliably recorded in Europe; detailed introductory material, glossary and appendix listing the herbarium material studied. A5 paperback.

No. 12 *Fumitories of Britain and Ireland* – R. J. Murphy. 2009. 121 pp., with descriptions, line drawings, black & white and full colour illustrations of 22 species, subspecies and varieties of fumitory in Britain and Ireland. detailed introductory material, glossary and summary of Vice-counties for which *Fumaria* taxa have been reliably recorded. A5 paperback. The first in a series of full colour handbooks.

No 13 *Grasses of the British Isles* – Tom Cope & Alan Gray. 2009. 612 pp., with descriptions, of 15 tribes, 67 genera and 220 species. The latter comprise 113 natives, 10 archaeophytes, 50 neophytes and 47 casuals; bamboos are not included. Keys to tribes, genera and species. Black & white illustrations by Margaret Tebbs. A5 paperback on thin paper; also hardback.

No 14. *Whitebeams, Rowans and Service Tees of Britain and Ireland* – Tim Rich, Libby Houston, Ashley Robertson and Michael Proctor. 2010. 223 pp., with descriptions of 52 native or naturalised *Sorbus* taxa in Britain and Ireland (44 species and 8 hybrids). 43 of the taxa are native, 35 of which are endemic to Britain and two to Ireland. 476 colour photographs, line drawings and maps. A4 hardback.

No 15. *Britsh Northern Hawkweeds* – Tim Rich & Walter Scott. 2011. 156 + iv pp., with a full account of the 21 species of British Northern Hawkweeds (*Hieracium* section *Alpestria),* 16 of which occur in Shetland, 4 in Scotland and 1 in England. Line drawings, silhouettes of herbarium material, detailed col. photos and general habitat shots are given for each species. A4 hardback

Other BSBI publications

Alien plants of the British Isles – E. J. Clement & M. C. Foster. 1994. 616 pp. Lists 3,586 recorded non-native species (of which 885 are established), with English names, frequency, status, origin, references to descriptions and illustrations, and selected synonyms. Paperback.

Alien grasses of the British Isles – T. B. Ryves, E. J. Clement & M. C. Foster. 1996. 234 pp. A companion volume to the last, listing over 700 non-native grasses; includes keys to bamboos and eight of the larger and more difficult genera and 29 pp. of drawings by G. M. S. Easy. Paperback.

Illustrations of alien plants of the British Isles – E. J. Clement, D. P. J. Smith & I. R. Thirlwell. 2005. 480 pp., including 444 full-page line drawings of introduced, naturalised and casually occurring alien plants in Britain and Ireland. The drawings are largely from a collection put together by the late David McClintock, originally for publication in his planned Volume 3 of *A New Illustrated British Flora*. A5 paperback.

Plant crib – T. C. G. Rich & A. C. Jermy. 1998, reprinted 2006. 400 pp. An expertly written identification guide for some 325 difficult taxonomic groups, with explanations, keys and illustrations of plant details. A4 paperback.

List of vascular plants of the British Isles – D. H. Kent. 1992. 400 pp. Nomenclature and sequence as in Clive Stace's *New Flora of the British Isles* (1991, 1997), with selected synonyms. Paperback. Supplied with five errata lists. Three supplements (published 1996, 2000 and 2006) are also available.

Vice-county census catalogue of vascular plants of Great Britain, the Isle of Man and the Channel Islands – C. A. Stace, R. G. Ellis, D. H. Kent & D. J. McCosh (eds). 2003. 432 pp. A full listing by species of the vice-counties from which vascular plants have been recorded. A5 paperback.

First records of alien plants in the wild in Britain and Ireland – D.. A. Pearman & C. D. Preston. 2003. 40 pp. Tables setting out the year(s) in which some 1,600 taxa were first recorded, with details of source, vice-county and some notes for mist entries. A5 paperback.

Altitudinal limits of British and Irish vascular plants – D. A. Pearman & R. W. M. Corner. 2nd edn 2004. 40 pp. Tables setting out maximum and minimum altitudes for some 1,500 taxa, with vice-county, locality, grid ref., recorder and date for most entries. A5 paperback.

Change in the British Flora 1987-2004 (A report on the BSBI Local Change survey) – M. E. Braithwaite, R. W. Ellis & C. D. Preston. 2006. 390 pp., with colour photographs, distribution maps, tables and graphs. A comparison of the results of two surveys of selected 2 km x 2 km squares. Large paperback.

Atlas of British and Irish brambles – A. Newton & R. D. Randall. 2004. 98 pp., with 330 hectad distribution maps of *Rubus* species, summaries of distribution and notes on changes. A5 paperback.

British alpine hawkweeds – David Tennant & Tim Rich. 2007. A monograph of British *Hieracium* section *Alpina*. 234 pp., with over 170 drawings and colour photographs and five paintings by Ramond C. Booth. All 39 taxa are described in detail, with their history, distribution maps, a gazetteer, habitats, ecology, biology, origins, cultivation, conservation status and details of relevant herbarium collections. A4 hardback.

Atlas of British and Irish Hawkweeds (Pilosella L. and Hieracium L.) – David McCosh & Tim Rich 2011. 500 pp., b&w maps plus 1 coloured distribution map .Based on a database of 19,000 records collected in the last 30 years and representing over 420 species. Each species account has Latin and English names, distribution map at hectad resolution, representative silhouette, brief notes, list of vice-counties where it has been recorded, and IUCN threat category. A5 paperback.

Botanical Links in the Atlantic Arc – S. J. Leach, C. N. Page, Y. Peytoureau & M. N. Sanford (eds). 2006. 336 pp., with colour photograph section, black-and-white photographs, maps and figures. A wide-ranging series of papers on the flora of the Atlantic coastal regions of Europe. Proceedings of an international conference held at Camborne, Cornwall, in 2003, published as BSBI Conference Report No. 24, dedicated to the memory of Dr Franklyn H. Perring. Hardback.

Current taxonomic research on the British and European Flora – J. P. Bailey & R. G. Ellis (eds). 2006. 156 pp., with colour photographs and text illustrations. Proceedings of a conference held at the University of Leicester in 2003 to mark the retirement of Prof. Clive Stace, published as BSBI Conference Report No. 25. Paperback.

50 Years of Mapping the British and Irish Flora 1962-2012 – M. Braithwaite & K. Walker (eds) 2012. 48 pp., with colour photographs and text illustrations. This booklet provides the background to the genesis of the New Atlas of the British and Irish Flora, it's successes and limitations and the initiatives that arose from it in the subsesquent decades. Prepared for the 2012 BSBI conference – A Great leap Forward.

Other publishers' books

Aquatic plants in Britain and Ireland – C. D. Preston & J. M. Croft. 1997. 365 pp. Accounts and distribution maps of 200 aquatic plants in 72 genera, with 72 line drawings by G. M. S. Easy. Large paperback reprint, published 2001 by Harley Books.

New Atlas of the British and Irish Flora – C. D. Preston, D. A. Pearman & T. D. Dines (eds). 2002. Out of print.

The Vegetative Key to the British Flora – John Poland & Eric Clement. 2009. 526 pp. A striking new approach the identification of nearly 3000 wildflowers, grasses, sedges, trees, shrubs, ferns and fern-allies to be found native, naturalised or casual in the British Isles. With numerous 'thumbnail' line drawings and 24 plates of colour photographs. Softback, privately published by John Poland, Southampton.